Combinational and Sequ

A hands-on approach using programmable log

Martin Rice

Combinational and Sequential Logic

A hands-on approach
using programmable logic

Martin Rice

Pearson Education Limited
Edinburgh Gate, Harlow
Essex CM20 2JE, England
and Associated Companies throughout the world

First published 2001

British Library Cataloguing in Publication Data
A catalogue entry for this title is available from the British Library

ISBN 0-582-43164-6

Set by 35 in Times 10/12 and Frutiger
Printed and bound in Great Britain by
Henry Ling Limited, Dorchester, Dorset

Contents

Preface

Occasionally junk mail is useful. Just as I was pondering how best to deliver the programmable logic section of the new HNC syllabus in digital electronics, a CD-ROM arrived containing just what I needed. Soon, the idea of teaching the whole of the subject by means of the XPLA software and 'Coolrunner' hardware seemed very attractive: the development system is easy to install and use, and the hardware can be reconfigured into all the circuits mentioned in the syllabus. No more messing around with 74 or 4000 series ICs in breadboard or wiring up trainer boards. Just define the circuit on a PC using a 'hardware description language', compile this script into a configuration data stream then send the design to the chip on a trainer board to test it.

The present book actually uses two approaches. In addition to making real LEDs light up in response to real input signals on a trainer board fitted with a programmable logic device, the visual indicators and interactive switches provided in the Electronics Workbench software have been exploited to illustrate digital theory in as graphic a format as possible. Indeed, readers may feel that the Electronics Workbench simulator and the simulation facilities embedded within the XPLA software are sufficient to gain a good insight into the field of digital electronics without the need for any hardware at all. However, engineering is about real things, so you are encouraged to build or buy the target hardware to see your designs come to life. The circuit diagram is given in Appendix A while construction and purchasing details are given in Appendix B.

The main text aims to cover the syllabus of the Edexcel unit 'Combinational and Sequential Logic'. It also covers the digital parts of the unit 'Digital and Analogue Devices and Circuits'. It follows a fairly conventional pattern, starting from basic concepts in Chapter 1, Boolean algebra in Chapter 2, combinational logic in Chapters 3 and 4, and sequential logic in Chapters 5 and 6. While all the chapters (apart from Chapter 2) refer extensively to the programmable logic chip on the target hardware, Chapter 7 discusses programmable logic more generally. Readers with no previous experience of digital electronics should be able to dive in at Chapter 1 without too much trouble. If the concepts of current and voltage are totally mysterious then you ought to do some background reading beforehand.

The text includes questions that are designed to check that you've actually understood the subject matter. Do try to get to the stage where you are confident that you know what the answers are to the questions. The correct answers are listed at the end of each chapter. There are also more extensive exercises based on Electronics Workbench and the XPLA development system for you to tackle. Again, answers are given at the end of each chapter.

There is a CD-ROM accompanying the book. This contains the XPLA software, some of the example design files discussed in the book, and the Electronics Workbench files. Instructions for installing the software are given in Appendix C.

In order to make the book as complete a teaching package as possible, some assignments are included that can be used as formal assessments for the two Edexcel units covered. Teachers and lecturers may wish to use them pretty much as given, or adapt them as they see fit. Assessment criteria have been given, based on the Edexcel guidelines. Opportunities for demonstrating 'Common' and 'Key' skills abound within the assignments, but have not been explicitly stated. Note that students would not be expected to complete all of the assignments, especially if they are following just the Digital and Analogue Devices and Circuits unit.

As well as being aimed at the Edexcel Electronics HNC market, the book will find use among a wider range of readers, including undergraduates on Electronic and General Engineering degree courses, and practising design engineers who have not yet discovered the delights of programmable logic.

The XPLA designs in the text are all entered using the Philips Hardware Description Language, PHDL. Schematic (circuit diagram) entry is possible, however, and Appendix D has been included as an introduction to the use of the XPLA schematic editor.

My thanks go to Chris Leeding at Pearson for encouraging me to write the book, and to my students at Newbury College who have given the text and assignments a trial run. I also thank Pat Kane at Xilinx for his support for this project. The guys at Albuquerque who wrote the XPLA software must be congratulated for producing such an easy to use piece of software, and for their helpful advice on pages 2, 42, 69 and 106 of the manual for version 2.04 of the software.

There is a website associated with this book at www.booksites.net/rice. Here you will find further examples and software to download, as well as any updates to the text.

Martin Rice
Newbury, Berkshire, UK
July 2000

Late news

The world of programmable logic changes fast. One thing that has changed during the time taken to write and produce this book is that Xilinx no longer support the XPLA software, and the PHDL language has been replaced by ABEL. The Coolrunner devices themselves are still supported, however; ABEL and PHDL are virtually identical; and software to replace XPLA is available and is included on the book's CD (Webpack ISE). Appendix E describes how to install and use the ISE software, and discusses the implications of changing from the XPLA to the ISE system.

The ISE system is much more versatile in terms of the range of devices and languages it will support compared to XPLA. From a teaching/learning point of view, however, the XPLA system has much to commend it. In particular, the ability to view the results of simulations in graphical form is easier to digest than the test vectors required for the ISE-ABEL system.

The recommended route from novice to useful engineer is thus to start with this book, using the XPLA system supplied, then try out the ISE system, as explained in Appendix E. To become an expert, teach yourself VHDL and/or Verilog, learn how to use all of the Webpack and associated software, get experience in big designs, then wait for the mega-salary offers to roll in!

1 Basic concepts

Introduction

What does a digital signal look like, and what can you do with one? In this first chapter you will learn about the nature of digital signals, and the basic ways digital signals can be processed. The chapter covers:

- input and output characteristics of digital logic devices
- graphical symbols used to represent digital processing elements
- mathematical symbols relevant to digital systems
- the binary number system
- Electronics Workbench exercises
- introduction to the XPLA software
- XPLA exercises
- introduction to the use of the CPLD demonstration board
- hardware exercises using the demonstration board

Digital signals: voltage levels, current values and fan-out

A digital signal can take on one of two possible states: HIGH or LOW. The different technologies used in the manufacture of digital devices have their own definitions of what constitutes a HIGH or a LOW. In this chapter the 74HC logic family operating from a 5V supply, and the 74LS devices are examined.

A 74HC device will regard any *input* signal between 0V and 1.5V as LOW, and signals between 3.5V and 5V as HIGH. These ranges are shown on the left of Figure 1.1. The devices themselves are guaranteed to produce *output* signals between 0V and 0.25V for a LOW and between 4.5V and 5V for a HIGH, although most signals will be even closer to 0V or 5V. See the right side of Figure 1.1.

Fig. 1.1 *Logic levels for 74HC family (5V supply)*

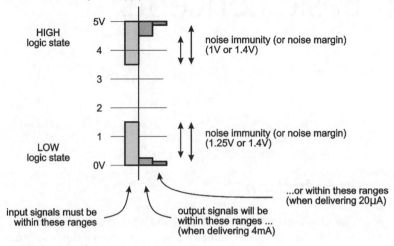

Noise immunity

Figure 1.1 also illustrates the concept of noise immunity. This is the amount of noise that can be added to an output signal yet still keep that signal within the acceptable range as far as other inputs are concerned. You can see that the noise immunity is better (i.e. greater) when the outputs are driving light loads (20μA) than when delivering maximum current (4mA).

Fan-out

Figure 1.1 indicates that currents as well as voltages are an important feature in considering digital signals. When developing a digital logic family, the general aim of a designer is to make sure that inputs take as little current as possible, but also to design outputs that can supply lots. This gives rise to large 'fan-out', whereby one output can drive many inputs.

For the 74HC series, very little current is needed at the inputs: less than 100nA. Outputs, on the other hand, can deliver relatively large amounts of current: a little over 4mA. The fan-out of the family is therefore very large: more than 4mA/100nA or 40,000!

The 74HC family was designed to replace older technologies, such as the 74LS series. A 74LS input requires a voltage between 2V and 5V to be recognised as a HIGH, and a current of 20μA to be fed into an input. A 74LS output can deliver 400μA, and still remain above 2.7V. This means that for a HIGH signal the (worst case) noise immunity is 0.7V, and the fan-out is 400μA/20μA = 20.

The figures for a 74LS LOW signal are as follows: the input voltage must be between 0V and 0.8V and inputs require 0.4mA to be drained out of them. An output can sink up to 8mA and still remain below 0.5V. For a LOW signal the noise immunity is thus just 0.3V, and the fan-out is 8mA/0.4mA = 20. These figures are summarised in Figure 1.2.

Fig. 1.2 *Signal characteristics for 74LS logic family*

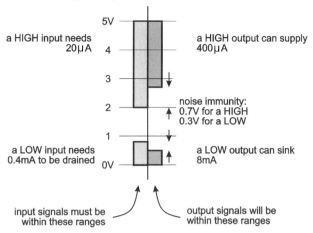

a HIGH input needs 20µA

a HIGH output can supply 400µA

noise immunity:
0.7V for a HIGH
0.3V for a LOW

a LOW input needs 0.4mA to be drained

a LOW output can sink 8mA

input signals must be within these ranges

output signals will be within these ranges

Most of the time your designs use various devices within the same logic family, and you don't need to worry about these things; as long as you keep within the fan-out capability, everything should work. The time when you do need to think about input and output characteristics is when you need to interface between logic families, or to some other input or output device. For instance what if you have a 74HC device driving a member of the 74LS family? This is shown in Figure 1.3. The top half of the diagram shows that there is not much of a problem if the signal is HIGH: each input requires just 20µA and the output can supply enough current for 200 of these. The lower half shows there to be more of a problem with a LOW: a 74HC output can only sink enough current to hold down ten 74LS inputs. The fan-out would thus be ten. Note that some members of the HC family have what's referred to as a 'bus driver' output stage. These are specifically designed for driving large numbers of devices all attached to a long PCB track, and have 50% more output current capability than 'standard' outputs. The fan-out for a bus-driver HC device to LS would be 15.

The noise immunity for the HC-to-LS situation would be 0.55V: the difference between the maximum acceptable at an LS input as a low (0.8V) and the maximum that an HC output will rise to when sinking 4mA (0.25V).

In fact, you don't have to interface HC and LS logic families because there is the 74HCT family. This is designed to have the benefits of HC (low operating power), but the logic levels and current capability are more compatible with the older, established LS devices.

Before leaving the subject of the voltages that can represent HIGH and LOW logic states, what happens if an input signal is above 5V, or below 0V? With the 74HC family there is a series resistor and two clamping diodes that allow the input to rise 1.5V above the positive supply rail, or 1.5V below the negative, and do no damage. This arrangement also helps to protect against short-lived input voltages considerably higher (or more negative) than this, which can often arise when static charges build up on people who handle circuits and chips. Note that it does not guarantee full anti-static protection,

Fig. 1.3 *Fan-out considerations for HC-to-LS compatibility*

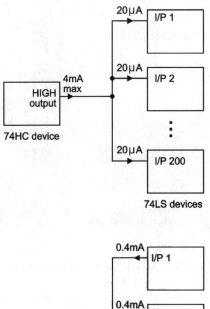

and precautions as recommended by the manufacturers should be taken when handling these devices.

Schmitt-trigger inputs

Another possibility is that an input signal lies somewhere between the allowed LOW and HIGH ranges. What happens, for instance, if the input is sitting bang in the middle of the range at 2.5V, the threshold between HIGH and LOW? For CMOS devices, the data sheets refer to this as the 'linear' region of operation, and a relatively large current will flow down through the chip from the 5V rail to 0V, increasing power dissipation. There's no problem as long as the input stays in this region for short periods of time only and most signals will indeed transition quickly between logic levels.

If you expect a slowly changing signal (the *User Guide* provided by Philips Semiconductors regards anything over 500ns rise/fall time as 'slow'!) then use a device having a specially designed 'Schmitt-trigger' input. This has a different threshold level for rising input signals and falling ones. For the 74HC14, for instance, a signal has to reach 2.6V before it is regarded as HIGH, while on the way down it has to go below 1.6V to achieve LOW status. The difference between these two levels is the 'hysteresis' of the Schmitt input, and prevents the output from behaving erratically if the input hovers around the nether regions between 'proper' HIGH and LOW voltages. This is demonstrated in the Electronics Workbench exercise later in this chapter.

Open drain (open collector) outputs

In the section above where fan-out was discussed, the current available at outputs was seen to be an important parameter contributing to the ability of one device to drive others. There is an output configuration – 'open drain' for HC or 'open-collector' for LS – that will not actually give any drive current at all. You might conclude that it would be totally incapable of driving other devices, and you would be right. However by adding a pull-up resistor it *can* drive other devices, and it has the advantage over normal outputs in that several outputs can be joined together.

The statement that open drain/open collector outputs have no drive current needs a little further explanation. These outputs *are* capable of sinking current when generating a LOW output, just like the normal-output members of the family. Their restriction is that they cannot source current when HIGH.

Fig. 1.4 *Wired-AND connection of open-collector outputs*

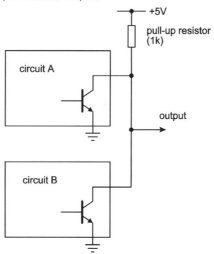

Figure 1.4 shows how to make a 'wired-AND' connection with open collector outputs. If circuit A's output transistor is on, the common output will be pulled LOW, irrespective of what circuit B is doing. Similarly, if circuit B turns its transistor on, the output will go LOW. Only when both transistors are off will the output be pulled HIGH by the pull-up resistor. This action is that of an AND gate, hence the term wired-AND. Confusingly, exactly the same circuitry is also called wired-OR. The definitions of AND and OR gates are discussed in more detail later in this chapter.

The open collector with pull-up resistor circuit is slower than the normal, active pull-up output, so is not used much now. Tri-state outputs have taken over where a number of outputs need to be joined to a common line. One job that open collector outputs are still sometimes used for is where the output signal voltage levels need to be shifted. If the pull-up resistor were connected to +15V, for instance, then the output signal would switch between 0V and a voltage close to +15V, depending on how much current the driven devices draw down through the pull-up resistor.

Tri-state outputs

Tri-state (or 3-state) outputs do not have some third logic level, different from HIGH or LOW, but the term means that the output can be made to take on no logic state at all. It is effectively disconnected – high impedance. Like the wired-AND connection, this allows several different devices to drive the same circuit node. All the devices except one will have their outputs disabled. By choosing which device has its output *en*abled, you can choose where the data for the node comes from. This is used extensively in computers where a data bus (a bus is just a collection of individual wires) connects the microprocessor, many memory devices and probably some input–output devices as well. Only one of these must be allowed to control the data on the bus at any time.

Supply voltages for logic families

The figures discussed above for the 74HC family assume that the circuit is being run from 5V: the traditional supply voltage for the LS and older logic families. 74HC devices will actually run on anything from 2V to 6V, however, with corresponding changes to HIGH and LOW logic levels, noise immunity and operating speed.

The logic family that has the largest range of supply voltage is the 4000 series. Like HC, this is CMOS, which means low operating power, but it is slower than HC. The 4000 series will work with supply voltages between 3V and 18V – ideal if you want to run a circuit from a 9V or 12V battery.

Data sheet symbols

The various voltage levels discussed so far all have symbols that the manufacturers use in their data sheets. Some are listed below.

- V_{OH} minimum output voltage for HIGH
- V_{OL} maximum output voltage for LOW
- V_{IH} minimum input voltage acceptable as HIGH
- V_{IL} maximum input voltage acceptable as LOW
- V_{TG} threshold input voltage, dividing HIGH from LOW
- I_O output current (negative values indicate out of device)
- I_I input current (negative values indicate out of device)
- I_{OL} output current, but specifically when the output is LOW

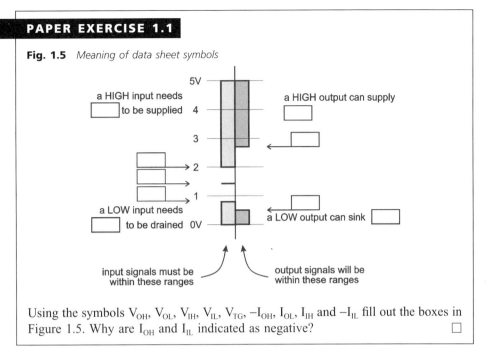

Fig. 1.5 *Meaning of data sheet symbols*

Using the symbols V_{OH}, V_{OL}, V_{IH}, V_{IL}, V_{TG}, $-I_{OH}$, I_{OL}, I_{IH} and $-I_{IL}$ fill out the boxes in Figure 1.5. Why are I_{OH} and I_{IL} indicated as negative? ☐

Acronyms

Several acronyms have been used in the discussion of logic families. The meanings of these acronyms are as follows: HC stands for High-speed CMOS; CMOS stands for Complementary MOS. Complementary means that FETs of both polarity types (n-channel and p-channel) are used. FET stands for Field-Effect Transistor. MOS is a particular type of FET: one based on a Metal layer, then an Oxide insulating layer, then the Silicon. HCT is HC that is compatible with the older TTL technology. TTL stands for Transistor–Transistor Logic. LS stands for Low-power Schottky, and is a variety of standard TTL. Schottky is the name of the chap who invented a particular type of diode (a.k.a. hot-carrier diode) that helps transistors switch quickly.

Digital signals: speed

The brief discussion given above about the high currents that may be drawn while the circuit is operating in its linear region if an input signal changes rather slowly from one logic state to another would lead you to assume that the quicker a signal rises or falls the better. Unfortunately, when the voltage level of signal A changes very rapidly it may cause a noise spike on signal B, which was just sitting there, supposedly at a steady level. The faster the edge (and the closer together the tracks) the greater this problem and, despite the noise immunity built into devices, erroneous switching may occur.

Signal rise and fall times are thus something of a compromise, and some devices have a 'slew-rate' control that allows a designer to choose the value of this parameter.

Some insight into the situation is gained from carrying out Fourier analysis of example signals. The maths is not covered here but the results are indicated below. Basically, fast edges give rise to high frequency signals at high amplitude, and it's these high frequency signals that AC couple through stray capacitance from one track to another. Figure 1.6 illustrates this point.

Fig. 1.6 *Fourier components of square waves with differing rise/fall times*

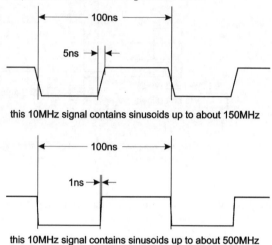

this 10MHz signal contains sinusoids up to about 150MHz

this 10MHz signal contains sinusoids up to about 500MHz

The rise and fall time for signals that are generated at 74HC outputs is typically 7ns when operating with a 5V supply. This increases to 19ns when a 2V supply is used.

Real signals don't have quite the shape indicated in Figure 1.6: instead of having sharp corners they curve over, as shown in Figure 1.7. This makes it more meaningful to define rise and fall times as the time taken to change between 10% and 90% of initial and final values.

Fig. 1.7 *Definitions of rise and fall times*

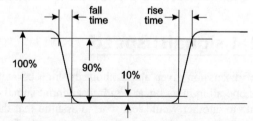

As well as rise and fall times, the other speed consideration is the time taken for an input signal to affect an output. This is referred to as the propagation delay and, for 74HC devices, is typically between 10ns and 20ns, more complex circuits taking longer to respond. Lower supply voltage also increases propagation delay.

Basic gates: the buffer

Having spent some time discussing digital signals themselves, we now start looking at what can be done with them. The simplest thing is to do nothing: the output is at the same logic state as the input. Such a device is called a buffer.

input ▷ output

Figure 1.8 gives the most commonly used symbol for a simple buffer, in accordance with the former standard set by the American National Standards Institute (ANSI). More recently (1984) the International Electrotechnical Commission (IEC) has set a standard for logic symbols that are particularly useful for representing more complex devices. The IEC symbols for the basic gates will be given towards the end of this chapter, but the old ANSI symbols will be used for now.

Although a buffer does nothing in terms of the logic state, it will introduce a propagation delay, and will increase the current drive.

Looking through the 74HC series, you can't actually buy a simple buffer, but what's referred to as a 'quad buffer/line driver; 3-state; output enable active LOW' is listed. It's the 74HC125.

The logic symbol for this is:

Fig. 1.9 *Buffer with tri-state output*

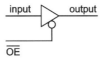

Being described as 'quad' means there are four of these in the single IC. Being described as a line driver implies the high output current capability (6mA rather than 4mA) discussed above.

The term 3-state means that the output can be HIGH, LOW or high impedance, as already discussed. The control signal for the output is the **Output Enable** (OE). When this is asserted, the output will take on one of the two normal states, depending on the logic at the buffer input. When the OE signal is not asserted, the output will go high impedance.

In the case of the 74HC125 the OE signal is asserted when it is LOW. It is therefore referred to as an 'active-LOW' signal. The little circle on the symbol indicates that this control signal is active LOW, as does the bar over the signal name ($\overline{\text{OE}}$).

Basic gates: the inverter, or NOT gate

As there are only two possible states for a digital signal, the next simplest thing after doing nothing is to change it from one state to the other and an inverter, or NOT gate, is used for this. The output will take on the opposite logic state to the input. The output is said to be the inverse, or complement, of the input.

The logic symbol for an inverter is shown below:

Fig. 1.10 *An inverter*

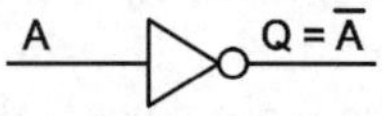

$$A \quad \rhd\!\!\circ \quad Q = \overline{A}$$

The A at the input of the gate and the $\overline{A}$ at the output show the Boolean algebra way of naming a signal and its complement. A bar over a signal's name shows that it has been inverted. The Q just represents the output signal. As before, the circle on the graphic indicates inversion.

The truth table for a NOT gate is shown below:

Fig. 1.11 *Truth table for an inverter*

input A	output Q
0	1
1	0

A truth table just lists all possible input situations, and states what the output does for each. The 0s and 1s represent logic states, 0 being LOW, 1 being HIGH. In some data sheets Ls and Hs are used instead of 0s and 1s. This convention assumes *positive* logic. (In *negative* logic a 0 is represented by a HIGH, and a 1 by a LOW.)

Basic gates: the AND gate

The AND gate has two or more input signals. The symbol for the two-input version is shown below:

Fig. 1.12 *An AND gate*

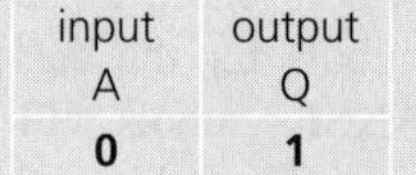

$$\begin{matrix} A \\ B \end{matrix} \quad \rceil\!\!) \quad Q = A.B$$

The input signals are A and B, and the output is shown as A.B The . is the Boolean algebra way of saying 'AND'. Sometimes it is omitted and the AND function would be written Q = AB.

The truth table for a two-input AND gate is shown below:

Fig. 1.13 *Truth table for an AND gate*

input A	B	output Q
0	0	0
0	1	0
1	0	0
1	1	1

This table shows that the only way to get a 1 at the output is if both the A *and* B inputs are 1. This is why the device is called an AND gate.

Another, equally important way to think of the operation of this gate is as follows: a 0 at either input forces the output to 0.

A three-input AND gate has the truth table as shown:

Fig. 1.14 *Truth table for 3-input AND gate*

input			output
A	B	C	Q
0	0	0	0
0	0	1	0
0	1	0	0
0	1	1	0
1	0	0	0
1	0	1	0
1	1	0	0
1	1	1	1

The output is a 1 only when A *and* B *and* C are all 1. A 0 at any input causes the output to be 0. The Boolean algebra description of a three-input AND gate is Q = A.B.C.

Basic gates: the OR gate

The symbol for a two-input OR gate is:

Fig. 1.15 *An OR gate*

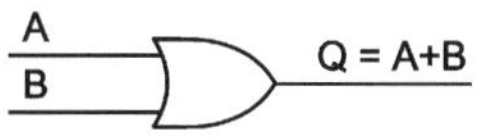

Note the Boolean algebra use of + to mean OR. The truth table is:

Fig. 1.16 *Truth table for an OR gate*

input		output
A	B	Q
0	0	0
0	1	1
1	0	1
1	1	1

The way this works is that the output is a 1 if A *or* B is 1, hence the name OR gate. The only way to get a 0 out is if both inputs are 0.

A three-input OR gate has the truth table:

Fig. 1.17 *Truth table for a three-input OR gate*

input			output
A	B	C	Q
0	0	0	0
0	0	1	1
0	1	0	1
0	1	1	1
1	0	0	1
1	0	1	1
1	1	0	1
1	1	1	1

Here you can see that a 1 on any input forces a 1 at the output. In Boolean algebra, $Q = A + B + C$.

Basic gates: the NAND gate

You have now seen all the building blocks used in digital circuits. Amazingly, all digital systems are build of just AND gates, OR gates and inverters. In theory, you don't even need the two sorts of gate, since you can build one from the other, as Chapter 2 discusses. There are a few more gates that are regarded as 'basic' however, and the NAND gate is the first to be examined. This can be thought of as an AND gate followed by an inverter.

Correspondingly, the logic symbol consists of an AND symbol followed by the small circle seen before. These small circles are sometimes referred to as 'inversion bubbles'.

Fig. 1.18 *A NAND gate*

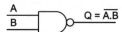

Note that the output is indicated with a single bar over the signal. The A and B signals are ANDed together to form A.B, then this is inverted to give $\overline{A.B}$.

The truth table can be constructed by ANDing the signals together, then inverting the result.

Fig. 1.19 *Truth table for NAND gate*

input			output
A	B	A.B	Q
0	0	0	1
0	1	0	1
1	0	0	1
1	1	1	0

In this table the A.B column shows the result of ANDing A and B together. The output of the gate, however, is the inverse of this, as shown in the final column.

For the NAND gate, inputs A *and* B must both be 1 to get a 0 out. Any 0s at the input cause the output to go to 1.

Basic gates: the NOR gate

Just as the NAND is AND followed by NOT, so NOR is OR followed by NOT:

Fig. 1.20 *A NOR gate*

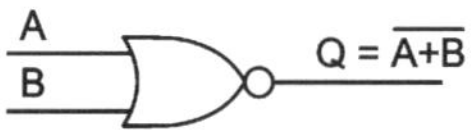

$$A \quad B \quad Q = \overline{A+B}$$

Note that first the A and B signals are ORed together to give $A + B$, then this signal is inverted to give $\overline{A+B}$.

The truth table can be constructed by taking the OR truth table and inverting:

Fig. 1.21 *Truth table for a NOR gate*

input			output
A	B	A + B	Q
0	0	0	1
0	1	1	0
1	0	1	0
1	1	1	0

For the NOR gate a 1 on any input forces a 0 at the output. Both inputs must be 0 to get a 1 out.

Basic gates: a summary

The symbols, Boolean algebra representation and action of the gates introduced above are summarised here.

Fig. 1.22 *Summary of basic gates*

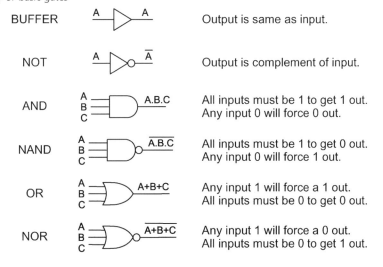

BUFFER	A ▷ A	Output is same as input.
NOT	A ▷○ $\overline{A}$	Output is complement of input.
AND	A B C — A.B.C	All inputs must be 1 to get 1 out. Any input 0 will force 0 out.
NAND	A B C — $\overline{A.B.C}$	All inputs must be 1 to get 0 out. Any input 0 will force 1 out.
OR	A B C — A+B+C	Any input 1 will force a 1 out. All inputs must be 0 to get 0 out.
NOR	A B C — $\overline{A+B+C}$	Any input 1 will force a 0 out. All inputs must be 0 to get 1 out.

The truth tables are not given, but can be deduced from the descriptions given of the way the gates act. In fact, it is better to remember these descriptions rather than trying to think in truth table terms. See if you can apply them to the following questions.

QUESTIONS

1.1 A 3-input AND gate has a 1 at its output. Which of the following input combinations can cause this?
(a) 000   (b) 010   (c) 101   (d) 111

1.2 A 4-input NAND gate has a 1 at its output. Which of the following input combinations can cause this?
(a) 0000   (b) 0101   (c) 1010   (d) 1111

1.3 A 3-input NOR gate has a 1 at its output. Which of the following input combinations can cause this?
(a) 000   (b) 010   (c) 101   (d) 111

1.4 A 4-input NOR gate has a 1 on one of its inputs. Its output will be?
(a) 0   (b) 1   (c) not enough information to tell   (d) 5V

For the following questions the available answers are:

(a) stay low
(b) stay high
(c) oscillate in phase with the clock input
(d) oscillate out of phase with the clock input

The 'clock' is a signal that oscillates between 0 and 1, 50 times a second.

QUESTIONS

1.5 An inverter (NOT gate) has the clock signal on its input. The output will . . . ?   (choose from (a), (b), (c) or (d) above)

1.6 A 2-input NAND gate has both inputs joined together, and to the clock signal. The output will . . . ?   (a), (b), (c) or (d)

1.7 A 2-input AND gate has the clock signal on one input and the other input is held permanently low.
The output will . . . ?   (a), (b), (c) or (d)

1.8 A 2-input NAND gate has the clock signal on one input and a permanent high on the other. The output will . . . ?   (a), (b), (c) or (d)

Fig. 1.23 *Circuit for questions 1.9–1.12*

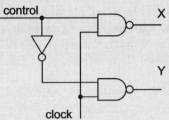

1.9 In Figure 1.23 above the control signal is permanently high. The output X will . . . ? (a), (b), (c) or (d)

1.10 In Figure 1.23 above the control signal is permanently high. The output Y will . . . ? (a), (b), (c) or (d)   ·

1.11 In Figure 1.23 above the control signal is permanently low. The output X will . . . ? (a), (b), (c) or (d)

1.12 In Figure 1.23 above the control signal is permanently low. The output Y will . . . ? (a), (b), (c) or (d)

PRACTICAL EXERCISE 1.1

This exercise uses Electronics Workbench to check out the input and output characteristics of the 74LS and 74HC logic families.

Run Electronics Workbench and open the file **fig1_24.ewb**. You should get a circuit like Figure 1.24 shown below. ☐

Fig. 1.24 *EWB investigation of logic input and output characteristics*

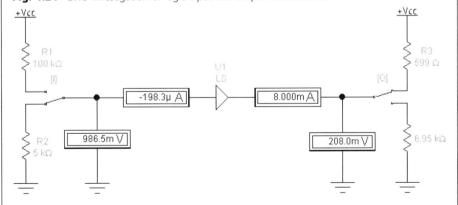

The input switch (operated by the I key on the keyboard) and the associated ammeter and voltmeter allow the input characteristics to be investigated. Similarly, the output characteristics are demonstrated by use of the O switch. The $+V_{CC}$ symbol is a connection to +5V, and the buffer circuit, U1, is operated from a +5V supply.

Right-click and choose **Component properties...** or double-click on the buffer circuit, click the **Models** tab and choose **ttl/LS** as the logic family. ☐

Use the **Edit** button and verify the following settings:

- V_{OH} = 3.4V (minimum output voltage for HIGH)
- V_{OL} = 0.4V (maximum output voltage for LOW)
- V_{IH} = 2.0V (minimum input voltage acceptable as HIGH)
- V_{IL} = 0.8V (maximum input voltage acceptable as LOW)
- V_{TG} = 1.3V (threshold input voltage dividing HIGH from LOW)
- T_{PLH} = 10ns (propagation delay for rising input edge)
- T_{PHL} = 10ns (propagation delay for falling edge)

LS input characteristics

Edit R1 and R2 to be just 1Ω. As you switch the input between HIGH and LOW you should find that the LS input current switches between +20µA and −400µA. This confirms the figures and direction of the current (into the input for HIGH, out of the input for LOW) given previously. Note that in Electronics Workbench, ammeters give positive readings if conventional current flows into the side with a lightly drawn border, and out from the side with the heavy line border. The convention in data sheets is that current flowing into a device is regarded as positive, while current flowing out is negative. ☐

With the values of R1 and R2 as shown (R1 = 100k pull-up, R2 = 5k pull-down) the circuit is near the borderline for legal logic levels at the input. When the input switch is set to LOW, only 198.3µA is drawn, and the input voltage rises to almost 1V. This is actually above the V_{IL} value of 0.8V, but below the threshold voltage, V_{TG} of 1.3V, so EWB still regards it as a LOW, and the buffer generates a good LOW at its output.

Experiment with different values for R2. What value for R2 results in a good, safe LOW input voltage of 0.1V? ☐

Investigate the situation for HIGH. What value for R1 will pull the input up to a good HIGH input level of 4.9? ☐

Why is R1 a different value from R2 for the previous two experiments? ☐

When designing circuits, it is recommended that you use a pull-up resistor rather than pull-down. For instance, Figure 1.25(a) is to be preferred over Figure 1.25(b): although it gives an active-low action, it has better noise immunity, and switches less current.

LS output characteristics

Turning to the output side, the values of R3 and R4 have been chosen to give the maximum recommended output currents for a standard 74LS device. As you can see from Figure 1.24, setting R3 to 599Ω causes exactly 8mA (the recommended

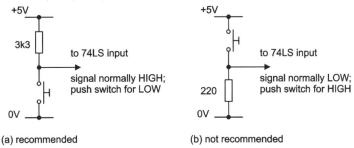

Fig. 1.25 *Use of pull-up and pull-down resistors at inputs*

+5V

3k3

to 74LS input

signal normally HIGH;
push switch for LOW

0V

(a) recommended

+5V

to 74LS input

signal normally LOW;
push switch for HIGH

220

0V

(b) not recommended

maximum) to flow when the output is LOW. The resulting output voltage is 0.208V, well below the 0.5V value of V_{OL}.

Switch the input switch up and the output switch down so that you can check the situation for an output set to logic HIGH. You should find that 400μA is drawn from the output and that the output voltage is just over 2.7V. This agrees with the 74LS specification for V_{OH} and I_{OH}. (It disagrees with the V_{OH} setting of 3.4V for the EWB model for the device. It would seem that the simulated internal circuitry requires V_{OH} to be set to 3.4V in order for the actual simulation to agree with real devices.) □

R3 and R4 have different values, reflecting the different drive capabilities of the output when HIGH and LOW. This leads to a recommended way of using the output to drive devices such as LEDs. It is better to connect them as shown in Figure 1.26(a) rather than 1.26(b). The output signal is active LOW, but capable of delivering more current.

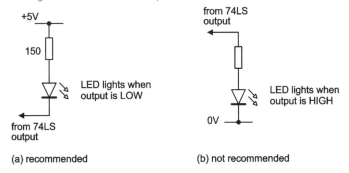

Fig. 1.26 *Driving devices from a 74LS output*

+5V

150

LED lights when
output is LOW

from 74LS
output

(a) recommended

from 74LS
output

LED lights when
output is HIGH

0V

(b) not recommended

Electronics Workbench can be used to simulate these ways of driving an LED. Add LEDs in series with R3 and R4, then edit each one to be red_LED type, with model parameters: junction potential: 1.5V; turn-on current: 0.015A □

Make a note that when you come to exit this simulation choose **No** when asked if you want to save the default LED library. □

Edit R3 and R4 so that they are both 150Ω. If you run the simulation with the output switch in the up position you should find that the top LED lights up (its two photon-arrows turn dark!) when the input switch is down. On the other hand, running the simulation with the output switch selecting the Figure 1.26(b) type of circuit, you cannot get the bottom LED to turn on. (Reducing R4 to 50Ω does allow the LED to illuminate, however.) □

HC input characteristics

Turning to the high-speed CMOS logic family, the 74HC device is much more symmetrical than the 74LS. Edit the buffer to be type CMOS HC, change R1 and R2 so that they are both 100k, and R3 and R4 so that they are both 150Ω. □

Run the simulator and check the input logic levels for both positions of the input switch. Are they well behaved, close to the V_{CC} or 0V rails? □

HC output characteristics

Now measure the output logic levels. Check that a LOW output, with the output switch up, sinks enough current to make the LED light up. What current do you get? What is the output voltage? Is it within the acceptable range for a logic LOW, i.e. 0–1.5V? □

Now check out the opposite situation: input HIGH, output switch down. Does the LED light up? What current do you get? What is the output voltage? Is it within the acceptable limits for a logic HIGH, i.e. 3.5–5V? □

HC buffer-type and open-drain output characteristics

Repeat the last two tests but with a buffer type HC circuit. Does the buffer type output drive the LEDs better than the normal HC output? □

Repeat the tests on the output capabilities of the buffer, but change the logic type to HC-OD (open drain). Does a LOW output turn on the top LED? Does a HIGH drive the bottom LED satisfactorily? □

Effect of measuring instrument input resistance

It is interesting to check how the measuring instruments themselves affect some readings in this particular set-up. On the input side, with the input switch set to HIGH, you should find that the voltmeter reads 4.539V. This reading is a little on the low side because the voltmeter itself is dragging the voltage down. If you double-click on the voltmeter you can increase its input impedance to 100MΩ. Now what does the HIGH level read? □

Schmitt-trigger input devices

The section earlier in this chapter on Schmitt-trigger inputs briefly discusses how they can help circuits switch cleanly even if input signals are changing slowly. The problem with slowly changing signals is that the inevitable noise will cause

Fig. 1.27 *Schmitt and ordinary inputs compared*

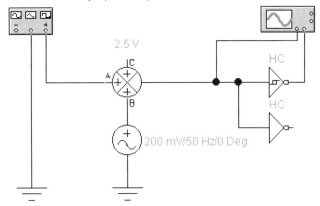

erratic switching of the output. This is demonstrated in the Electronics Workbench circuit shown in Figure 1.27. Run Electronics Workbench and open the file **fig1_27.ewb**. □

The device in the centre of the figure is a 'three-way voltage summer'. Here it adds 200mV of 50Hz noise to a slowly changing (1Hz) 2.5V triangle wave. It also adds in 2.5V DC offset. The coefficients of the summer should be: Input A offset voltage = 2.5; Input A gain = 1; Output gain = 1. All the others should be 0. The signal generator should be set for 1Hz, 50% duty cycle, 2.5V amplitude and 0V offset. The AC voltage source should be set to 200mV amplitude, 50Hz. The oscilloscope settings should be 0.2s/div and 2V/div for the A and B inputs. Other settings should be 0. □

Under the **Analysis \ Analysis Options…** menu choose the **Instruments** tab and set (tick the box) for the **Oscilloscope Pause** after each screen option. □

With the settings given above there should be no noise added to the triangle wave. Run the simulation, open the oscilloscope and enlarge the oscilloscope display. Drag the red and blue vertical hairlines to the points where the input signal (the triangle wave) causes the output (the rectangular wave) to switch states. What input voltage causes the output to switch when the input is falling? How about when it is rising? How much hysteresis is there? Do the figures agree with those given in the paragraph above on Schmitt-trigger inputs? (No, they don't! But they are close to those given in the data book for a 74HCT14, rather than the 74HC14.) □

Now move the oscilloscope channel B input to the *ordinary* inverter's output and repeat the experiment. How much hysteresis is there for the simulated ordinary inverter? □

Now add in the noise by setting the Input B gain (note gain, not offset) in the summer to 1. Re-run the simulation, and note all the glitches on the output of the inverter, as Figure 1.28 illustrates. □

Finally, move the scope B input back to the Schmitt-trigger inverter output, run the simulation, appreciate the clean switching of the output and make sure you know *why* it's so nice. □

Fig. 1.28 *Output glitches caused by slow, noisy input signal*

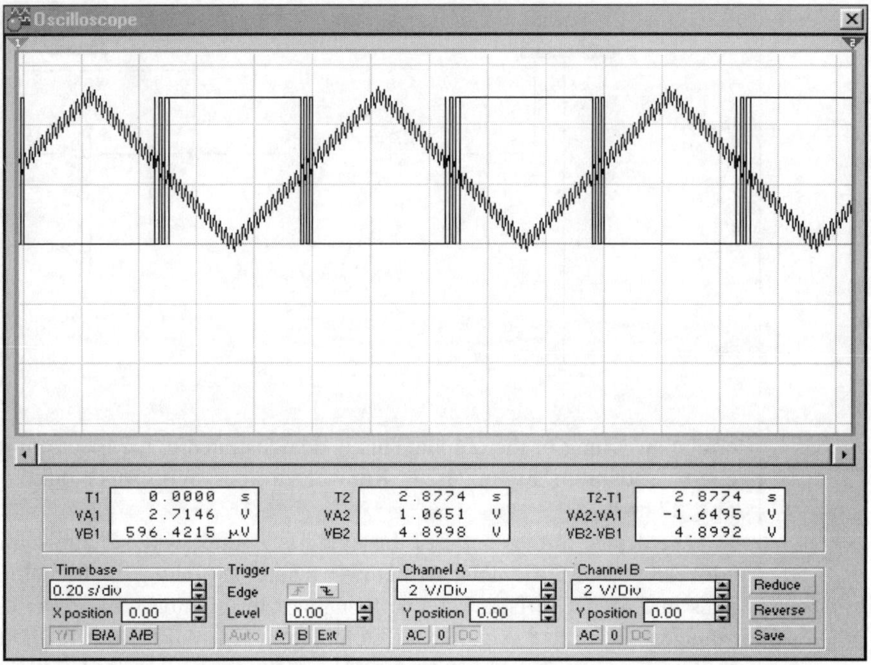

There is one more thing you can do. Click the **B/A** button on the time base. This tells you how the output (B) depends on the input (A), the *transfer characteristic* of the device. You should notice that it resembles the little symbol inside the triangle of the Schmitt-trigger inverter.   □

PRACTICAL EXERCISE 1.2

This exercise uses the XPLA software and the demonstration board hardware to verify the function of the digital processing elements that have been covered in this chapter. If you don't have the hardware, you will still be able to simulate the results, but you need the demonstration board to switch real switches and see real LEDs light up!

The demonstration board contains a 'Complex Programmable Logic Chip' (CPLD) that can be programmed to perform many different logic operations, from the basic gates that have been covered in this chapter to the counters, state machines and more advanced digital systems that you will cover later. The board also contains a few switches that can set the levels of input signals, and LEDs that can display the states of output signals.

In order to use the demonstration board the following steps are necessary:

---

1. Run the XPLA software, and type in a description of your required circuit, using the editor.
2. Save your description, then compile it.
3. Optionally, simulate the action of the circuit ('Functional simulation').
4. Get the software to work out how to fit the circuit into the CPLD chip on the demonstration board. Optionally re-simulate ('Timing simulation').
5. Run the ISP download software and send the design to the chip on the board.
6. Test the design.

Step 1

If the software has been installed using the default options you can start step 1 by pressing: **Start \ Programs \ XPLA Professional \ XPLA Professional**. When the **Project Panel** is shown (see Figure 1.29) click on the **Project** menu then **New...** to open the **New Project** window. ☐

You can arrange your work as you wish, but it is a good idea to create a folder for each project, and this can be done using the file management facilities within the **New Project** window. Use the drop-down window in the **Save in**: field to navigate to a suitable location in the file structure, then use the **Create New Folder** button to do just that. For the purposes of this book, a folder called **xplawork** was created on the c: drive, and for this chapter a folder within **xplawork** called **basic_gates** was made. ☐

Having created a folder for your project, you need to name the project. As well as being a suitable name for the folder, **basic_gates** is a suitable name for the project. Having chosen a name, type it in the **File name** field, set the **Save as type** field to **PRJ files (*.prj)**, then click the **Save** button. ☐

Fig. 1.29 *XPLA Project Panel after a few initialising procedures*

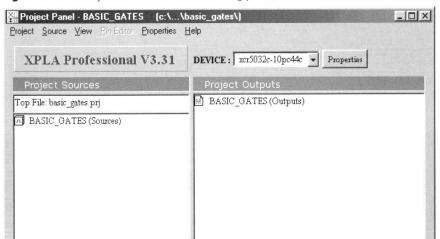

The next step is to choose a particular device as the target for your design. This is done with the **Devices** field of the **Project Panel**. Use the drop-down facilities to choose a **5V device \ 5032 \ xcr5032c-10pc44c** device. The **Project Panel** should now look something like Figure 1.29. ☐

You can now complete Step 1 by using the XPLA editor to type a description of the circuit to be configured within the chip. Click the **Source** menu and choose **New File...** to open the **Create New File** dialog box. Select PHDL as the **Type** of design entry method you wish to use, and enter a name for your design; **basic_gates** is a suitable name for the file. Enter the file name in the **Name** field then click the **New** button. The XPLA editor should open with a few headings already present. ☐

(If you have followed the suggestions given above, you will now have a folder named **basic_gates** containing both a project called **basic_gates.prj**, and a file called **basic_gates.phd**.)

The PHDL file should be completed as Figure 1.30. PHDL stands for Philips Hardware Description Language, and is the language that will be used throughout this book.

Fig. 1.30 *PHDL code for AND gate*

```
MODULE  basic_gates
TITLE    'First experiment with PHDL: a three-input AND gate'

DECLARATIONS
A, B, C               pin 4,6,8;          "INPUTS
AOUT, BOUT, COUT, Q   pin 16,17,18,27;    "OUTPUTS

EQUATIONS

AOUT = A;
BOUT = B;
COUT = C;
Q = A & B & C;

END
```

When you have finished typing the file, click the **Save** button to save it. ☐
An explanation of the PHDL file follows.

The first line of any PHDL file starts with the **MODULE** keyword, followed by the name of the module. The **TITLE** is optional, but useful for documentation purposes. Comments are essential for documentation purposes. A **"** indicates that what follows on that line is a comment.

The **DECLARATIONS** section declares the names of all the signals that are used in the design. This design uses three inputs and four outputs. The pin connections may also be given, as they are in this example. Referring to Appendix A, the circuit diagram of the demonstration board, you can see that signal **A** will be controlled by SW1, signal **B** by SW2, and signal **C** by SW3. The outputs **AOUT**, **BOUT** and **COUT** are included so that the logic level of the input switches can be indicated by elements of the bar graph.

The required behaviour of the design is defined in the **EQUATIONS** section. In this example the first three lines simply connect the three outputs directly to the three inputs, for monitoring purposes. The last line implements the AND gate. Note the use of the **&** sign to represent AND. Boolean algebra uses a dot (.) of course, but dots are used for other purposes in PHDL.

Note the use of the semi-colon (**;**) at the end of each statement. The final line of any PHDL file should contain just the keyword **END** (and no full stop).

Step 2
Having typed in and saved the source code, it is now time to process it, so return to the **Project Panel** and click the **Compile** button. After a little computer activity, the process should finish, and the message **Compiler executed successfully with no error**! should appear in the status bar of the **Project Panel**. If your PHDL file contained some error, then you may not get this message, but an error report in the log file, instead. If this happens, read the error report, sort out the problem, remember to save the corrected PHDL file, then re-compile.   □

Step 3
Getting the file to compile means that the XPLA software can understand what you have written but it doesn't mean that your design will necessarily do what you want it to. The simulation facilities of XPLA do give you a chance to check out the likely behaviour of your design, however. For this design you need to simulate all possible input states, and check that the Q output goes HIGH when, and only when, all three inputs are HIGH.

Click on the **FunSim** . . . button. The XPLA simulator should run, and automatically display the three input and four output signals. All the signals should be crosshatched, meaning that the simulator has not yet worked out what the actual logic levels should be on the various signals. Before attending to the signals however, set the simulation period to 1000ns by deleting a few 0s in the **Simulate Until** field, then press the **Enter** key on the keyboard. The time scale across the top of the display should run from 0 to 1000.   □

Logic levels need to be set on the input signals so that, when the **Run** button is pressed, the simulator can work out what will happen to the outputs. The normal way to ensure the inputs are exercised through all possible combinations is to make them count in binary. The binary number system is discussed later, but making the three signals toggle on and off at frequencies that progressively halve will achieve this.

Click the **Create Clk** button to open the **Clock Setting** dialog box. Check that the **Cycle Length** is set to 100ns, and the **Duty Cycle** is set to 50%.

Ensure that the **Start Value** is **Start** at 0, then click **Accept**. The message in the **Clock Setting** dialog box should tell you to select a signal, so click on signal **A**. You should see a nice 10MHz square wave displayed for signal **A**. Don't close the **Clock Settings** dialog box – you now need to set signal **B** to 5MHz, and signal **C** to 2.5MHz. Set the **Cycle Length to** 200ns, click **Accept**, then signal **B**. Finally, set the **Cycle Length** to 400ns, click **Accept**, then signal **C**. Now you can close the **Clock Settings** dialog box by pressing **Done**.   □

Fig. 1.31 *Simulation results for 3-input AND gate*

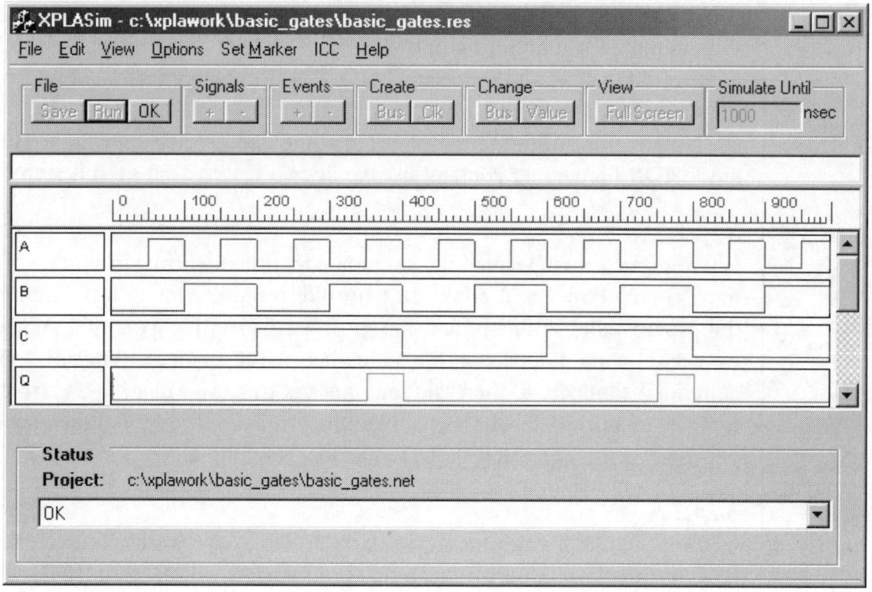

Having set the input signals it is now time to see how the design behaves. Click the **Run** button and wait for the simulation software to do its stuff, then check that the Q output does indeed go HIGH when, but only when, all three inputs are HIGH, i.e. between 350 and 400ns, and between 750 and 800ns, as shown in Figure 1.31.

Figure 1.31 has had the AOUT, BOUT and COUT signals removed. You can do this if you wish by means of the **Signals** button. The other signal not showing is the # check. This signal indicates if there are any nasty glitches (short spikes) on any of the internal circuit nodes. Hopefully, it will indicate LOW for the duration of all your simulations.

Before leaving the simulator there is one more thing you can check: the propagation delay. This is the time taken for an input change to affect the output. From Figure 1.31 it looks as if the output changes as soon as all three inputs go high, but if you double-click on a waveform near the 350ns point, you zoom in. (Double-clicking the right-hand mouse button zooms back out again.) Keep double-clicking until you get the '**Maximum resolution reached!!!**' message, but check each time you zoom that you can still see the rising edge of the Q signal. It should soon become clear that the input and output signals do not change simultaneously. □

It should be possible to use the time scale at the top of the display to measure the propagation delay, but it seems to get a bit out of step as the zoom facility is used. The delay can be measured, however, by using the **Set Marker** facility instead.

Use the **View \ Full Screen** button to zoom out to view the whole of the simulation period, then click the **Set Marker** menu item at the top of the simulation window. Nothing much will happen, except that the **Set Marker** item will become greyed out. If you press the mouse button just to the left of the rising edge of signal

A at 350ns and keep it pressed a little while, a vertical marker line will attach itself to that edge. The number in red at the top of the marker gives the time co-ordinate of the edge. Now move the mouse just to the left of the rising edge on the **Q** signal and press (and hold) the mouse button again. A second line should appear, drawn through the rising edge on the **Q** signal. The information at the top of this line gives the time co-ordinate of this edge in red, but also the time interval between the two markers in blue. The blue number gives the propagation delay for the AND gate – 3ns. This is a nominal value. A more realistic value will be discovered later. ☐

You can clear the markers by pressing the **Clear Marker** menu item at the top of the simulation window.

Step 4

That completes the 'functional simulation' of the design, and it looks as if your AND gate design should work! You can now move on to step 4: fitting the design to the chip that you have in mind as a target. Close down the simulator, check that the **Project Panel** indicates the correct chip in the **Device field (xcr5032c-10pc44c)** and press the **Fit** button. After a little while the XPLA software should work out how to fit your design onto your chosen chip, generating a total of eight output files viewable in the **Project Outputs** window. This completes step 4. ☐

Before downloading the design to the chip, it is worth revisiting the simulator, but this time hit the **TimeSim . . .** button. The simulator window should reappear, with the signals set up as you left them. Click on the **Run** button, wait for the simulation to finish, then use the **Set Marker** facility again to check the propagation delay. You should find that the delay is reported as 10ns. This is a realistic estimate of the propagation delay, based on the actual chip chosen for the design. The '10' in the part number refers to the propagation delay of the chip. There are versions with 7ns and 6ns delays available, at greater cost. ☐

Step 5

Having checked as thoroughly as you can that the design is likely to work, it's time to download the design to the target hardware, step 5. The XPLA PC-ISP software is used for this but before running the software you need to connect the target board to the PC by means of the ISP download cable. This plugs into the 10-pin rectangular connector on the target board and to the parallel port (remove any printer cable connected) on the PC. ☐

Apply 9V unregulated, centre-positive DC power to the target board. ☐

Now start the download software by pressing **Start \ Programs \ XPLA PC-ISP Programmer \ XPLA PC_ISP**. ☐

The software looks at the parallel port to find out what type of cable you are using, and if that cable is connected to any devices. It should find an ISP HyperCable/Board and 1 JTAG device, and report this in the message window of the programmer software. ☐

(If you do run the ISP software before making the connection between the PC and the target board you will have to establish communications by clicking

HyperCable \ Check connection. If there is still a problem click on the **Port Setup...** menu and ensure that neither the Altera nor Xilinx cables are selected. Also check that the correct address of the parallel port is selected (**Auto Port Select** should work, but you could try setting the specific value: normally 378 hex), click OK and hit **HyperCable \ Check connection** again.)

You now have to tell the programmer three things: which device you are targeting, which file contains the design that you wish to download, and what you want the programmer to do. Double-click on the **Device Name** cell on row 1 of the **Device** tab of the **Configure JTAG chain devices** window. Select **XCRx032_CA** from the list that pops up. ☐

Now double-click in the **Design File Name** cell on row 1. A window should open that allows you to find your design file, which should be a JEDEC type.

Navigate to your file, select it then click **Open**. For the example in this chapter the path to the file is **c:\xplawork\basic_gates\basic_gates.jed**. ☐

Finally, double-click the **Operation** cell, and select **Prog_&_Verify**. ☐

The Programmer window should look like Figure 1.32.

Downloading can now start: click the **Execute** button, watch the messages and wait a second or so for the process to complete. ☐

Step 6

Step 6 is where you actually test the finished hardware. The three large slide switches control the input signals to the AND gate configured inside the PLD chip,

Fig. 1.32 *Programmer software ready to download*

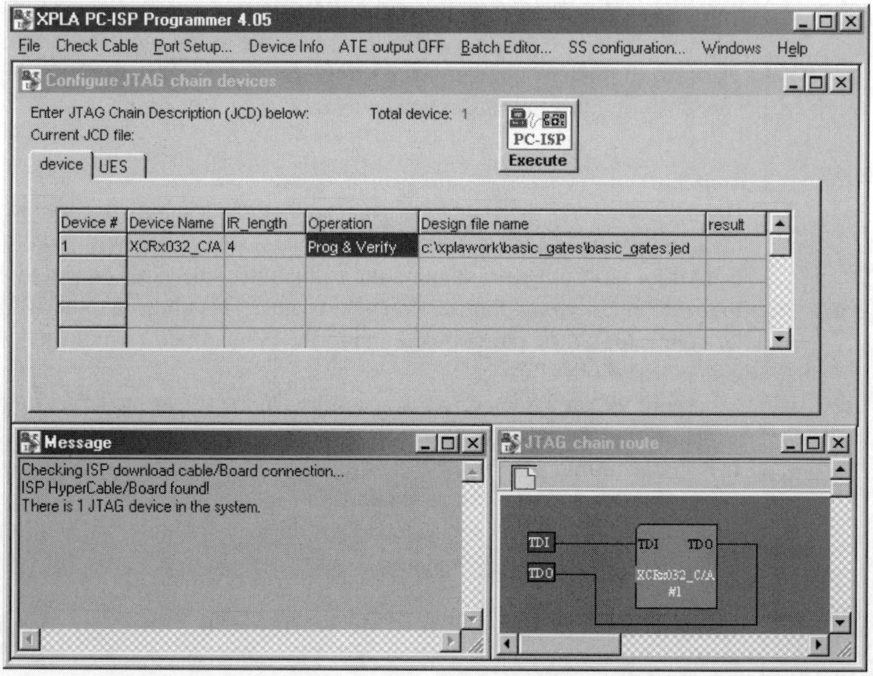

and the three left-hand LEDs of the bar-graph display monitor the states of these signals. The right-hand LED indicates the state of the output of the AND gate. Switch SW4d (the right-hand one of the DIL switch) has to be closed (up) for the bar graph to be operative.

What do you have to do to the three switches to make the output go high? Is this in accordance with the truth table of a three-input AND gate? □

Having spent a considerable amount of effort learning how to use the XPLA software, you should go back over the six steps of the process, but this time implementing a three-input OR gate.

The only difference as far as the design is concerned is that the PHDL file should contain the OR function Q = A # B # C; instead of the AND function Q = A & B & C; Note the use of # to mean OR.

Assuming that the XPLA and PC_ISP software packages are already running, it should take you about one minute to amend the PHDL file, save it, compile it, simulate the design, fit the design to the chip, and download the new design to the target board. □

In similar quick fashion, you should check out the NAND and NOR functions. The inversion symbol is ! Thus you could have Q = !A for simple inversion of one signal, or Q=!(A&B&C); for NAND, and Q=!(A#B#C); for NOR. □

While you have the software running, try out the exclusive-OR function by amending the defining equation to Q = A $ B $ C; Make a note of the results. What do you have to do to the inputs to make the output go high? □

This exercise tests out a variation of the little circuit given in Figure 1.23. The new circuit is shown in Figure 1.33.

Fig. 1.33 *Clock demultiplexer*

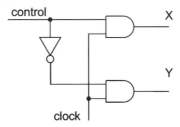

The circuit should send the clock signal to output X if the Control is HIGH but to output Y if it's LOW. Taking an input signal and switching to this output or that one is called 'demultiplexing'.

The PHDL code for this is given in Figure 1.34.

Fig. 1.34 *PHDL code for clock demultiplexer*

```
MODULE  basic_gates
TITLE   'two-way demultiplexer'

DECLARATIONS
clock, control    pin 43,14;     "clock, push switch
X, Y              pin 16,27;     "left, right LEDs

EQUATIONS

X = control & clock;
Y = !control & clock;

END
```

Use the XPLA editor to enter this design, save as **demux.phd**, or some such name, remove any existing source file from the project and replace it with this one. □

Compile, fit, download and test. The 555 timer circuit in the top left of the demonstration board generates the clock signal. You can adjust its frequency by means of the variable resistor in that area of the board. Check that either the left or right LEDs in the bar graph flash, depending on whether or not the microswitch is pressed. □

It should be clear from this circuit why the AND functions are referred to as 'gates'. They act as gates across a signal path and are opened to let the clock signal through when the control signal is in the correct logic state.

An alternative way of thinking about the circuit is 'if the control signal is high the clock should come out on connection X, else on connection Y'. The PHDL language supports such thinking, as the code in Figure 1.35 shows.

Fig. 1.35 *PHDL code for clock demultiplexer*

```
MODULE  basic_gates
TITLE   'two-way demultiplexer'

DECLARATIONS
clock, control    pin 43,14;     "clock, micro switch
X, Y              pin 16,27;     "left, right LEDs

EQUATIONS

when (control == 0) then X = clock;
else Y = clock;

END
```

Try out this code. Note the use of **when** rather than **if**, and **==** rather than just **=**. The double-equals sign is used when a condition is being tested, while single-equals is used to connect signals together.

Edit the previous PHDL module, save, compile, fit, download and test. It should behave exactly as the original design, except that the default side for the LED to flash is on the left. □

As a final variation on this theme, design a circuit that will flash the left-hand LED if the three-position slide switch is pushed to the left, the right LED when pushed to the right, but neither when it's in the middle. You will need to refer to the circuit diagram of the demonstration board (Appendix A) for further information, such as the pin numbers. Answers are given at the end of this chapter. □

PRACTICAL EXERCISE 1.4

In this exercise the input and output characteristics of the **xcr5032c-10pc44c** CPLD chip are investigated. You need to have a copy of the circuit diagram (Appendix A) to refer to. A digital multimeter is suitable for making the measurements. The bare terminal pin near the two transistors is a 0V test point. SW4d should be closed (up) initially.

Input characteristics

The 4.7k resistors in SIL resistor pack RN1 act as pull-downs when the switches are open. The 1k resistors in the DIL resistor pack RN4 protect connections A0 through A9 of the PLD chip in the event of a conflict between an I/O pin being programmed as a LOW output and the corresponding switch being connected HIGH. The DIL pack also provides a convenient set of pins to make voltage measurements. The bottom side of the DIL pack corresponds to the left side on the schematic. RN4a is at the left-hand end of the DIL pack.

Measure the voltage at the bottom end of RN4a when SW1 is down (open circuit). What current must be flowing through the pull-down resistor? □

Now set SW1 HIGH and measure the voltage on the bottom and top sides of RN4a. What current must be flowing into then PLD input pin? □

Don't worry if you get 0 for some of your answers. Your measurements are telling you that the input pins take very little current – less than you can detect.

Output characteristics

Switch SW1 up so that the left-hand LED of the bar graph illuminates. Measure the voltage at the anode of the LED. You can access this node by means of the corresponding pin of the connector socket just above the LED. □

The voltage you have just measured is the PLD output voltage while it is delivering enough current to illuminate the LED. The no-load output voltage can be measured by open-circuiting the LED path. Create this condition by opening SW4d. Note the new output voltage. □

Close SW4d so that the LED comes back on again and measure the voltage on the cathode of the LED. You can access this circuit node on the component side of the board via the top end of R7. □

Calculate the current flowing through the current limit resistor, R7, and hence the current delivered by the PLD output pin. From your knowledge of the open-circuit and on-load output voltages, and the on-load current, calculate the Thévenin output resistance of the PLD. □

(See end of chapter for typical results.)

Binary numbers, decimal numbers and hexadecimal numbers

As already discussed, signals in digital systems can take one of two possible states: either HIGH or LOW. Similarly, the digits in the binary number system can take one of two possible states: either 1 or 0. Hence, digital systems and binary numbers are natural bedfellows; digital systems are basically machines for manipulating binary numbers.

Decimal numbers are the numbers we use every day, of course, but they don't have an easy relationship to binary numbers. Hexadecimal numbers do have a nice relationship to binary numbers, and are easier for humans to use than binary.

Decimal numbers

The decimal number 1904 means 'one thousand, nine hundred and four'. Written in powers of 10, $1904 = 1 \times 10^3 + 9 \times 10^2 + 0 \times 10^1 + 4 \times 10^0$. The decimal number system may be described as 'base ten'. Ten different symbols are needed for a base ten system. The ten different symbols are 0, 1, 2, 3, 4, 5, 6, 7, 8 and 9.

When counting up in decimal you go through all ten digits, then, when you run out, you add another column, whose digits are worth ten times those on their right. Perhaps you knew that already!

Binary numbers

The binary number 1101 means 'one eight, one four and one'. Written in powers of 2, $1101 = 1 \times 2^3 + 1 \times 2^2 + 0 \times 10^1 + 1 \times 2^0$. The binary number system may be described as 'base two'. Two different symbols are needed for a base two system. The two different symbols are 0 and 1.

When counting up in binary you go through both digits, then, when you run out, you add another column, whose digits are worth twice those on their right.

Binary numbers are normally written with the 'weightiest' on the left and 'lightest' on the right, just like the decimal system. The terms 'most significant bit' (MSB) and 'least significant bit' (LSB) are used respectively for these concepts. The term 'bit' is derived from *binary* dig*it*.

Hexadecimal numbers

The hexadecimal number 190F means 'one lot of 4096, nine lots of 256 and eff'. Written in powers of 16, $190F = 1 \times 16^3 + 9 \times 16^2 + 0 \times 16^1 + F \times 10^0$. The hexadecimal number system may be described as 'base sixteen'. Sixteen different symbols are needed for a base sixteen system. The sixteen different symbols are 0, 1, 2, 3, 4, 5, 6, 7, 8, 9, A, B, C, D, E and F. Sometimes the symbols 0, 1, 2, 3, 4, 5, 6, 7, 8, 9, a, b, c, d, e and f are used, or a mixture of the two sets.

A is worth one more than 9 (hold two hands up and count the fingers and thumbs: that many). F is worth one more than E (hold three hands up and count the fingers and thumbs: that many).

When counting up in hexadecimal you go through all sixteen digits, then, when you run out, you add another column, whose digits are worth sixteen times those on their right.

Relationship between the three number systems

Figure 1.36 shows what happens when you start counting up in the three number systems, starting at 0 and using the rules given above.

As mentioned above, there's not much of a relationship between decimal and the other two systems. If you need to do a conversion, just use a calculator.

Fig. 1.36 *Decimal, binary and hexidecimal numbers*

decimal	binary	hex
0	0	0
1	1	1
2	10	2
3	11	3
4	100	4
5	101	5
6	110	6
7	111	7
8	1000	8
9	1001	9
10	1010	A
11	1011	B
12	1100	C
13	1101	D
14	1110	E
15	1111	F
16	1 0000	10
17	1 0001	11
18	1 0010	12
...	...	...
31	1 1111	1F
32	10 0000	20
...	...	...
255	1111 1111	FF
256	1 0000 0000	100
...	...	...
4095	1111 1111 1111	FFF
4096	1 0000 0000 0000	1000
...	...	...
6415	1 1001 0000 1111	190F
6416	1 1001 0001 0000	1910
...	...	...

The relation between binary and hex is much closer. The pattern set in the first 16 entries (from decimal 0 to 15) just repeats itself indefinitely thereafter.

The binary digits have been grouped in fours to emphasise the relationship. Each hex digit always maps across to the same 4-bit binary pattern. Study the last two entries in the table and make sure you can see what's happening. Basically, you can pack four binary digits into one hex digit.

Two technical terms

A group of eight binary digits is called a 'byte'. A group of four is a 'nibble'. Presumably the latter term started life as a joke, but now it's official computerese.

IEC symbols for basic gates

As mentioned earlier, the IEC standard gives different symbols for the basic gates from the ones that have been used in this chapter. While the IEC standard is taking over for more complex devices, the older symbols are still very widely used for the basic gates. You will come across the IEC versions in some situations, however, such as when an AND function is embedded into a more complex device, so here they are.

Fig. 1.37 *IEC symbols for basic functions*

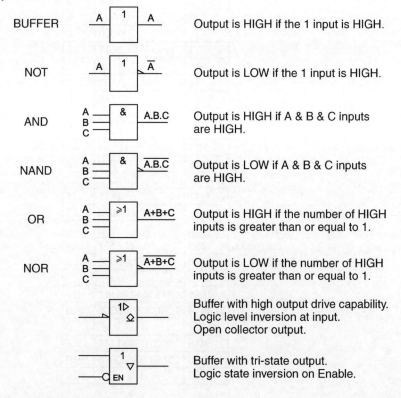

BUFFER		Output is HIGH if the 1 input is HIGH.
NOT		Output is LOW if the 1 input is HIGH.
AND		Output is HIGH if A & B & C inputs are HIGH.
NAND		Output is LOW if A & B & C inputs are HIGH.
OR		Output is HIGH if the number of HIGH inputs is greater than or equal to 1.
NOR		Output is LOW if the number of HIGH inputs is greater than or equal to 1.
		Buffer with high output drive capability. Logic level inversion at input. Open collector output.
		Buffer with tri-state output. Logic state inversion on Enable.

The & 'general qualifying symbol' clearly means AND. The ≥1 symbol for the OR gate means 'if 1 or more of the inputs are HIGH'. The half arrow 'polarity indicator' can be used at an input or an output to signify logic level inversion. The small circle negation symbol can also be used, but means logic state inversion, rather than voltage inversion, a distinction reflecting the possibilities of using either positive or negative logic. Generally, the half-arrows are used outside a device outline while the circle is used within.

Summary

This chapter has introduced digital signals and the fundamental logic operations that can be carried out on them. You should now be familiar with AND gates, OR gates and inverters, and with NAND and NOR gates. You should know about the input and output characteristics of the LS and HC logic families, and, if you have carried out practical exercise 1.4, with the input and output characteristics of the CPLD chip on the demonstration board.

The XPLA software has been introduced, and you should now know how to run the editor, compiler, fitter and pre- and post-fitting simulators. If you have the demonstration board, you should know how to download a design to it using the XPLA PC-ISP software, and how to use the board to test out basic designs.

ANSWERS TO QUESTIONS

1.1 **(d)**: Being an AND gate, the only way to get the output to go HIGH is for all three inputs to be HIGH.

1.2 **(a)**, **(b)** and **(c)**: Any input LOW forces a NAND gate output to go HIGH, so the only *in*correct answer is (d).

1.3 **(a)**: Any input HIGH forces a NOR gate output LOW. The output is HIGH, however so none of the inputs can be HIGH.

1.4 **(a)**: Any input HIGH forces a NOR gate output LOW.

1.5 **(d)**: An inverter will reproduce a clock signal at its output, but inverted, i.e. out of phase with the input.

1.6 **(d)**: Tying the two inputs of a NAND gate together turns it into an inverter.

1.7 **(a)**: A LOW input forces the output LOW for an AND gate. The gate is 'closed', preventing the signal from getting through.

1.8 **(d)**: The NAND gate is 'open' allowing the signal through, but it inverts it as well.

1.9 **(d)**: This is the same situation as 1.8.

1.10 **(b)**: The LOW from the inverter on the bottom NAND gate will force a HIGH out.

1.11 **(b)**: The LOW on the top NAND gate will force a HIGH out.

1.12 **(d)**: The inverter generates a HIGH at its output, so the bottom NAND will be enabled, and allow an inverted clock signal to emerge on output Y.

Paper exercise 1.1

Fig. 1.38 *Definitions of terms*

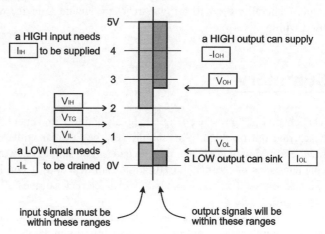

I_{IL} and I_{OH} are both given as negative because these currents flow *out* from the device.

Practical exercise 1.3

Referring to the circuit diagram of the demonstration board you can see that the slide-switch, SW6, is connected to pins 1 and 2 of the PLD. Naming the pin-2 signal `left` and the pin-1 signal `right`, the DECLARATIONS section should read:

```
clock, left, right  pin 43,2,1;  "INPUTS
X, Y                pin 16,27;   "OUTPUTS
```

The EQUATIONS section should consist of just

```
when left then X = clock;
when right then Y = clock;
```

Note that `when left...` is equivalent to `when (left == 1)...` Equivalently, you could write

```
X = clock & left;
Y = clock & right;
```

Practical exercise 1.4

Figure 1.39 illustrates the picture you should have in mind, with some typical values. The top part shows the off-load situation. The measured output voltage is the same as the Thévenin voltage.

The lower section shows what happens when current is drawn from the output. The output voltage drops because the current has to flow through the output resistance. The value of the current can be calculated considering the voltage across the 330Ω resistor. Thus

---

Fig. 1.39 *Typical values when calculating PLD output resistance*

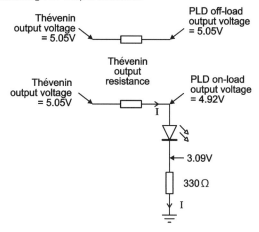

$$I = \frac{V}{R} = \frac{3.09}{330} = 9.36\text{mA}$$

This current causes a voltage drop of $5.05 - 4.92 = 0.13$V. Thus the Thévenin output resistance is

$$R = \frac{V}{I} = \frac{0.13}{9.36 \times 10^{-3}} = 13.9\Omega$$

Note that these measurements were made on version 1.0 of the demonstration board. This had a 330Ω current limit resistor for the LEDs. Version 1.1 uses 470Ω.

2 Boolean algebra

Introduction

Mathematicians are amazingly brilliant people who spend their time fiddling around with symbols, and inventing rules for manipulating those symbols. Some time later, they discover that the new mathematical systems they have created can be used very effectively to describe the real world. Occasionally, the new mathematics even reveals things about the world that would not otherwise have come to light. Engineers also take up the ideas and apply them to their particular discipline and find new ways to solve design problems.

George Boole (1815–1864) was an English mathematician whose work is now used to solve problems in digital electronics. He came from a pretty ordinary background so taught himself Greek and Latin to try to get ahead. He took up a post as a schoolteacher, and became interested in mathematics, reading (and mastering) the works of Laplace and Lagrange. He made friends with Augustus De Morgan (1806–1871) and joined in the debate of the time about logic. Boole wanted to change the subject from one conducted using English sentences into one with a mathematical basis and, in 1847, he published a short book, *The Mathematical Analysis of Logic*, which contains the basis of what's now referred to as Boolean algebra. In 1854 Boole amplified his ideas in a larger volume, *Investigation into the Laws of Thought*. For good measure, as well as inventing an algebra for logic, Boole developed the algebra of the D-operator that can be used to solve differential equations (*Treatise on Differential Equations*, 1859).

In Chapter 1 you were introduced to some of the ideas of Boolean algebra. This chapter covers:

- the five pairs of axioms that define Boolean algebra
- seven further useful logic identities
- the principle of duality
- De Morgan's Laws
- applications of Boolean algebra to circuits – pure NAND and NOR-gate circuits
- circuit simplification
- Σ and Π terminology
- canonical forms
- Electronics Workbench and XPLA exercises

You may find this chapter a bit difficult to digest, since it is mainly theoretical. The important skills are the ability to 'multiply out' and 'add out' brackets, to apply De Morgan's rules, and to apply the principle of duality in order to simplify Boolean expressions. The ability to use the Σ and Π notation is also important. Following through the detailed derivation of the secondary logic identities is less important; it has been included to show how just five axioms (or rather five pairs of axioms) led to the whole of Boolean algebra.

Some practical exercises are included in order to verify the theoretical predictions. Your new skills in Boolean algebra will come in useful when trying to understand what the XPLA software sometimes does to your input equations.

The axioms of Boolean algebra

In chess there are basic rules that determine how you can move the various pieces. In mathematics a rule that determines how you can manipulate symbols is called an axiom. Using the symbols introduced in Chapter 1, the axioms of Boolean algebra are given in Figure 2.1.

Fig. 2.1 *The axioms of Boolean algebra*

1a	$A + B = B + A$
1b	$A.B = B.A$
2a	$A + B + C = A + (B + C) = (A + B) + C$
2b	$A.B.C = A.(B.C) = (A.B).C$
3a	$A.(B + C) = A.B + A.C$
3b	$A + (B.C) = (A + B).(A + C)$
4a	$A + 0 = A$
4b	$A.1 = A$
5a	$A + \overline{A} = 1$
5b	$A.\overline{A} = 0$

Discussion of the axioms

Different algebras have different axioms, and glancing at the list of Figure 2.1, a lot of the rules look pretty similar to 'ordinary' algebra. This can be both helpful and confusing. It's helpful since there isn't a whole new set of symbols to become familiar with, and some of the rules will seem obvious. However, this can lull one into a false sense of security because some of the axioms do not work for ordinary algebra and lead to some surprising or, at least unfamiliar, results. In the following section each pair of axioms will be briefly examined and interpreted in terms of the concepts introduced in Chapter 1.

Commutative law

1a $A + B = B + A$
1b $A.B = B.A$

The pair of rules 1a and 1b say that Boolean quantities 'commute'. That is, you can swap the positions of the two variables and nothing changes. In practical terms this means that the two inputs of an OR gate or an AND gate are equivalent.

Fig. 2.2 *The commutative law for AND gates: A.B = B.A*

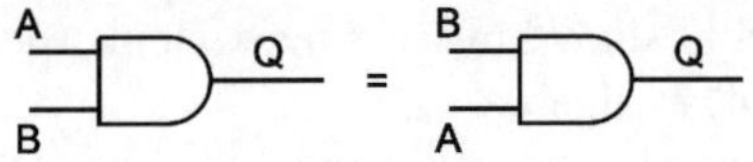

Associative law

2a $A + B + C = A + (B + C) = (A + B) + C$
2b $A.B.C = A.(B.C) = (A.B).C$

Rules 2a and 2b constitute the 'associative law', and tell us how to make OR and AND gates with more than two inputs.

Fig. 2.3 *The associative law for OR gates: A + B + C = (A + B) + C*

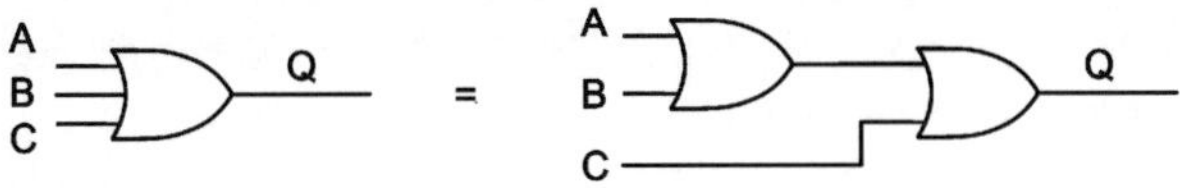

Distributive law

3a $A.(B + C) = A.B + A.C$
3b $A + (B.C) = (A + B).(A + C)$

So far, everything looks like ordinary algebra. Rule 3a looks like 'multiplying out a bracket'. Rule 3b is a bit different from ordinary algebra, though; you might describe it as 'adding out a bracket'. In mathematical language, in Boolean algebra both the + and . operators are said to distribute over the other. In ordinary algebra . distributes over +, but not the other way round.

It is not immediately obvious that either of these two rules is applicable when thinking in terms of gates. On the other hand, one looks as likely as the other does. Figures 2.4 and 2.5 show the gate versions of rules 3a and 3b respectively.

Fig. 2.4 *The distributive law for AND: A.(B + C) = A.B + A.C*

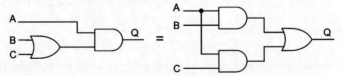

Fig. 2.5 *The distributive law for OR: A + (B.C) = (A + B).(A + C)*

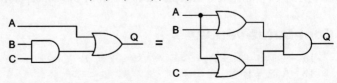

These two identities will be reconsidered later, but meanwhile, what about the fourth pair of axioms?

Identity elements

4a $A + 0 = A$
4b $A.1 = A$

Again, these equations look like ordinary algebra but have a special meaning when applied to logic. Mathematically speaking, 0 is defined as the identity element for the + operator, while 1 is the identity element for . since the operations in 4a and 4b leave the variable identical to what it was before.

Derivation of AND and OR truth tables

The identity axioms can be used to derive the truth tables for the AND and OR gates, as given in Chapter 1.

Thus, taking axiom 4a and setting A to 0 gives $0 + 0 = 0$. Setting A to 1 gives $1 + 0 = 1$. The commutative rule allows the 1 and the 0 to be swapped over to obtain $0 + 1 = 1$.

To get the fourth line of the truth table, i.e. $1 + 1 = 1$, takes a bit more work:

we may write	$A + A.1 = A + A$ (since, by rule 4b, $A.1 = A$)
using rule 3b, however,	$A + A.1 = (A + A).(A + 1)$
thus	$A + A = (A + A).(A + 1)$
and so, using rule 4b again	$A + 1 = 1$

Setting A to 1 gives the required fourth line of the truth table, $1 + 1 = 1$.

Answer the following questions to derive the four lines of the AND truth table.

QUESTIONS

2.1 Taking rule 4b and setting A to 0 gives . . . ?
  (a) $0.0 = 0$ (b) $0.1 = 0$ (c) $1.0 = 0$ (d) $1.1 = 1$

2.2 Taking the answer to Q1 and applying rule 1b gives . . . ?
  (a) $0.0 = 0$ (b) $0.1 = 0$ (c) $1.0 = 0$ (d) $1.1 = 1$

2.3 Taking rule 4b and setting A to 1 gives . . . ?
  (a) $0.0 = 0$ (b) $0.1 = 0$ (c) $1.0 = 0$ (d) $1.1 = 1$

2.4 Which rule allows you to write $A.(A + 0) = A.A$?

2.5 Which rule allows you to write $A.(A + 0) = A.A + A.0$?

2.6 From 2.4 and 2.5 $A.A = A.A + A.0$
  Which rule now allows you to deduce that $A.0 = 0$?

2.7 Taking 2.6 and setting A to 0 gives . . . ?
  (a) $0.0 = 0$ (b) $0.1 = 0$ (c) $1.0 = 0$ (d) $1.1 = 1$

Figure 2.6 summarises the results, giving the truth tables for OR and AND.

Fig. 2.6 *OR and AND truth tables re-stated*

A	B	A + B	A	B	A.B
0	0	0	0	0	0
0	1	1	0	1	0
1	0	1	1	0	0
1	1	1	1	1	1

Complement law

5a $A + \overline{A} = 1$
5b $A.\overline{A} = 0$

These two axioms define what the complement or inverse of a Boolean variable is. Taking rule 5a, setting A to 0 and looking at the second line of the OR truth table shows that $\overline{0}$ must be 1.

QUESTIONS

2.8 Taking rule 5b and setting A to 1 gives . . . ?
(a) $0.0 = 0$ (b) $0.1 = 0$ (c) $1.0 = 0$ (d) $1.\overline{1} = 0$

2.9 Which line of the AND truth table can now prove that $\overline{1} = 0$?

Further logic identities

The five pairs of fundamental axioms given above can be used to derive other secondary logic identities that are useful when manipulating Boolean algebra expressions. Some of these are derived and discussed below.

Forcing inputs

6a $A + 1 = 1$
6b $A.0 = 0$

These two rules were established during the derivation of the AND and OR truth tables during the discussion of the rules 4a and 4b.

From equation 6a you can deduce that a 1 on an OR gate input forces a 1 at the output, irrespective of the value of the other input.

2.10 Rule 6b implies . . . ?
  (a) a 0 on an OR gate input forces a 0 out
  (b) a 1 on an OR gate input forces a 1 out
  (c) a 0 on an AND gate input forces a 0 out
  (d) a 1 on an AND gate input forces a 1 out

Redundancy

7a $A + A = A$
7b $A.A = A$

7a can be shown to be the case by looking at the first and last lines of the OR truth table. If A happens to be 0 you get $0 + 0 = 0$, and setting A to 1 gives $1 + 1 = 1$, both of which comply with the rules of Boolean algebra. Thus $A + A = A$, whichever value A takes. Similarly $A.A = A$.

8a $A + A.B = A$
8b $A.(A + B) = A$

These identities are not so obvious. To prove the first of these, we need to show that the equation is true for any value of A. Suppose A is 0. We need to prove that $0 + 0.B = 0$:

we may write $0 + 0.B = 0 + 0$ (by rule 6b)
                        $= 0$ (by rule 7a)

So 8a is true if $A = 0$. Now set A to 1. Does $1 + 1.B = 1$? Yes, by rule 6a. Thus, whichever value A takes, $A + A.B = A$.

You can prove the second identity in a similar fashion, by showing that $A.(A + B) = A$ whatever the Boolean value of A.

2.11 If $A = 0$ you need to show that $0.(0 + B) = 0$. Which rule asserts this to be the case?

2.12 If $A = 1$ you need to show that $1.(1 + B) = 1$. Which rule asserts that $1.(1 + B) = 1.1$?

2.13 Which rule asserts that $1.1 = 1$?

Complementary redundancy

9a $A + \overline{A}.B = A + B$
9b $A.(\overline{A} + B) = A.B$

These are similar to 8a and 8b, but instead of the A term being repeated it appears in its complement form. The first of these can be proved by 'adding out' the implied brackets:

$$A + (\overline{A}.B) = (A + \overline{A}).(A + B) \quad \text{(rule 3b)}$$
$$= 1.(A + B) \quad \text{(rule 5a)}$$
$$= A + B \quad \text{(rule 4b)}$$

The second can be proved by 'multiplying out' the actual brackets:

$$A.(\overline{A} + B) = A.\overline{A} + A.B \quad \text{(line 1)}$$
$$= 0 + A.B \quad \text{(line 2)}$$
$$= A.B \quad \text{(line 3)}$$

QUESTIONS

2.14 Which rule has been used in line 1?

2.15 Which rule has been used in line 2?

2.16 Which rule has been used in line 3?

De Morgan's laws

10a $\quad \overline{A} + \overline{B} = \overline{A.B}$
10b $\quad \overline{A.B} = \overline{A} + \overline{B}$

These remarkable identities can be proved by truth tables.

Fig. 2.7 *Truth table proof that $\overline{A} + \overline{B} = \overline{A.B}$*

1	2	3	4	5	6	7
A	B	$\overline{A}$	$\overline{B}$	$\overline{A} + \overline{B}$	A.B	$\overline{A.B}$
0	0	1	1	1	0	1
0	1	1	0	1	0	1
1	0	0	1	1	0	1
1	1	0	0	0	1	0

Columns 1 and 2 of Figure 2.7 give the four possible combinations of 0 and 1 that A and B can take. Columns 3 and 4 invert these values, to obtain $\overline{A}$ and $\overline{B}$. The fifth column ORs columns 3 and 4 together to give $\overline{A} + \overline{B}$. The sixth column ANDs A and B together to give A.B and the final column inverts this to give $\overline{A.B}$. But look! Columns 5 and 7 are identical, proving that $\overline{A} + \overline{B} = \overline{A.B}$.

PAPER EXERCISE 2.1

Complete Figure 2.8 to prove that $\overline{A}.\overline{B} = \overline{A+B}$.

Fig. 2.8 *Truth table proof that $\overline{A}.\overline{B} = \overline{A+B}$ (for you to complete)*

1	2	3	4	5	6	7
A	B	$\overline{A}$	$\overline{B}$	$\overline{A}.\overline{B}$	A + B	$\overline{A+B}$
0	0	1	1			
0	1	1	0			
1	0	0	1			
1	1	0	0			

Double inversion

11   $\overline{\overline{A}} = A$

If you invert a signal then invert it again, you end up the same way you started.

This identity is easy to prove since 0 and 1 are the only two values a Boolean variable can take, and, as axioms 5a and 5b imply, they are the complement of each other. Think of a Boolean value. Now invert it. Now invert that. What do you get?

Boolean logic identities

The set of logic identities derived from the axioms is listed here.

Fig. 2.9 *Derived Boolean logic identities*

6a	A + 1 = 1
6b	A.0 = 0
7a	A + A = A
7b	A.A = A
8a	A + A.B = A
8a	A.(A + B) = A
9a	A + $\overline{A}$.B = A + B
9b	A.($\overline{A}$ + B) = A.B
10a	$\overline{A}$ + $\overline{B}$ = $\overline{A.B}$
10b	$\overline{A}.\overline{B}$ = $\overline{A+B}$
10c	$\overline{A+B}$ = A.B
10d	$\overline{A.B}$ = A + B
11	$\overline{\overline{A}}$ = A

Two additional identities have crept in: 10c and 10d. These are not really new, but are just two more manifestations of De Morgan's laws. 10c has been derived by complementing both sides of identity 10a, then using the double inversion rule to get rid of both inversion bars on the right-hand side:

thus $\qquad \overline{A} + \overline{B} = \overline{A.B}$

so $\qquad \overline{\overline{A}+\overline{B}} = \overline{\overline{A.B}}$

giving $\qquad \overline{\overline{A}+\overline{B}} = A.B$

10d can be derived from 10b in a similar fashion.

Note that all four versions of De Morgan's laws can be remembered by thinking:

break/join the bar, change the sign

The distributive rules: do they apply to logic gates?

Axioms 3a and 3b cannot be proved: they are part of the *definition* of Boolean algebra. However, it is worth checking that they are at least consistent with our logic gate interpretation of Boolean algebra. It's not at all obvious from drawing the gate circuits that they are – see Figures 2.4 and 2.5 above – but they can be checked using truth tables.

Rule 3a is: $A.(B + C) = A.B + A.C$. To investigate this we need to see what happens to the left-hand side and the right-hand side for all eight possible combinations of 1s and 0s for A, B and C. If they always agree, then we will be happy.

Fig. 2.10 *Truth table investigation of rule 3a: A.(B + C) = A.B + A.C*

1	2	3	4	5	6	7	8
A	B	C	B + C	A.(B + C)	A.B	A.C	A.B + A.C
0	0	0	0	0	0	0	0
0	0	1	1	0	0	0	0
0	1	0	1	0	0	0	0
0	1	1	1	0	0	0	0
1	0	0	0	0	0	0	0
1	0	1	1	1	0	1	1
1	1	0	1	1	1	0	1
1	1	1	1	1	1	1	1

Here, columns 1–3 list the possible states of the 'inputs'. Column 5 gives the result for the left-hand side of the identity and column 8 for the right-hand side. You can see that columns 5 and 8 are identical, so we can accept the first distributive rule for Boolean algebra.

Repeat the exercise using Figure 2.11 to demonstrate the relevance of the 'adding out' rule. As before, you should find that columns 5 and 8 hold the same data as each other.

Fig. 2.11 *Truth table investigation of rule 3b: A + (B.C) = (A + B).(A + C)*

1	2	3	4	5	6	7	8
A	B	C	B.C	A + (B.C)	A + B	A + C	(A + B).(A + C)
0	0	0					
0	0	1					
0	1	0					
0	1	1					
1	0	0					
1	0	1					
1	1	0					
1	1	1					

Duality

You will have noticed that the axioms and derived identities have generally been given in pairs. You may also have noticed that to get from one of the pairs to the other you just swap the + and . symbols, (and swap any 0 and 1 values). This is called the principle of duality. It means you can halve the number of things you need to remember.

Duality also means that if you can describe a circuit or logic problem using a certain Boolean algebra equation, you may be able to find another (perhaps simpler) way of looking at the situation by swapping all the AND and OR functions, and by inverting all the variables. De Morgan's laws can be derived from this principle:

suppose	$Q = A + B$
then, by duality,	$\bar{Q} = \bar{A}.\bar{B}$
inverting both sides gives	$Q = \overline{\bar{A}.\bar{B}}$ (since $\bar{\bar{Q}} = Q$)
thus	$A + B = \overline{\bar{A}.\bar{B}}$

This, of course, is one of the De Morgan identities.

De Morgan's laws in pictures

The Boolean algebra statements of De Morgan's laws are one way of stating them, but it's perhaps easier to remember them using symbols.

The two central equalities show that you can use one gate to do the job of another if you surround it with inversion bubbles. The two outer equalities say that if you slide the inversion bubble from one end of the symbol to the other, then change the shape of the symbol as well. The inversion bubbles at the input to the symbols are used extensively to help a reader of a circuit diagram understand the function that a designer

Fig. 2.12 *De Morgan's laws in symbols*

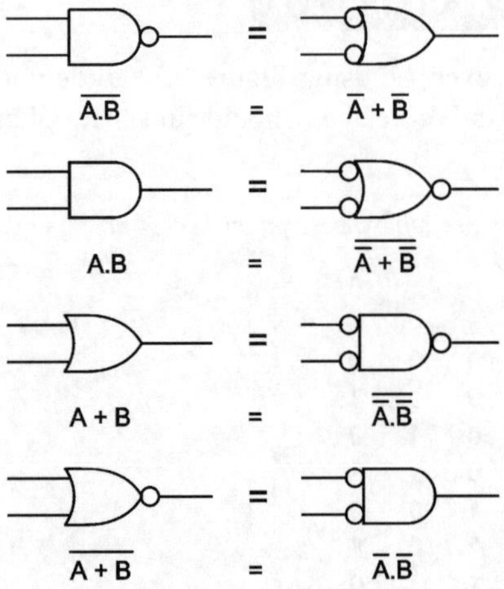

$$\overline{A.B} \quad = \quad \overline{A} + \overline{B}$$

$$A.B \quad = \quad \overline{\overline{A} + \overline{B}}$$

$$A + B \quad = \quad \overline{\overline{A}.\overline{B}}$$

$$\overline{A + B} \quad = \quad \overline{A}.\overline{B}$$

intends. For instance if a signal (X) needs to go HIGH only when two others (A and B) are both LOW then the designer thinks Figure 2.13.

Fig. 2.13 *'I want X to go HIGH when A and B are both LOW'*

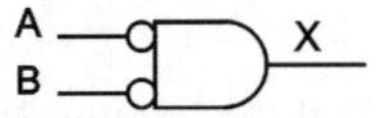

But if the requirement is that signal X needs to go LOW when either A or B is HIGH then the designer thinks Figure 2.14.

Fig. 2.14 *'I want X to go LOW when either A or B is HIGH'*

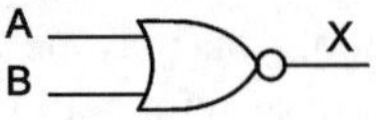

De Morgan's law tells us that these two statements are logically equivalent and a two-input NOR gate would be used for either of them. Drawing them the way the designer thinks is a great aid to understanding, and is very much to be encouraged.

De Morgan's laws in words

'Chicken and chips please.'

'Are you sure? Chips aren't very good for you, you know. Wouldn't you prefer something with less cholesterol? A baked potato perhaps?'

'No, no. *Chips* please!'

'Well I'm only thinking of your health, sir. And about those poor chickens, cooped up all day. Spare a thought for them and have a baked potato and cheese . . .'

'*Chicken* please! Two tasty fried chicken thighs, with lots of salty, fatty skin.'

'I really don't think you are wise . . .'

'Please listen. Do you understand De Morgan's laws? If it isn't chicken or it isn't chips then I do *not* want it, thank you very much.'

NAND-gate-only circuits

One of the implications of De Morgan's laws is that you could make any digital system using just NAND gates. You can make an inverter by joining the two inputs together; you can make an AND by inverting the output, and you can make an OR by inverting the inputs. As an example, suppose a signal Q depends on signals A, B and C thus:

$$Q = A.B.\overline{C} + A.\overline{B}.C + \overline{A}.B.C + A.B.C$$

(One way to think about this is that Q goes HIGH if at least two of the three inputs are HIGH.)

Drawn using AND gates, OR gates and inverters, the circuit to implement this statement would be Figure 2.15.

Fig. 2.15 *Straightforward implementation of $Q = A.B.\overline{C} + A.\overline{B}.C + \overline{A}.B.C + A.B.C$.*

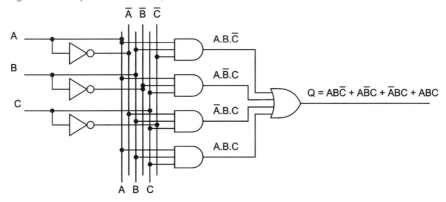

The first step towards implementing this circuit in NAND gates only is to put inversion bubbles all around the OR gate, and turn it into an AND, in accordance with the third diagram of Figure 2.12 above.

Fig. 2.16 *First step towards NAND implementation of circuit*

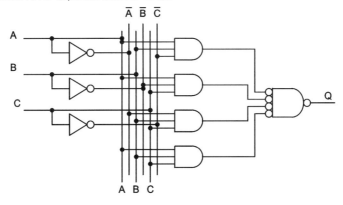

The second step is to slide the inversion bubbles from the input side of the four-input NAND to the outputs of the AND gates, as shown in Figure 2.17.

Fig. 2.17 *Circuit almost converted to NAND gates only*

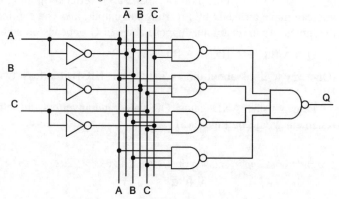

The final step is the minor one of replacing the NOT gates with NANDs.

Fig. 2.18 *Circuit converted to NAND-gate implementation*

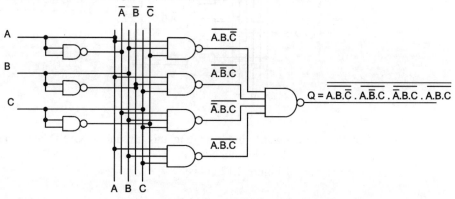

It's no longer clear that the circuit will do what it is supposed to do, namely give a HIGH output in response to a majority of the inputs being HIGH. The Boolean algebra equation describing the final circuit is given in Figure 2.18 and it takes a straightforward application of De Morgan's laws to prove that the final circuit is logically equivalent to the first.

$$Q = \overline{\overline{A.B.\overline{C}}.\overline{A.\overline{B}.C}.\overline{\overline{A}.B.C}.\overline{A.B.C}}$$

$$= \overline{\overline{A.B.\overline{C}}} + \overline{\overline{A.\overline{B}.C}} + \overline{\overline{\overline{A}.B.C}} + \overline{\overline{A.B.C}} \qquad \text{(break bar, change sign)}$$

$$= A.B.\overline{C} + A.\overline{B}.C + \overline{A}.B.C + A.B.C \qquad \text{(rule 11: double inversion)}$$

Why should you wish to use a load of NAND gates instead of ANDs and ORs? Well, you don't generally buy gates one at a time, but in ICs with three or four to a package, so you may be able to reduce the package count by this sort of trick.

NOR-gate-only circuits

What you can do with NANDs you can also do with NORs. Given the principle of duality, it would be surprising if you couldn't. One way to obtain a NOR-gate implementation of the two-or-more-inputs-HIGH-detector circuit is to start by taking the dual of the original equation. Instead of writing

$$Q = A.B.\overline{C} + A.\overline{B}.C + \overline{A}.B.C + A.B.C$$

you can invert all the variables, change the signs and write

$$\overline{Q} = (\overline{A} + \overline{B} + C).(\overline{A} + B + \overline{C}).(A + \overline{B} + \overline{C}).(\overline{A} + \overline{B} + \overline{C})$$

Inverting both sides gives

$$Q = \overline{(\overline{A} + \overline{B} + C).(\overline{A} + B + \overline{C}).(A + \overline{B} + \overline{C}).(\overline{A} + \overline{B} + \overline{C})}$$

This equation can be implemented with the circuit shown in Figure 2.19.

Fig. 2.19 *Straightforward implementation of $Q = \overline{(\overline{A} + \overline{B} + C).(\overline{A} + B + \overline{C}).(A + \overline{B} + \overline{C}).(\overline{A} + \overline{B} + \overline{C})}$*

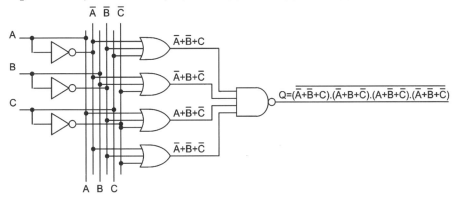

The four-input NAND gate can be turned into an OR by sliding the inversion bubble from its output side to its input side, in accordance with the top diagram of Figure 2.12.

Fig. 2.20 *First step towards NOR implementation of circuit.*

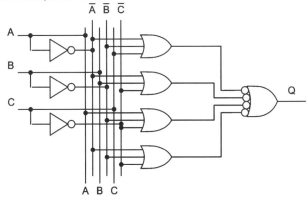

As before, the second step involves sliding the inversion bubbles along their wires.

Fig. 2.21 *Circuit almost converted to NOR gates only*

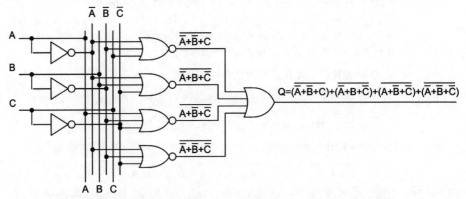

The final steps are fairly trivial. The three inverters are replaced with NOR gates with their inputs tied together. The four-input OR has to be replaced with a four-input NOR, followed by an inverter, in the form of yet another NOR with its inputs tied together.

Does this circuit still look like one whose output goes HIGH if most of its inputs are HIGH? A Boolean algebra proof using De Morgan's laws again shows that it does.

$$Q = \overline{\overline{A} + \overline{B} + C} + \overline{\overline{A} + B + \overline{C}} + \overline{A + \overline{B} + \overline{C}} + \overline{\overline{A} + \overline{B} + \overline{C}}$$
$$= \overline{\overline{\overline{A}.\overline{B}.\overline{C}}} + \overline{\overline{\overline{A}.B.\overline{C}}} + \overline{\overline{A.\overline{B}.\overline{C}}} + \overline{\overline{\overline{A}.\overline{B}.\overline{C}}} \quad \text{(De Morgan)}$$
$$= A.B.\overline{C} + A.\overline{B}.C + \overline{A}.B.C + A.B.C \quad \text{(double inversion)}$$

Circuit simplification

You have seen that the same logic function (in the example above, indicating that two or more of three inputs are HIGH) can be implemented in a number of different circuits. How many different ways are there? Which is the simplest?

There are infinitely many ways to implement a given circuit and in the next chapter you will be introduced to some methods for finding the simplest ones. For now, one or two examples are given showing how Boolean algebra can be used to simplify a circuit.

One method is like ordinary algebra and consists in looking for 'common factors' – rule 3a. Taking the example $Q = A.B.\overline{C} + A.\overline{B}.C + \overline{A}.B.C + A.B.C$ again, look at the last two terms – B.C is a common factor.

$$Q = A.B.\overline{C} + A.\overline{B}.C + \overline{A}.B.C + A.B.C$$
$$= A.B.\overline{C} + A.\overline{B}.C + (\overline{A} + A).B.C$$
$$= A.B.\overline{C} + A.\overline{B}.C + B.C \quad \text{(since, by rule 5a, } \overline{A} + A = 1)$$

Well, the expression has been reduced from four terms to three, so it's simpler. The process of looking for a common factor was particularly helpful in this case because of the way the $\overline{A}$ and the A 'cancelled out'.

Look at the original expression again. Had the A.B factor from the first and last terms been factored out then a similar thing would have happened, and also if the A.C factor from the second and last terms had been factored out. What a shame there aren't enough A.B.C terms for all three of these to have been possible. Well, by rule 7a $(A + A = A)$ it *is* possible. You can duplicate terms if you want to, so we can add in as many A.B.C terms as needed.

$$Q = A.B.\overline{C} + A.B.C + A.\overline{B}.C + A.B.C + \overline{A}.B.C + A.B.C \qquad \text{(rule 7a)}$$
$$= A.B.(\overline{C} + C) + A.C.(\overline{B} + B) + B.C.(\overline{A} + A) \qquad \text{(rule 3a)}$$
$$= A.B + A.C + B.C \qquad \text{(rules 5a \& 4b)}$$

Isn't that nice? The circuit is shown in Figure 2.22.

Fig. 2.22 *Simpler circuit to indicate if two or more inputs are HIGH*

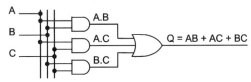

PAPER EXERCISE 2.3

As an exercise in creating NAND-only circuits, convert Figure 2.22 to such a circuit.

A similar exercise can be used on the OR-gate version of the circuit. Starting from the dual of the original equation we may write

$$\overline{Q} = (\overline{A} + \overline{B} + C).(\overline{A} + B + \overline{C}).(A + \overline{B} + \overline{C}).(\overline{A} + \overline{B} + \overline{C})$$
$$= (\overline{A} + \overline{B} + C).(\overline{A} + B + \overline{C}).(\overline{A} + B + \overline{C}).(\overline{A} + \overline{B} + \overline{C}).(A + \overline{B} + \overline{C}).(\overline{A} + \overline{B} + \overline{C})$$
$$\text{(rule 7a)}$$
$$= (\overline{A} + \overline{B} + C.\overline{C}).(\overline{A} + \overline{C} + B.\overline{B}).(A.\overline{A} + \overline{B} + \overline{C}) \qquad \text{(rule 3b)}$$
$$= (\overline{A} + \overline{B}).(\overline{A} + \overline{C}).(\overline{B} + \overline{C}) \qquad \text{(rules 5b \& 4a)}$$

Therefore $\qquad Q = \overline{(\overline{A} + \overline{B}).(\overline{A} + \overline{C}).(\overline{B} + \overline{C})} \qquad \text{(rule 11)}$
$$= \overline{(\overline{A} + \overline{B})} + \overline{(\overline{A} + \overline{C})} + \overline{(\overline{B} + \overline{C})} \qquad \text{(rule 10a)}$$

The method is analogous to the one used before, as you can see by comparing the rules used – 7b instead of 7a, and so on. The tricky bit to see is the third line, where rule 3b has been invoked, but that's just because you are more familiar with ordinary algebra than with this Boolean stuff!
The circuit is shown in Figure 2.23.

Fig. 2.23 *Another way to build the two-or-more-inputs-HIGH circuit*

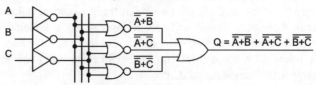

$$Q = \overline{\overline{A+B}} + \overline{\overline{A+C}} + \overline{\overline{B+C}}$$

Comparing Figures 2.22 and 2.23, you can spot that De Morgan easily converts one into the other. Imagine sliding the inversion bubbles from the outputs of the inverters to the inputs of the two-input OR gates. All those inversion bubbles will turn them into ANDs, and there's Figure 2.22.

PRACTICAL EXERCISE 2.1

According to Boolean algebra, all the circuits shown in Figures 2.15–2.23 are equivalent. In this exercise you use Electronics Workbench to simulate them, and verify that the software agrees with the maths. The relevant files are supplied on the CD and are named **fig2_15.ewb**, **fig2_17.ewb**, **fig2_19.ewb**, **fig2_21.ewb**, **fig2_22.ewb** and **fig2_23.ewb**. A screen dump of **fig2_15.ewb** is shown below.

Fig. 2.24 *Electronics Workbench version of Figure 2.15*

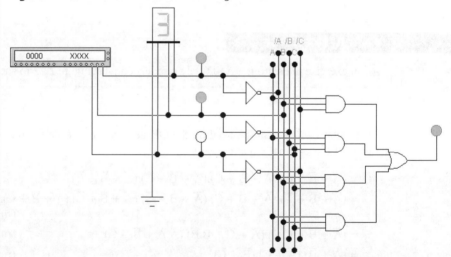

Run Electronics Workbench, open each file in turn, and check that they all give a HIGH output if two or three of the inputs are HIGH. The three inputs are generated automatically by the **Word Generator** and the pattern set thereon is a binary up counter. A new member of the sequence is output every second. The logic state of each input is monitored by a probe, but the set of inputs is also interpreted as a three-bit binary number, and displayed on the decoded seven-segment display.

Verify that for each circuit the output probe does indeed go HIGH each time at least two of the inputs are HIGH, i.e. for binary values 3, 5, 6 and 7. □

Σ and Π terminology

The Electronics Workbench exercise actually used a seven-segment display to show the binary value of the input signal. Now, the various input signals may not necessarily be thought of as forming a binary number, but it is a convenient way of describing the way a system behaves, or is required to behave. In the case of the circuits under discussion, the output could be described as $Q = \Sigma(3,5,6,7)$.

The Σ sign is used because of the way it is used in ordinary algebra to represent the sum of a series. (Σ is the capital letter sigma, Greek for S.) The + sign in the expression $Q = A.B.\overline{C} + A.\overline{B}.C + \overline{A}.B.C + A.B.C$ doesn't mean 'add', of course, and the . doesn't mean multiply, but the format is referred to as 'sum of products' and $Q = \Sigma(3,5,6,7)$ is taken to mean just the same as $Q = A.B.\overline{C} + A.\overline{B}.C + \overline{A}.B.C + A.B.C$.

To convert from one format to the other is straightforward, provided you know which input is which in terms of way they have been combined to form the binary number. Here A is taken as the LSB, and C the MSB. Thus $A.B.\overline{C}$ becomes 110 (MSB on right), which becomes 011 (MSB on left) i.e. 3 in decimal. $A.\overline{B}.C = 101$ (either way round!) = 5, and so on.

The duality principle would lead to the idea that there should be a similar shorthand for a 'product of sums' expression, and so there is. This is where the Π sign comes in. (Π is the capital letter pi, Greek for P.) You might think that if, for example, $\overline{Q} = (\overline{A} + \overline{B} + C).(\overline{A} + B + \overline{C}).(A + \overline{B} + \overline{C}).(\overline{A} + \overline{B} + \overline{C})$ then you would write $\overline{Q} = \Pi(4,2,1,0)$ by analogy with the Σ format. In fact, however, the convention is to write $\overline{Q} = \Pi(3,5,6,7)$. The 'values' of the individual terms are calculated by taking a variable that is present in its true form to be worth 0, but one that is complemented is given the value 1. Binary weightings are assigned as for the Σ situation; here A is the LSB and C the MSB.

Using these conventions, the duality principle can be stated:

if $\quad\quad Q = \Sigma(\mathbf{S})\quad$ then $\quad \overline{Q} = \Pi(\mathbf{S})$
and if $\quad Q = \Pi(\mathbf{S})\quad$ then $\quad \overline{Q} = \Sigma(\mathbf{S})$

Here, **S** refers to some set of values, like the set (3,5,6,7) used above.

QUESTIONS

2.17 Suppose Q depends on three signals A, B and C such that $Q = \Sigma(1,3,4)$, taking A is the LSB and C as the MSB. The equivalent Boolean algebra expression is . . . ?
(a) $Q = (\overline{A}.\overline{B}.C) + (\overline{A}.B.C) + (A.\overline{B}.\overline{C})$
(b) $Q = (A.\overline{B}.\overline{C}) + (A.B.\overline{C}) + (\overline{A}.\overline{B}.C)$
(c) $\overline{Q} = (A + B + \overline{C}).(A + \overline{B} + \overline{C}).(\overline{A} + B + C)$
(d) $\overline{Q} = (\overline{A} + B + C).(\overline{A} + \overline{B} + C).(A + B + \overline{C})$

2.18 Suppose, as above, that Q depends on three signals A, B and C such that $Q = \Sigma(1,3,4)$, taking A is the LSB and C as the MSB. The dual of this statement is . . . ?
(a) $Q = \Sigma(1,3,4)$
(b) $Q = \Pi(1,3,4)$
(c) $\overline{Q} = \Sigma(1,3,4)$
(d) $\overline{Q} = \Pi(1,3,4)$

2.19 Suppose again that Q depends on three signals A, B and C such that
Q = Σ(1,3,4), taking A is the LSB and C as the MSB. The dual of this
statement is . . . ?
(a) Q = $(\overline{A}.\overline{B}.C) + (\overline{A}.B.C) + (A.\overline{B}.\overline{C})$
(b) Q = $(A.\overline{B}.\overline{C}) + (A.B.\overline{C}) + (\overline{A}.\overline{B}.C)$
(c) $\overline{Q}$ = $(A + B + \overline{C}).(A + \overline{B} + \overline{C}).(\overline{A} + B + C)$
(d) $\overline{Q}$ = $(\overline{A} + B + C).(\overline{A} + \overline{B} + C).(A + B + \overline{C})$

First and second canonical forms, minterms and maxterms

The two ways (Σ and Π) of expressing a Boolean function as well as being referred to
as sum-of-products and product-of-sums are also known as first and second canonical
forms, respectively. If an expression is given in canonical form each term in the expres-
sion contains every input variable. Thus Q = $A.B.\overline{C} + \overline{A}.\overline{B}.C + \overline{A}.B.C + A.B.C$ is
in first canonical form, but Q = A.B + A.C + B.C, although a sum-of-products type
expression, and equivalent to the first, is not in canonical form since, for instance,
variable C is missing from the first term. Similarly, Q = $(A + B + \overline{C}).(A + \overline{B} + \overline{C})$.
$(\overline{A} + B + C)$ is in second canonical form, but Q = (A + B).(A + C).(B + C) isn't.

- A 'product' term (like A.B.C) is known as a 'minterm'.
- A 'sum' term (like A + B + C) is known as a 'maxterm'.

Conversion between canonical forms

Duality takes you from one canonical form to the other, but gives you the inverse of
the original function. There's another principle that can be used to obtain the other
canonical form, with the output the same way up, so to speak.

First, the set, **B**, containing all the possible input binary values needs to be defined.
Thus, for a three input system, **B** = (0,1,2,3,4,5,6,7). The conversion process can now be
stated:

if   Q = Σ(**S**)   then   Q = Π(**B** − **S**)
and if   Q = Π(**S**)   then   Q = Σ(**B** − **S**)

Thus, if Q = Σ(1,3,4) then Q = Π(0,2,5,6,7). In other words, the values of the maxterms
in the Π version of the function are found by selecting the ones missing from the
minterms of the Σ version, and *vice versa*. Remember the different way of evaluating a
maxterm from a minterm, however.

The statement 'if Q = Σ(1,3,4) then Q = Π(0,2,5,6,7)' would be written out as a full
Boolean algebra statement as:

if   Q = $(A.\overline{B}.\overline{C}) + (A.B.\overline{C}) + (\overline{A}.\overline{B}.C)$
then   Q = $(A + B + C).(A + \overline{B} + C).(\overline{A} + B + \overline{C}).(A + \overline{B} + \overline{C}).(\overline{A} + \overline{B} + \overline{C})$

Yet more ways to make a two-or-more-inputs-HIGH detector

Returning to the circuit discussed above (Figure 2.15, for instance) we now have another way to build the circuit. The original circuit definition was given as:

$$Q = A.B.\overline{C} + A.\overline{B}.C + \overline{A}.B.C + A.B.C \qquad (or\ Q = \Sigma(3,5,6,7))$$

This can now be instantly converted to $Q = \Pi(0,1,2,4)$, or

$$Q = (A + B + C).(\overline{A} + B + C).(A + \overline{B} + \overline{C}).(A + B + \overline{C})$$

By 'multiplying in' a couple more $(A + B + C)$ terms, using rule 7a, then 'factorising' out, a simpler expression can eventually be derived:

$$Q = (A + B + C).(\overline{A} + B + C).(A + B + C).(A + \overline{B} + C).(A + B + C).(A + B + \overline{C})$$
$$= (A + \overline{A}).(B + C).(B + \overline{B}).(A + C).(C + \overline{C}).(A + B)$$
$$= (B + C).(A + C).(A + B)$$

Figure 2.25 shows the circuit.

Fig. 2.25 *One more way to build a two-or-more-inputs-HIGH detector circuit*

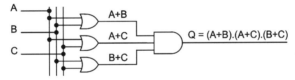

Does this work? It is exactly the same as Figure 2.22, but with the gate types swapped. Surely you can't just swap all the gates over and expect a circuit still to work. Well, generally, no you can't, but in this particular case it works. Verify with Electronics Workbench and **fig2_25.ewb**.

You can, of course, use Boolean algebra to prove that it's the same:

$$Q = (A + B).(A + C).(B + C) \qquad (Figure\ 2.25)$$
$$= (A + B).(A.B + A.C + C.B + C.C)$$
$$= A.A.B + A.A.C + A.C.B + A.C.C + B.A.B + B.A.C + B.C.B + B.C.C$$
$$= A.B + A.C + A.B.C + A.C + A.B + A.B.C + B.C + B.C$$
$$= A.B + A.C + B.C + A.B.C$$
$$= A.B + A.C + B.C \qquad (Figure\ 2.22)$$

QUESTION

2.20 Which rules have been used in the above proof?

This chapter has been quite theoretical, but should have given you a feel for the ways Boolean algebra expressions can be converted. The XPLA software does this kind of thing automatically when it is changing the expressions that a designer might enter into versions that will fit better to the hardware inside the CPLD chip. On the whole, it prefers to use AND gates rather than ORs. Even basic expressions like the ones you used in Chapter 1 are altered. For instance, if you enter the expression Q = A # B it will turn this into !Q = !A & !B, the De Morgan (or dual) equivalent.

You should recall from Chapter 1 that the PHDL software uses # to signify OR, & to mean AND, and ! to show inversion. Using the Boolean algebra symbols used in the rest of this Chapter, the XPLA conversion above would read 'Q = A + B is turned into $\overline{Q} = \overline{A}.\overline{B}$'.

The present exercise involves entering some of the expressions discussed in this chapter into the XPLA software, then taking a look at what it does to them. With your new knowledge of Boolean algebra you should be able to check that the optimised equations it generates are equivalent to the ones you entered.

Run the XPLA software, then create a new project. Call the new project **boolean_algebra** or something like that, and save it somewhere safe! ☐

Now create a new PHDL source file for the project. Call it **fig2_15** or something similarly meaningful. ☐

Give the module a name, such as **boolean_algebra**, and enter some brief description of the module under the **Title** field. ☐

The **DECLARATIONS** section should list inputs **A**, **B** and **C** on pins 4, 6 and 8, and an output **Q** on pin 16. ☐

The **EQUATIONS** section should reflect the equation associated with Figure 2.15, namely $Q = A.B.\overline{C} + A.\overline{B}.C + \overline{A}.B.C + A.B.C$. You could enter this as:

```
Q = A&B&!C # A&!B&C # !A&B&C # A&B&C;
```
☐

Note that in PHDL the **&** sign takes precedence over the **#**, just as × takes precedence over + in ordinary algebra, so there is no need for brackets (or even spaces) when entering the expression given above for Q.

Save the file, and compile. ☐

Now, by double-clicking on it, view the optimised equations version of the file, **fig2_15.ph1**, or similar. You should find that the XPLA software has created the Figure 2.22 version of the Boolean expression. ☐

Now amend the defining equation to that given for Figure 2.25, save, compile, and check the optimised equations. You should again find it creates the Figure 2.22 version. ☐

Try a NAND-gate-only version of the circuit, such as Figure 2.18, or the NAND-gate version of Figure 2.22. (The PHDL version of the Figure 2.18 equation is Q = !(!(A&B&!C)&!(A&!B&C)&!(!A&B&C)&!(A&B&C));.) You should find that you end up with the dual of the Figure 2.25 equation. ☐

Check the target device is set to **xcr5032c-10pc44c**, fit and use the PC-ISP software to download any of these versions to the hardware. Verify that the left LED lights up if most of the big slide switches are in the up position. □

Now try your hand at the $\Sigma(1,3,4)$ expression. Enter the Boolean equation for this, save, compile, fit and download. Verify that the left LED lights if the three slide switches represent the numbers 1, 3 or 4. Note that for this exercise the left-hand switch (SW1) is the LSB and the right-hand one is the MSB. □

Check the optimised equation that the XPLA software has generated. Use Boolean algebra to prove that it is equivalent to $\Sigma(1,3,4)$. □

Since they are equivalent, you should get the same results if you enter $\Pi(0,2,5,6,7)$ instead of $\Sigma(1,3,4)$ for Q. Do you? Can you prove that $\Pi(0,2,5,6,7) = \overline{A}.\overline{B}.C + A.\overline{C}$? □

Try entering some random Boolean expression of three variables, compiling, examining the optimised equation, and then use Boolean algebra to prove the equivalence of the expression as entered and the optimised version. □

Summary

In this chapter the rules (axioms) of Boolean algebra have been introduced. You have seen how they come in dual pairs, and how just five pairs of axioms are needed in order to establish all the mathematics used in analysing the logical behaviour of digital circuits.

By the use of De Morgan's laws and the duality principle (either the mathematical version, or the 'picture' version) you should be able to convert any circuit into one that uses just NAND gates or just NORs. You should be familiar with the Σ ('sum-of-products' first canonical form) and Π ('product of sums' second canonical form) terminology for describing how the output of a circuit depends on its inputs.

Electronics Workbench has been used to simulate/verify logic circuit designs, with the word generator creating suitable input stimuli. The XPLA software has been shown to be capable of simplifying expressions, and you should be able to prove, by Boolean algebra, that the simplified expressions are equivalent in their logical operation to the ones entered.

Although Boolean algebra has been used to manipulate expressions from one format to another, the business of finding the simplest version has been touched upon but not investigated fully. This is the subject of the next chapter.

ANSWERS TO QUESTIONS

2.1 $0.1 = 0$ **(b)**
2.2 $1.0 = 0$ **(c)**
2.3 $1.1 = 1$ **(d)**
2.4 4a
2.5 3a
2.6 4a

2.7 $0.0 = 0$ **(a)**

2.8 $1.\overline{1} = 0$ **(d)**. If you thought (c) was the answer then you were *assuming* what you were trying to prove.

2.9 **Line 3**

2.10 **(c)**

2.11 **6b**: 0.anything = 0

2.12 **6a**

2.13 **7b** or **4b**

2.14 **3a**

2.15 **5b**

2.16 **4a**

2.17 **(b)**

2.18 **(d)**

2.19 **(d)**

2.20 **3a** to get to line 2; **3a** to get to line 3; **7b** to get to line 4; **7a** to get to line 5; **8a** to get to line 6

ANSWERS TO EXERCISES

Paper exercise 1.1
Figure 2.26: columns 5 and 7 are identical for every possible combination of A and B, so proving that $\overline{A}.\overline{B} = \overline{A+B}$.

Fig. 2.26 *Figure 2.8 completed*

1	2	3	4	5	6	7
A	B	$\overline{A}$	$\overline{B}$	$\overline{A}.\overline{B}$	A + B	$\overline{A+B}$
0	0	1	1	**1**	0	1
0	1	1	0	**0**	1	0
1	0	0	1	**0**	1	0
1	1	0	0	**0**	1	0

Paper exercise 2.2
Figure 2.27: columns 5 and 8 are identical for all possible combinations of A, B and C, so proving that $A + (B.C) = (A + B).(A + C)$.

Fig. 2.27 *Figure 2.11 completed*

1	2	3	4	5	6	7	8
A	B	C	B.C	A + (B.C)	A + B	A + C	(A + B).(A + C)
0	0	0	0	0	0	0	0
0	0	1	0	0	0	1	0
0	1	0	0	0	1	0	0
0	1	1	1	1	1	1	1
1	0	0	0	1	1	1	1
1	0	1	0	1	1	1	1
1	1	0	0	1	1	1	1
1	1	1	1	1	1	1	1

Paper exercise 2.3

Figure 2.28 shows how the circuit in Figure 2.22 may be converted into a NAND-gate-only circuit.

Fig. 2.28 *Converting Figure 2.22 to a NAND-gate-only version*

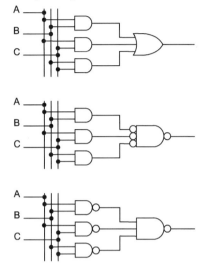

Practical exercise 2.2

You should find that the XPLA software optimises the equation $Q = \Sigma(1,3,4)$ into $Q = A.\overline{C} + \overline{A}.\overline{B}.C$. The proof that these are equivalent is:

$$Q = A.\overline{B}.\overline{C} + A.B.\overline{C} + \overline{A}.\overline{B}.C$$
$$= (\overline{B} + B).A.\overline{C} + \overline{A}.\overline{B}.C \qquad \text{(rule 3a)}$$
$$= A.\overline{C} + \overline{A}.\overline{B}.C \qquad \text{(rules 5a \& 4b)}$$

The XPLA software optimises the equation $Q = \Pi(0,2,5,6,7)$ into the same expression. The proof that these are equivalent is:

$$Q = (A + B + C).(A + \overline{B} + C).(\overline{A} + B + \overline{C}).(A + \overline{B} + \overline{C}).(\overline{A} + \overline{B} + \overline{C})$$
$$= (A + C + B.\overline{B}).(\overline{A} + \overline{C} + B.\overline{B}).(A.\overline{A} + \overline{B} + \overline{C}) \qquad \text{(rules 3b \& 7a)}$$
$$= (A + C).(\overline{A} + \overline{C}).(\overline{B} + \overline{C}) \qquad \text{(rules 5b \& 4a)}$$
$$= (A + C).(\overline{C} + \overline{A}.\overline{B}) \qquad \text{(rule 3b)}$$
$$= A.\overline{C} + A.\overline{A}.\overline{B} + C.\overline{C} + C.\overline{A}.\overline{B} \qquad \text{(rule 3a)}$$
$$= A.\overline{C} + \overline{A}.\overline{B}.C \qquad \text{(rules 5b, 6b \& 4a)}$$

3 Circuit minimisation

Introduction

'I need a circuit that will allow the motor to run only when the guard is in place, and the operator is pressing either this push-switch on the right, or that one on the left. For maintenance purposes, it can also run even when the guard is removed, provided *both* of the switches are pressed and the special key-switch is operated.'

One way to analyse such a 'combinational logic' problem is to think carefully about it, then write down a Boolean algebra expression that describes the required circuit. Another way, more tedious but possibly more reliable, is to list all the possible combinations of inputs (switch settings in this example) and then say exactly what the output should do (let the machine run or not). The list containing all possible input combinations and the corresponding output state is a truth table, like the ones covered in previous chapters. Once you have a truth table it is a straightforward task to extract a Boolean algebra expression for the problem, and then design a suitable circuit.

How do you ensure that the *simplest* circuit has been devised? In 1953 the engineer M. Karnaugh devised a graphical technique (the 'Karnaugh map') that helps you spot the simplest system for small-scale problems (those with five or less input variables). In 1952 W.V. Quine published a paper on simplifying truth functions and in 1956 E. McCluskey developed it into an algorithm suitable for any size of problem and capable of being implemented by computer.

This chapter covers:

- truth table analysis of circuit requirements
- extraction of both Σ and Π Boolean algebra expressions from a truth table
- use of Karnaugh maps to minimise circuits with up to five variables
- use of the Quine–McCluskey method to minimise circuits
- use of Electronics Workbench to devise minimised circuits from truth tables
- use of Electronics Workbench to derive truth tables from circuits
- use of XPLA software to minimise circuits
- truth table syntax for PHDL code
- parity, Gray code and miscellaneous other combinational logic problems
- static hazards
- an extended assignment

Solving a problem by truth table

Taking the problem posed in the introduction, and labelling the input signals L, R, G and K (Left push-switch, Right push-switch, Guard and Key-switch), the truth table defining the required behaviour of the output M (Motor) is shown in Figure 3.1.

Fig. 3.1 *Initial truth table for guarded machine*

	inputs				output
	L	R	G	K	M
0	0	0	0	0	0
1	0	0	0	1	0
2	0	0	1	0	0
3	0	0	1	1	0
4	0	1	0	0	0
5	0	1	0	1	0
6	0	1	1	0	1
7	0	1	1	1	?
8	1	0	0	0	0
9	1	0	0	1	0
10	1	0	1	0	1
11	1	0	1	1	?
12	1	1	0	0	0
13	1	1	0	1	1
14	1	1	1	0	?
15	1	1	1	1	?

The exercise of creating the truth table has, in this case, revealed that the original description of the requirement is incomplete. What should happen in the case that the guard is in place *and* the key-switch is operated when one of the push-switches is pressed? Rows 7 and 11 have ? in the output column to highlight this query. For the purposes of this exercise we will assume that the motor should run. Row 3 also has both the guard and key-switch at logic 1, but neither push-switch pressed, so we would not expect the output to go live.

In row 14 the guard is in place and *both* push-switches are pressed. For the sake of argument, let us assume that the motor can run in this situation. Similarly, a 1 will be entered for the last row where all the input signals are 1. The new truth table can be drawn up as Figure 3.2.

It is now very straightforward to write down a Boolean expression for M:

$$M = \bar{L}.R.G.\bar{K} + \bar{L}.R.G.K + L.\bar{R}.G.\bar{K} + L.\bar{R}.G.K + L.R.\bar{G}.K + L.R.G.\bar{K} + L.R.G.K$$

Using the Σ notation introduced in the previous chapter, this could also be written M = $\Sigma(6,7,10,11,13,14,15)$, taking L to represent the MSB of the input. This could be implemented in a circuit comprising four inverters, seven four-input AND gates, and a seven-input OR. The question arises, is there a simpler circuit?

Fig. 3.2 *Second truth table for guarded machine*

	inputs				output
	L	R	G	K	M
0	0	0	0	0	0
1	0	0	0	1	0
2	0	0	1	0	0
3	0	0	1	1	0
4	0	1	0	0	0
5	0	1	0	1	0
6	0	1	1	0	1
7	0	1	1	1	1
8	1	0	0	0	0
9	1	0	0	1	0
10	1	0	1	0	1
11	1	0	1	1	1
12	1	1	0	0	0
13	1	1	0	1	1
14	1	1	1	0	1
15	1	1	1	1	1

An examination of the Boolean expression shows that the first two terms (rows 6 and 7) could be combined: $\overline{L}.R.G.\overline{K} + \overline{L}.R.G.K = L.R.G.(\overline{K} + K) = \overline{L}.R.G$ Other simplifications could also be made, such as rows 10 and 14, 13 and 15, etc.

This leads to the idea that if the truth table were laid out in a different manner these combinations would be easier to spot. Enter the Karnaugh map. This contains exactly the same information as the truth table, but displayed in a two-dimensional array, arranged so that if neighbouring cells both have 1s then they can be combined. Even better, if a rectangular group of four or eight neighbouring cells are all 1, they can also be combined into a single Boolean term.

In a truth table half the rows have a given input variable HIGH, and the other rows show it LOW. Similarly, on a Karnaugh map, half of its area represents an input variable as 'true' while in the other half it's 'false'. Figure 3.3 shows how to construct a Karnaugh map for a system with four input variables, A, B, C and D.

Fig. 3.3 *Four-variable Karnaugh map truth regions*

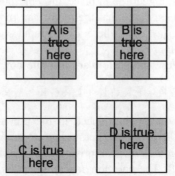

In Figure 3.4 these four diagrams have been superimposed.

Fig. 3.4 *Karnaugh map cell locations and minterm values*

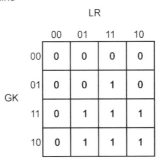

AB

		00	01	11	10
	00	0	4	12	8
	01	1	5	13	9
CD	11	3	7	15	11
	10	2	6	14	10

From the way the rows and columns are labelled around the outside of Figure 3.4 you can see that (as in Figure 3.3) the whole of the right-hand half of the map shows where A is 1 ('true'). B is true in the central vertical area, C in the bottom half, and D in the central horizontal area. Note the sequencing of the AB and CD values across the top and down the sides of the Karnaugh map. In this sequence only one variable at a time ever changes value when moving from one row to an adjacent one, or between adjacent columns. This is known as 'Gray' code, as opposed to a binary sequence. The idea still holds when 'rolling over' from one end back to the beginning.

Figure 3.4 also gives the minterm values, assuming A to be the MSB, D the LSB. Take a look at cell 15. According to Figure 3.3, every input variable is true in this particular cell. Hence A AND B AND C AND D are true here: A.B.C.D. You can also read off the minterm value just by the 'grid reference' of the cell, reading across then down (AB then CD). To convert a truth table into a Karnaugh map, the output values of the truth table are placed in the appropriate cells of the Karnaugh map, row 0 to cell 0, row 1 to cell 1, and so on.

The result for this example is shown in Figure 3.5.

Fig. 3.5 *Karnaugh map for guarded machine*

LR

		00	01	11	10
	00	0	0	0	0
	01	0	0	1	0
GK	11	0	1	1	1
	10	0	1	1	1

You can now see how the Karnaugh map works. It has placed the 1s from rows 6 and 7 of the truth table right next to each other, indicating that they can be combined. Similarly, rows 10 and 14, and rows 13 and 15. Even better than that, the 1s from rows 6, 7, 14 and 15 are all next to each other in a nice rectangular block, indicating that these four rows can be combined.

The information on the Karnaugh map for the guarded machine can be grouped as shown in Figure 3.6 to give the simplest expression for M.

Fig. 3.6 *Karnaugh map groupings for guarded machine*

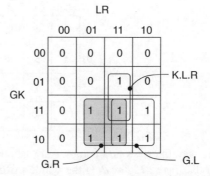

By considering which variables are true inside a particular grouping you can work out the Boolean expression for that grouping. G is true for instance, in the bottom half of the map, so G is true inside the greyed square. R is true in the central vertical area of the map, so the greyed square is the region where *both* these variables are true. The expressions for the other two regions have been derived in similar fashion. It is now possible to write down the minimised Boolean expression for M:

$$M = G.R + G.L + K.L.R$$

Having gone through the exercise, it now seems obvious, perhaps, that the motor should run when the guard is in place and the right button is pressed, or the guard is in place and the left button is pressed, or the key-switch is operated and both buttons are pressed. The process has forced us to examine all possible input states, however, and we are confident that there will be no unexpected actions when unexpected combinations of inputs are present.

PAPER EXERCISE 3.1

It is worth putting Chapter 2's work on Boolean algebra into use to check what has happened as the four minterms in the grey square have been combined into the one expression. The grey square (call it W) is $\Sigma(6,7,14,15)$.

$$
\begin{aligned}
W &= \bar{L}.R.G.\bar{K} + \bar{L}.R.G.K + L.R.G.\bar{K} + L.R.G.K \\
&= \bar{L}.R.G.(\bar{K} + K) + L.R.G.(\bar{K} + K) \\
&= \bar{L}.R.G + L.R.G \\
&= (\bar{L} + L).R.G \\
&= R.G
\end{aligned}
$$

Do the same for the other block of four. □

Notice that minterm 15 is involved in all three of the groupings. This repeated use of a minterm reflects logic identity 7a: $A = A + A$.

Repeat the work done so far in this chapter, but assume that the motor should *not* run if the guard is in place and the key-switch is operated. (The reasoning here might be that the key to the key-switch is an important part of the safety system, and it should not be possible to run the machine in normal operational mode if the key is inadvertently left in place after maintenance work has been carried out.)

Assume, as before, that if both buttons are pressed and the guard is in place, then the motor can run.

Re-create the truth table. ☐

Draw up the Karnaugh map for the new system. ☐

Deduce the new minimised Boolean expression for M. ☐

Check your work against the answers given at the end of the chapter. ☐

Karnaugh maps and Π (product of sums) expressions

Looking at the 1s on a Karnaugh map is equivalent to considering the Σ version of the Boolean expression. From Chapter 2 you know that for every Σ version (obtained by 'summing' minterms) there is a Π version (obtained by 'multiplying' maxterms.) The maxterms are those found by removing the minterms from the complete set of terms.

In a Karnaugh map the 1s are the minterms, the complete set is the total set of cells, so the maxterms must be the 0s. This means that you can get the Π expression for a system by looking at the 0s on a Karnaugh map, writing down the maxterm for each 0 (or 'rectangular' group of two, four or eight 0s) and multiplying (ANDing) them together. The result for the (first version of) the guarded machine is shown in Figure 3.7.

Fig. 3.7 *Extracting a 'product-of-sums' expression from a Karnaugh map*

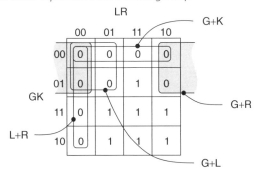

From the figure you can see that M = (L + R).(G + R).(G + L).(G + K). Note how the expressions for the individual groups are obtained. Consider the greyed group. This group happens to be formed by wrapping around from one edge of the map to the other, but it is the area where G is LOW and R is LOW. Had it contained 1s and a sum-of-products expression been sought, then it would be defined as $\overline{G}.\overline{R}$. Here, however, it contains 0s and we are seeking a product-of-sums expression. This means that the inverse of each relevant variable is written into the term, which are then ORed together instead of being ANDed. Thus $G + R$ rather than $\overline{G}.\overline{R}$. (Compare the way maxterms are evaluated when using the Π notation.)

This particular truth table (and Karnaugh map) contains seven 1s and nine 0s and the sum-of-products minimised expression has turned out to be simpler than the product-of-sums expression – three two-input AND gates ORed together rather than four two-input OR gates ANDed together. It is generally the case that if a truth table contains more 1s than 0s the simpler expression is the sum-of-products version, but if there are more 0s than 1s then the product-of-sums expression is simpler. If you want to, you can invert the 1s and 0s by redefining the output as active LOW rather than active HIGH. This is illustrated in Figure 3.8.

Fig. 3.8 *Karnaugh map for $\overline{M}$*

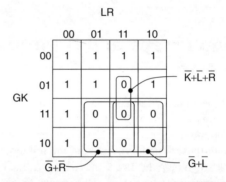

From Figure 3.8 we may write $\overline{M} = (\overline{G} + R).(\overline{G} + \overline{L}).(\overline{K} + \overline{L} + \overline{R})$.

By inverting both sides of this equation, and applying De Morgan's laws it is easy to get back to the original sum-of-products expression for M:

$$M = \overline{(\overline{G} + R).(\overline{G} + \overline{L}).(\overline{K} + \overline{L} + \overline{R})} = \overline{(\overline{G} + R)} + \overline{(\overline{G} + \overline{L})} + \overline{(\overline{K} + \overline{L} + \overline{R})}$$
$$= \overline{\overline{G}}.\overline{R} + \overline{\overline{G}}.\overline{\overline{L}} + \overline{\overline{K}}.\overline{\overline{L}}.\overline{\overline{R}} = G.R + G.L + K.L.R$$

As a fourth alternative, you may also choose to group the 1s in the map for $\overline{M}$ to get another expression for $\overline{M}$, as shown in Figure 3.9.

Fig. 3.9 *Extracting an expression for $\overline{M}$ from a Karnaugh map for $\overline{M}$*

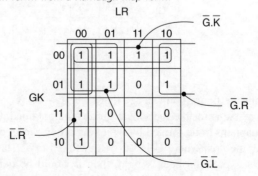

From Figure 3.9 we may write $\overline{M} = \overline{L}.\overline{R} + \overline{G}.\overline{L} + \overline{G}.\overline{R} + \overline{G}.\overline{K}$.

Confused? Let's go over the four ways to get an expression from a Karnaugh map.

- Figure 3.6. Map for M; 1s grouped; sum-of-products expression for M.

    $M = G.R + G.L + K.L.R$

- Figure 3.7. Map for M; 0s grouped; product-of-sums expression for M.

    $M = (L + R).(G + R).(G + L).(G + K)$

- Figure 3.8. Map for $\overline{M}$; 0s grouped; product-of-sums expression for $\overline{M}$.

    $\overline{M} = (\overline{G} + \overline{R}).(\overline{G} + \overline{L}).(\overline{K} + \overline{L} + \overline{R})$

- Figure 3.9. Map for $\overline{M}$; 1s grouped; sum-of-products expression for $\overline{M}$.

    $\overline{M} = \overline{L}.\overline{R} + \overline{G}.\overline{L} + \overline{G}.\overline{R} + \overline{G}.\overline{K}$

Thus you can get both sum-of-products and product-of-sums expressions for both M and $\overline{M}$.

Remember the duality principle? Figures 3.6 and 3.8 form a dual pair, as do Figures 3.7 and 3.9. It all hangs nicely together!

PAPER EXERCISE 3.3

Create the equivalent Karnaugh maps and resulting expressions for M and $\overline{M}$ as Figures 3.7, 3.8 and 3.9 but making the same assumptions about the system behaviour as for Paper exercise 3.2. ☐

PRACTICAL EXERCISE 3.1

Electronics Workbench will do the work of minimising a Boolean expression for you. It always generates a sum-of-products expression, but is a useful timesaving facility.

Run Electronics Workbench and read the **Help** for the **Logic Converter**. ☐

Use the **Logic Converter** facility (find the **Logic Converter** in the **Instruments** menu bar) to enter the truth table of Figure 3.2. You will need four inputs, A, B, C and D. Note how the input combinations are created automatically as you click the input buttons. Assigning the variables L, R, G and K to A, B, C and D respectively, enter the output data, i.e. 1s in rows 6, 7, 10, 11, 13, 14 and 15. ☐

Now click the second of the conversions buttons (truth table to Boolean expression). You should find that the **Logic Converter** has generated the first canonical form expression for the output. (Inverted variables are shown by a single quote mark. Thus A' means $\overline{A}$.) ☐

Now click the third button (truth table to simplified Boolean expression) and see the minimised Boolean expression for the truth table. Check that it's the same as the expression derived above from Figure 3.6. ☐

Now click the fifth button (Boolean expression to circuit). The software will instantly create the circuit for you. Electronics Workbench insists on using two-input gates for everything, but apart from that minor drawback, the **Logic Converter** provides a very useful tool. □

Delete the circuit just created and press the bottom button. This will create a NAND-gate only version of the circuit. □

Finally, delete the NAND-gate-only circuit, reset all the truth table outputs to 0 and enter the Figure 3.7 equation for M in the Boolean expression field at the bottom of the **Logic Converter** window, bearing in mind that L is A, etc. Now press the fourth button (Boolean expression to truth table). The truth table should be re-created. □

Pressing the third button will now turn the product-of-sums expression into the minimised sum-of-products version. □

The only facility not yet examined is the first button. This turns a circuit into a truth table. In order to use this you need a circuit to analyse, and the one that would implement the Figure 3.8 Karnaugh map is provided on the CD as **fig3_10.ewb**. Attach the inputs of the circuit to the inputs of the **Logic Converter** (L to A, R to B, G to C and K to D), and the output of the circuit to the output of the **Logic Converter**. Press the top conversion button. You should find that the truth table for $\overline{M}$ has been deduced. □

Fig. 3.10 *Electronics Workbench circuit to implement* $\overline{M} = (\overline{G} + \overline{R}).(\overline{G} + \overline{L}).(\overline{K} + \overline{L} + \overline{R})$

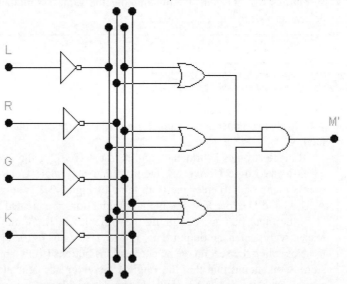

Pressing the truth table to simplified Boolean expression button will generate the sum-of-products expression for $\overline{M}$. Check it against the equation for Figure 3.9. □

Karnaugh maps for three-input systems

It's easy to reduce the four-variable Karnaugh map to suit a system with just three inputs. The next example shows how.

Consider the truth table below. The output is 1 if an odd number of the inputs are 1. This is referred to as an odd *parity* detector. Slightly confusingly, it is also referred to as *even* parity *generator* since, taking the total number of 1s on inputs and output, there is always an even number of 1s – none, two or four.

Fig. 3.11 *Truth table for even parity generator*

	input			output
	A	B	C	Q
0	0	0	0	0
1	0	0	1	1
2	0	1	0	1
3	0	1	1	0
4	1	0	0	1
5	1	0	1	0
6	1	1	0	0
7	1	1	1	1

The Karnaugh map for this is shown in Figure 3.12.

Fig. 3.12 *Karnaugh map for even parity generator*

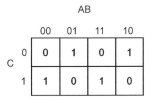

The lack of any rectangular groupings on the map shows that it is not possible to simplify the Boolean description of the system. This information in itself is valuable in that it saves you wasting time trying to achieve the impossible. The Boolean expression for the system is $Q = \overline{A}.\overline{B}.C + \overline{A}.B.\overline{C} + A.\overline{B}.\overline{C} + A.B.C$. You would need four three-input AND gates, a four-input OR, and three inverters.

Although the chequer-board pattern shown in Figure 3.12 doesn't point to simplification in terms of AND or OR gates, it does suggest implementation in terms of exclusive-OR devices. This gate was briefly discussed in Chapter 1. They are available as ICs in the 74HC and 4000 logic families (74HC86 or 4030B quad two-input exclusive-ORs) and the entire circuit for the even-parity generator can be implemented using just two two-input exclusive-ORs.

The truth table for the exclusive-OR is shown in Figure 3.13.

Fig. 3.13 *Truth table for exclusive-OR gate*

inputs		output
A	B	Q
0	0	0
0	1	1
1	0	1
1	1	0

The exclusive-OR function is thus the same as the ordinary-OR, except for the situation in which both inputs are HIGH. (The exclusive-NOR function is similarly defined: it is the same as ordinary-NOR, except for the situation in which both inputs are HIGH.)

PAPER EXERCISE 3.4

Draw the Karnaugh map for the two-input device and verify that the chequer-board pattern is revealed. ☐

The traditional and IEC circuit symbols for the exclusive-OR gate are shown in Figure 3.14.

Fig. 3.14 *Traditional and IEC symbols for exclusive-OR gate*

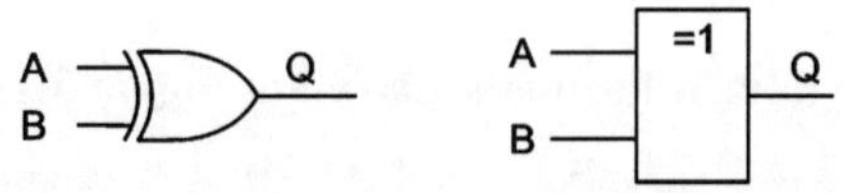

The '=1' qualifying symbol in the IEC version refers to the requirement that exactly 1 of the inputs be HIGH to give a HIGH at the output.

PAPER EXERCISE 3.5

The circuit for the even-parity generator is shown in Figure 3.15.

Fig. 3.15 *Even-parity generator*

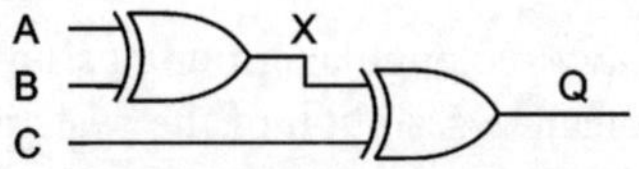

Use a truth table to verify that the circuit works as required. ☐
Using three gates, devise a four-input even-parity generator. ☐

Another application of the exclusive-OR gate: a Gray code to binary converter

Gray code has been discussed briefly with reference to the bit pattern sequence around the borders of Karnaugh maps, but it has a property that makes it useful for mechanical

---

encoders. This property is the way the code only ever changes in one digit between adjacent values. A mechanical system may be bordering between two such values, but the read out will only dither between these two values. By contrast, a binary encoded system is prone to wildly erroneous data. For instance, if bordering between 7 and 8, the readout might be 0111 or 1000 (OK) or a mixture of these two readings, like 0000 or 1111 (not so good!)

To count in Gray go like this: start with all 0s. To generate the next code change the single right-most bit that will give you a new number. Thus

Fig. 3.16 *Counting in Gray code*

	A	B	C	D
0	0	0	0	0
1	0	0	0	1
2	0	0	1	1
3	0	0	1	0
4	0	1	1	0
5	0	1	1	1
6	0	1	0	1
7	0	1	0	0
8	1	1	0	0
9	1	1	0	1
10	1	1	1	1
11	1	1	1	0
12	1	0	1	0
13	1	0	1	1
14	1	0	0	1
15	1	0	0	0

Following the algorithm, you get from 0 to 1 by changing bit D from 0 to 1. To get to 2 you can't change D because that would take you back to 0, so change C instead. To get to 3 you do change D, because that's the right-most bit that you can change and get a new value.

You can now see how a mechanical system dithering between 7 and 8 can only generate 0100 or 1100, i.e. 7 or 8. The same applies to any two adjacent numbers, even 15 and 0.

So it's a useful code, but you might want to convert it to a pure binary code, and this is where the exclusive-OR gate comes in handy. Before discussing the circuit you need to be aware of a different way of looking at the exclusive-OR function – as a conditional inverter. Consider its truth table.

Fig. 3.17 *Truth table for exclusive-OR gate*

inputs		output
A	B	Q
0	0	0
0	1	1
1	0	1
1	1	0

Notice that when A is LOW, Q is just the same as B. When A is HIGH, however, Q is the complement of B. Signal B gets inverted when input A is HIGH.

Now take another look at the Gray code counting scheme, and compare it to binary counting.

Fig. 3.18 *Gray to binary conversion*

	Gray				binary			
	W	X	Y	Z	A	B	C	D
0	0	0	0	0	0	0	0	0
1	0	0	0	1	0	0	0	1
2	0	0	1	1	0	0	1	0
3	0	0	1	0	0	0	1	1
4	0	1	1	0	0	1	0	0
5	0	1	1	1	0	1	0	1
6	0	1	0	1	0	1	1	0
7	0	1	0	0	0	1	1	1
8	1	1	0	0	1	0	0	0
9	1	1	0	1	1	0	0	1
10	1	1	1	1	1	0	1	0
11	1	1	1	0	1	0	1	1
12	1	0	1	0	1	1	0	0
13	1	0	1	1	1	1	0	1
14	1	0	0	1	1	1	1	0
15	1	0	0	0	1	1	1	1

Taking the A output, this is exactly the same as the W input, so the part of circuitry to convert from Gray to binary will consist of a piece of wire from the W input to the A output.

Generating the B output looks almost as easy until you get to row 8. Up until then, the B output is the same as the X input. From there on, X needs to be inverted to generate B. The facilities of a controlled inverter (= exclusive-OR) are required, the W/A signal being used to control whether X gets inverted.

Similarly, C is the same as Y, provided B is LOW, but it is the complement of Y when B is HIGH. Finally, Z inverted under control from C will generate D. The circuit is thus as shown in Figure 3.19.

Fig. 3.19 *4-bit Gray to binary converter*

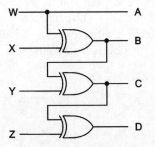

This example shows how it is possible sometimes just to 'see' a solution by inspecting the truth table, rather than using any formal method to arrive at a solution. If you do draw up the Karnaugh maps the chequer-board patterns point you in the direction of exclusive-OR gates, however.

One final point: the design of Figure 3.19 is neat, but does have a timing problem. A changes instantaneously with W, but there is a propagation delay before B changes, then another before C does, then another before D does. This rippling down of information from A to D may re-introduce the momentary errors in output code that the Gray counting scheme was employed to eliminate.

PAPER EXERCISE 3.6

Run the Electronics Workbench file **fig3_19.ewb** to see the effect. Note that the parameters for the propagation delay have been increased so that the effects are made visually obvious. When the software warns about 'Models Clash' choose **Use circuit model**. Run the simulation and note the ripple effect at the output, and the rather troubled way that the display counts. ☐

When you quit the file or close the program choose **No** when asked if you want to save the changes made to the default digital library. ☐

Karnaugh maps for five-input systems

Returning to the use of Karnaugh maps, the way to cope with a five-input system is to draw two four-input maps, one showing the situation with the fifth input LOW, and the other with the fifth input set HIGH. The 1s (or 0s) are grouped in the usual way on each map, but groupings between corresponding positions on the two maps are also checked. The example below (Figure 3.20) shows the kind of thing.

Fig. 3.20 *5-variable Karnaugh map*

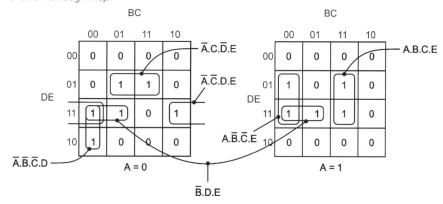

The example shows $Q = \Sigma(2,3,5,7,11,13,17,19,23,29,31)$, i.e. the prime numbers up to 31, taking A as the MSB. After simplification using the Karnaugh map:

$$Q = \overline{A}.\overline{B}.\overline{C}.D + \overline{A}.C.\overline{D}.E + \overline{A}.\overline{C}.D.E + A.\overline{B}.\overline{C}.E + A.B.C.E + B.D.E$$

Quine–McCluskey method for circuit minimisation

The Karnaugh map technique can be extended to six variables. You draw four four-variable maps next to each other, with the two omitted variables being set to 00, 01, 11 and 10 on each map. Loops are generated in two dimensions on each map, but also in the third dimension between maps, as indicated in Figure 3.20. This is somewhat unwieldy, and with larger numbers of input variables a new technique is needed. Quine and McCluskey developed a tabular method suitable for implementation as a computer program, and this is outlined below. It is the technique used by Electronics Workbench to do its simplification.

Taking the prime-number detector $Q = \Sigma(2,3,5,7,11,13,17,19,23,29,31)$ as an example, the Quine–McCluskey method is as follows.

Step 1 (Figure 3.21)

Group the minterms according to how many 1s each has. Thus minterm 2 is 00010 (one 1), while minterm 31 is 11111 (five 1s). (Had the minterm 0 been included, a column for no 1s would have been needed.)

Fig. 3.21 *Minterms grouped according number of 1s*

one 1 minterm		two 1s minterm		three 1s minterm		four 1s minterm		five 1s minterm	
dec	binary	dec	binary	dec	binary	dec	binary	dec	binary
2	00010	3	00011	7	00111	23	10111	31	11111
		5	00101	11	01011	29	11101		
		17	10001	13	01101				
				19	10011				

Step 2 (Figure 3.22)

Compare minterms in adjacent columns. All pairs that differ in just one bit are combined. (The equivalent process on a Karnaugh map would be to loop all adjacent pairs.) Thus minterms 2 and 3 can be paired, as can 29 and 31, etc. The paired minterms are now written out in binary with a × to show the 0/1 combination. The new minterm pairs are again grouped into those containing no 1s, one 1, two 1s etc.

Any minterm that cannot be so combined is called an 'implicant'. These are the equivalent of isolated 1s on a Karnaugh map, and the full Boolean expression for these minterms will appear in the final expression for the overall function.

Here, all the minterms in the first table have been combined into pairs, so there are no implicants at this stage.

Fig. 3.22 *Minterm pairs grouped according to number of 1s*

one 1 minterm pairs		two 1s minterm pairs		three 1s minterm pairs		four 1s minterm pairs	
decimal	binary	decimal	binary	decimal	binary	decimal	binary
2,3	0001×	3,7	00×11	7,23	×0111	23,31	1×111
		3,11	0×011	13,29	×1101	29,31	111×1
		5,13	0×101	19,23	10×11		
		17,19	100×1				

Step 3

This is a repeat of step 2, but attempting to create pairs of pairs. Minterm pairs in adjacent columns are compared and any that differ in one bit can be combined. The only example in this case is 3,7 can be combined with 19,23, creating the minterm quad 3,7,19,23: ×0×11.

The minterm pairs not so combined are further implicants and are added to those (if any) found at step 2. The implicants at this stage are all the pairs apart from 3,7 and 19,23.

Steps 4 & 5

The process is repeated, generating pairs of quads, pairs of eights, etc, and noting the implicants at each stage. In this example no further steps like this are possible.

Last step

Some of the implicants that have been discovered by this method might be redundant, and the last step is to discover the essential ('prime') ones. The prime implicants are those that, if left out, would mean that one or more of the original minterms would be left out. A table is created which lists all the implicants and the original minterms they contain. If an original minterm appears in only one implicant, then that implicant is a prime one. Figure 3.23 shows the idea.

Fig. 3.23 *Prime and redundant implicants*

implicants		original minterms										
decimal	binary	2	3	5	7	11	13	17	19	23	29	31
2,3	0001×	✓	✓									
3,11	0×011		✓			✓						
5,13	0×101			✓			✓					
7,23	×0111				✓					✓		
13,29	×1101						✓				✓	
17,19	100×1							✓	✓			
23,31	1×111									✓		✓
29,31	111×1										✓	✓
3,7,19,23	×0×11		✓		✓				✓	✓		

The darker rows in the table show the redundant implicants. They are the ones that contain minterms that are already covered by the other (prime) implicants.

The minimised Boolean expression for Q thus comprises implicants (2,3), (3,11), (5,13), (17,19), (29,31), (3,7,19,23). The binary codes for these implicants leads to the actual Boolean expression. Thus (2,3) has the code 0001× which means $\overline{A}.\overline{B}.\overline{C}.D.E + \overline{A}.\overline{B}.\overline{C}.D.\overline{E}$. This reduces to just $\overline{A}.\overline{B}.\overline{C}.D$. In other words, the ×s do not appear in the terms, but just act as place markers. Thus, $Q = \overline{A}.\overline{B}.\overline{C}.D + \overline{A}.\overline{C}.D.E + \overline{A}.C.\overline{D}.E + A.\overline{B}.\overline{C}.E + A.B.C.E + \overline{B}.D.E$, as obtained from the Karnaugh map method, Figure 3.20.

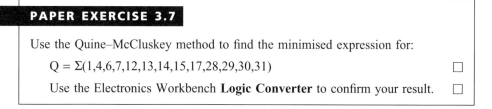

PAPER EXERCISE 3.7

Use the Quine–McCluskey method to find the minimised expression for:

Q = Σ(1,4,6,7,12,13,14,15,17,28,29,30,31) ☐

Use the Electronics Workbench **Logic Converter** to confirm your result. ☐

In practical exercise 3.1 the requirement for a design was entered into Electronics Workbench simply by filling in a truth table. The software analysed the table, minimised it and created the circuit automatically. The XPLA software allows you to do the same, and this is covered in this exercise. Run XPLA Professional, create a new project (e.g. Ch3) and create a new PHDL source file (e.g. **Prime.phd**) for the project. Set the **DEVICE** to **xcr5032c-10pc44c**.   ☐

Give the module a name (e.g. **Prime**) and add some title information.   ☐
Declare five inputs, A to E, and an output Q.   ☐
Under the equations section enter the data in Figure 3.24.

Fig. 3.24 *Using a truth table in PHDL*

```
equations
;
truth_table([A,B,C,D,E]  ->  Q)
                      0   ->  0;      "0 and 1 are not
                      1   ->  0;      "defined as prime numbers
                      2   ->  1;
                      3   ->  1;
                      4   ->  0;
                      5   ->  1;
                      6   ->  0;
                      7   ->  1;
                      8   ->  0;
                      9   ->  0;
                     10   ->  0;
                     11   ->  1;
                     12   ->  0;
                     13   ->  1;
                     14   ->  0;
                     15   ->  0;
                     16   ->  0;
                     17   ->  1;
                     18   ->  0;
                     19   ->  1;
                     20   ->  0;
                     21   ->  0;
                     22   ->  0;
                     23   ->  1;
                     24   ->  0;
                     25   ->  0;
                     26   ->  0;
                     27   ->  0;
                     28   ->  0;
                     29   ->  1;
                     30   ->  0;
                     31   ->  1;
END
```

Note the ; before the truth table. There is no obvious reason why this is needed but the design won't compile unless it is present.

The square brackets around the list of input variables turns the list into a binary-weighted set. It is then possible to assign values to the set, allowing the 32 input/output requirements to be defined as shown.　☐

Save the file and compile it. If there are any errors, read the information, try to correct the information in the **.phd** file, checking that it is exactly the same as that given above, save and re-compile.　☐

Take a look at the optimised-equations file: that's the one with the **.ph1** extension. Interestingly, a different optimisation has taken place from the one that the Quine–McCluskey algorithm gives. In terms of a five-variable Karnaugh map, the loops have been made as shown in Figure 3.25.

Fig. 3.25 *XPLA optimisation of prime-numbers function*

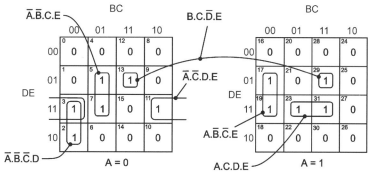

As you can see, this is a perfectly valid way of grouping the 1s, although the 3,7,19,23 quad has not been created.　☐

Does it work? The timing simulator can be used to verify correct operation, so click the **Fit** button, then the **TimeSim...** button.　☐

Some input signals need to be defined, and the easiest way to exercise the design is to create a five-bit binary number that increases steadily from 00000 to 11111 (0 to 31). First, set the **Simulate Until** box to 2000ns, and press the **Enter** key on the keyboard.　☐

Now click the **Create Clk** button, set the **Cycle Length** to 800, **Start Value** to 0, Accept, then click on **signal A**.　☐

Repeat for signals B, C, D and E, but with **Cycle Lengths** of 400, 200, 100 and 50 respectively. Close the **Clock Setting** dialog box by clicking the **Done** button.　☐

Press the **Run** button, and verify that the Q output goes high when (and only when) the input is a prime number, taking signal A as the MSB. Zoom in a few times (by double-clicking the left mouse button) and use the **Set Marker** facility to verify the propagation delay is 10ns.　☐

Note: There is a facility for joining displayed signals together into a bus, and for the software to display the value of the bus. This would be very useful here to check that the output goes high at the correct times. Unfortunately, it isn't possible to include clock signals into a bus, so you will just have to read off the binary values, and convert them to decimal numbers.

Static hazards

This does not refer to the problems of static electric charges blowing up delicate electronic components, as mentioned briefly in Chapter 1, but to the situation whereby outputs momentarily change state when they should remain static.

For the current design, you should find that the design appears to work satisfactorily, with the output signal going HIGH whenever the input is a prime number. However, it is important to check for static hazards when the input changes from one prime number to another. The output should remain HIGH, of course. To test for this, the input binary value needs to sequence through all the prime numbers, rather than counting up in binary. The easiest way to achieve this is edit the **Simulation Control Language** file that controls the way the simulator behaves.

PRACTICAL EXERCISE 3.3

Click the **File** menu item in the top bar of the **XPLASim** window then select **Open Text File…** Check that the **Files of type** field of the **Open** dialog box is set to **SCL Files (*.scl)**, then navigate to the folder where you have saved your current work. You should find the **.scl** file listed there relevant to the current design. Select it, then click **Open**. You should get something like the listing in Figure 3.26. □

Fig. 3.26 *Simulation Control Language file*

```
*   C:\xplawork\prime.scl
*   Thu Dec 30 12:07:00 1999
*   XPLA-Sim (2.1d)

*   These Signals Will Be Viewable After Running The
Simulator

P A, B, C, D, E, Q

*   These Are The Initializations.

IT 1 (VCC)

*   These Are The Signal Transitions For The Simulation

S  0 ( 400, 800,  ETC) A
S  0 ( 200, 400,  ETC) B
S  0 ( 100, 200,  ETC) C
S  0 ( 50,  100,  ETC) D
S  0 ( 25,  50,  ETC) E

SU TIME = *+2000
*   SU TIME = 2000

F
```

The five clock signals are defined using the s (sequence) command. You should be able to see how these definitions have been created automatically from the **Clock Settings** that you entered earlier. The P command controls which signals will be 'printed', the SU TIME command controls the **Simulate Until** parameter. F means **Finish**, while IT (**Initialise To**) has been used here, by default, to set the signal vcc to 1. Lines starting with * are comments. See the **Help** system for further details.

Edit the five s lines so that they read:

```
S 0 (400 ,850 ) A
S 0 (150 ,200 ,350 ,500, 750 ,900 ,1050 ,1100 ) B
S 0 (250 ,550 ,700 ,1000 ) C
S 0 (50 ,300, 450 ,600 ,650, 800, 950, 1200 ) D
S 0 (100 ,1150 ) E
```

Make sure you have all the syntax exactly right, with no extra commas, etc. – the software tends to crash if it cannot parse the **.scl file** successfully. Note that the command lines must start with a blank space before the s. Save the amended file, but *don't* run the simulation yet. ☐

The simulator still has the old **.scl** file in its memory and, at the next run of the simulator, will save it over the top of the one you have carefully altered. To prevent it from doing so, click the **File \ Open...** menu, select and open the new **.scl** file into the simulator's memory. You should find the new pattern of input signals displayed. ☐

Now it is safe to run the simulation. You should find a couple of glitches in the output signal: one at 260ns and the other at 710ns. ☐

At this point the bus facility *can* be used to group and evaluate the amended input signals. Click the **Create Bus** button (click OK first, if necessary, to un-grey the facility). When the **Adding Bus** dialog box appears, select signals A, B, C, D and E, and copy them to the **Bus Elements** field, using the right-pointing button in the window. Give the bus a name, e.g. **IN**, hit the **Display** button then **Done**.

If the bus value is given in hex, click the **Options \ Bus Value \ Decimal** menu item. Run the simulation again. You should find the glitches occur when the input changes value from 5 to 13, and from 31 to 29. ☐

Where have the glitches come from? A detailed explanation would require a very detailed knowledge of the circuitry inside the CPLD chip and the data books do not give this amount of detail. The kind of thing that is going on, however, is illustrated in Figure 3.27 below.

When signal A goes LOW, signal B goes HIGH. If the delay through the inverter were zero, then the two events would happen simultaneously, there would be no time when A and B were both LOW, and there would be no glitch. In reality, signal B remains LOW for a short time after A goes LOW, so the OR gate momentarily sees two LOWs, and the glitch appears. Note that the propagation delay through the OR gate is not shown in the diagram.

Fig. 3.27 *Glitch caused when signal A goes LOW*

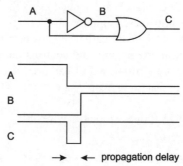

From this example you would expect the glitch width to be the same as the propagation delay of the inverter. If you examine the simulator output waveform the glitch lasts 2ns which agrees with the specification for the propagation delay of the individual gates within the CPLD chip. The glitch that occurs when the input data changes from 31 to 29 involves one of the input signals (signal D) going LOW, which again makes sense in terms of the discussion given above. The 5–13 glitch must be caused by some internal signal making a HIGH-to-LOW transition.

The reason some transitions cause glitches while others don't is worth investigating. Consider the three-input system Q = Σ(1,3,6,7). The Karnaugh map is shown in Figure 3.28.

Fig. 3.28 *Karnaugh map for Q = Σ(1,3,6,7)*

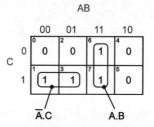

The minimised expression for Q is thus A.B + $\overline{A}$.C and the circuit is shown in Figure 3.29 below.

The timing diagram illustrates why the transition from 111 to 011 (cell 7 to cell 3 of the Karnaugh map) causes a glitch, but the reverse transition (011 back to 111) doesn't. The inverter delays the LOW-to-HIGH edge on $\overline{A}$, allowing the two LOWs to coincide at the input to the OR with a brief LOW appearing at Z. When the transition is in the other direction it is the HIGH logic state that persists, but this has no effect on the OR gate. (Signals B and C are not shown on the timing diagram, but remain HIGH throughout.)

Transitions between cells 1 and 3 never cause a glitch since it is signal B that changes between these cells. The other two signals remain in states that ensure a permanent HIGH at the OR gate input – A is permanently LOW so W doesn't change, and X remains HIGH throughout.

Fig. 3.29 *Transitions from 111 to 011 and back again*

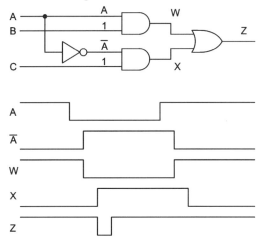

One way to overcome the glitch problem is to add redundant terms to the Boolean expression covering the transitions between loops. Thus, the Karnaugh map should be looped as shown in Figure 3.30 to ensure that there are no glitches caused by changes between adjacent cells.

Fig. 3.30 *Extra loop introduced to eliminate static hazard glitches*

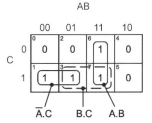

The circuit is shown in Figure 3.31. Now there will be no glitch when the input changes from 111 to 011 since the output from the BC AND gate remains HIGH.

Fig. 3.31 *Glitch-free transition with extra AND gate*

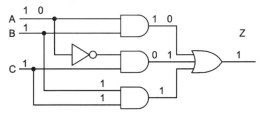

This technique will guarantee that there will be no static hazards when a single input changes state. It doesn't cover the situation when two or more inputs change, as when, for example, moving from cell 1 to cell 6.

PRACTICAL EXERCISE 3.4

Returning to the circuit to detect when a prime number is present at its five-bit input, we have two expressions for the logic: one derived from the Karnaugh map depicted in Figure 3.20, and one from the XPLA software and Karnaugh map shown in Figure 3.25. The first Karnaugh map has bigger loops, leading to $Q = \overline{A}.\overline{B}.\overline{C}.D + \overline{A}.C.\overline{D}.E + \overline{A}.\overline{C}.D.\overline{E} + A.\overline{B}.\overline{C}.E + A.B.C.E + \overline{B}.D.E$. With bigger loops there is less chance of glitches, so it is worth trying this expression as the definition of the system rather than using the truth table.

Run the XPLA software and open the project/file created in practical exercise 3.2. Amend the **.phd** file as follows:

- under the `equations` section add the expression for Q thus:

```
Q = !A&!B&!C&D  #  !A&C&!D&E  #  !A&!C&D&E  #  A&!B&!C&E
    #  A&B&C&E  #  !B&D&E;
```

- turn the truth table stuff into one big comment by enclosing it between a `/*` before the `truth_table` keyword and a `*/` after the last truth table entry. ☐

Save the amended file, compile it, fit the design and run the timing simulator. The simulator should open with the same input signals as before. Run the simulation. Do you get any glitches now? ☐

Summary

This chapter has covered the way a combinational logic problem can be tackled by firstly defining it in terms of a truth table, then minimising the resultant Boolean expression by means of a Karnaugh map or Quine–McCluskey tabular algorithm. Both sum-of-product and product-of-sums type expressions have been covered.

Electronics Workbench and XPLA software have been used to carry out the process automatically, from inputting the design requirements by means of a truth table, to obtaining minimised Boolean expressions for the solution, and implementing the solution in terms of logic gates. The Electronics Workbench software uses the Quine–McCluskey algorithm to minimise the solution, but it was found that the XPLA software uses a different process.

The problem of static hazards has been discussed and a method, involving adding extra redundant loops on a Karnaugh map, for eliminating such glitches has been given. This solves the problem provided only one input changes state at a time. The design generated by the XPLA software to detect whether a five-bit number was prime was found to be susceptible to static hazards in two situations, according to the timing simulation software. The design generated by the Quine–McCluskey method appeared to be free from such problems.

In this chapter you have been introduced to a variety of ways to solve problems in combinatorial logic. This assignment gives you an opportunity to demonstrate that you can apply them to the problem of driving the seven-segment displays on the demonstration board that accompanies this book.

With reference to the circuit diagram of the demonstration board (Appendix A) the top segment of the seven-segment display is referred to as segment 'a'. Segments b, c, d, e and f follow in sequence clockwise around the outside of the display. Segment g is the central segment. Each of these seven segments comprises a red LED; an eighth LED forms the decimal point.

The anode connection of each LED is taken to the pins of the display as indicated on the circuit diagram, but all the cathodes are linked together internally. The common cathode connection is brought out via the V- pin. In order to make a particular segment light up, its anode connection must be taken HIGH (via its current limiting 330Ω resistor) and the transistor for the display turned on. Thus, when pins 41 and 28 of the CPLD chip go HIGH, segment 'a' of IC1b shines.

Numbers and letters can be displayed by getting the appropriate LEDs to illuminate. This, if segments a, b, g, e and d turn on, it will look something like the number 2. Segments a, e, f and g will display an F.

Task 1

Construct seven truth tables showing how the state of each segment depends on the four-bit binary input. Segment a has been partially completed for you. Note that you will need to ensure that it is possible to display all ten decimal digits plus the six hex digits. Obviously, each displayed digit should be unique so that there is no ambiguity as to which digit is displayed.

Fig. 3.32 *Truth tables for display segments (to be completed)*

W	X	Y	Z	a	b	c	d	e	f	g
0	0	0	0	1						
0	0	0	1	0						
0	0	1	0	1						
0	0	1	1	1						
0	1	0	0							
0	1	0	1							
0	1	1	0							
0	1	1	1							
1	0	0	0							
1	0	0	1							
1	0	1	0							
1	0	1	1							
1	1	0	0							
1	1	0	1							
1	1	1	0	1						
1	1	1	1	1						

inputs / outputs

Task 2

Enter the design using the XPLA software. Note that the `truth_table` syntax can accept multiple output variables as well as inputs. Indeed, the whole design could be entered quite neatly by such means:

```
truth_table([W,X,Y,Z]  ->  [a,b,c,d,e,f,g])
              0         ->  [1,1,1,1,1,1,0];
              1         ->  [0,1,1,0,0,0,0];
             ...            ...
             ^hF        ->  [1,0,0,0,1,1,1];
```

In order to demonstrate that you have grasped the content of this chapter, however, think up as many ways as you can to enter the design, using different methods for different outputs.

Remember to turn the appropriate transistor on. `TR = 1;` will set the variable `TR` permanently HIGH.

Task 3

Compile, fit, carry out timing simulations and download the design to the target hardware to ensure that your design works as required. Refer to the circuit diagram (Appendix A) for pin numbers. This information can be entered in the **.phd** file, or you can use the pin editor facility to allocate pins. Use the **Properties** dialog box to specify whether the **.phd** file or the **.paf** file should be used for determining how the pins are allocated.

Check for static hazards. Discuss which transitions might cause static hazards for which outputs. Design test sequences that would reveal them. Comment on the importance of eliminating such glitches for this particular application.

Task 4

Write an account of the work done. Include listings of any **.phd** or **.scl** files used, Karnaugh maps, etc. Discuss the design methods you used, what results you were expecting, how you tested the design and the results that were obtained.

Coverage

This assignment covers the last two of the three assessment criteria for the combinational logic aspects of Outcome 3 of the Edexcel/BTEC H-level unit 'Digital and Analogue Devices and Circuits'.

Grading criteria

Pass

- 'Design digital electronic circuits' (derive a suitable way to drive at least two of the segments)
- 'Test digital electronic circuits' (at least one of the designs simulated; design downloaded to target hardware and tested, with an account given of method and results)

There are opportunities to gain evidence towards Merit and Distinction grades for the 'Digital and Analogue Devices and Circuits' unit, as the following examples suggest.

Merit

- 'Use a range of methods and techniques to collect, analyse and process information/ data' (use a range of methods to derive Boolean expressions for the various segments of the display)
- 'Apply and analyse detailed knowledge and skills, using relevant theories and techniques' (analyse the Karnaugh maps to pin-point likely static hazards)
- 'Coherently present and communicate work using technical language accurately' (task 4)

Distinction

- 'Check validity when collecting, analysing and processing complex information/ data' (discuss validity of information presented by XPLA simulation software, etc.)
- 'Evaluate and synthesise relevant theories and techniques to generate and justify conclusions' (discuss appropriateness of different techniques for deriving Boolean expressions, discuss importance of glitches in this application)
- 'Show an individual approach in presenting and communicating work coherently, using technical language fluently' (task 4)

ANSWERS TO EXERCISES

Paper exercise 3.2

Figures 3.33 and 3.34 show the revised truth table and Karnaugh map.

Fig. 3.33 *Figure 3.2 revised for new version of guarded machine*

	inputs				output
	L	R	G	K	M
0	0	0	0	0	0
1	0	0	0	1	0
2	0	0	1	0	0
3	0	0	1	1	0
4	0	1	0	0	0
5	0	1	0	1	0
6	0	1	1	0	1
7	0	1	1	1	0
8	1	0	0	0	0
9	1	0	0	1	0
10	1	0	1	0	1
11	1	0	1	1	0
12	1	1	0	0	0
13	1	1	0	1	1
14	1	1	1	0	1
15	1	1	1	1	0

Fig. 3.34 *Figure 3.6 revised for new version of guarded machine:* $M = G.\bar{K}.R + G.\bar{K}.L + \bar{G}.K.L.R$

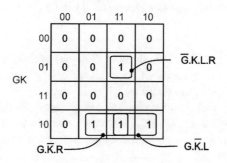

Paper exercise 3.3

Figures 3.35, 3.36 and 3.37 show the revised Karnaugh maps and expressions.

Fig. 3.35 *Equivalent of Figure 3.7 for re-defined guarded machine:* $M = (L + R).(G + K).(G + R).(\bar{G} + \bar{K}).(G + L)$

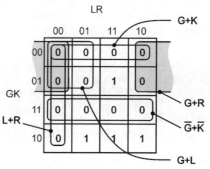

Fig. 3.36 *Figure 3.8 revised:* $\bar{M} = (\bar{G} + K + \bar{R}).(\bar{G} + K + \bar{L}).(G. + \bar{K} + \bar{L} + \bar{R})$

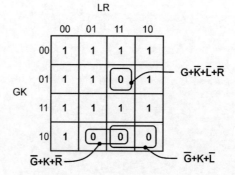

Fig. 3.37 *Figure 3.9 revised:* $\overline{M} = \overline{L}.\overline{R} + \overline{G}.\overline{K} + \overline{G}.\overline{R} + G.K + \overline{G}.\overline{L}$

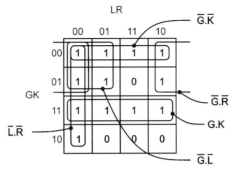

Paper exercise 3.7

Step 1
Group minterms according to number of 1s (Figure 3.38).

Fig. 3.38 *Step 1 of the Quine–McCluskey method completed*

one 1 minterm		two 1s minterm		three 1s minterm		four 1s minterm		five 1s minterm	
dec	binary	dec	binary	dec	binary	dec	binary	dec	binary
1	00001	6	00110	7	00111	15	01111	31	11111
4	00100	12	01100	13	01101	29	11101		
		17	10001	14	01110	30	11110		
				28	11100				

Step 2
Create minterm pairs (Figure 3.39). No implicants generated at this stage.

Fig. 3.39 *Step 2 of the Quine–McCluskey method completed*

one 1 minterm pairs		two 1s minterm pairs		three 1s minterm pairs		four 1s minterm pairs	
decimal	binary	decimal	binary	decimal	binary	decimal	binary
1,17	×0001	6,7	0011×	7,15	0×111	15,31	×1111
4,6	001×0	6,14	0×110	13,15	011×1	29,31	111×1
4,12	0×100	12,13	0110×	13,29	×1101	30,31	1111×
				14,15	0111×		
				14,30	×1110		
				28,30	111×0		

Step 3
Create minterm quads (Figure 3.40). (1,17) and (4,6) implicants generated at this stage. Note that some quads have been generated twice. This has no particular significance.

Fig. 3.40 *Step 3 of the Quine–McCluskey method completed*

one 1 minterm quads		two 1s minterm quads		three 1s minterm quads	
decimal	binary	decimal	binary	decimal	binary
4,12,6,14	0x1x1	6,7,14,15	0x11x	13,15,29,31	x11x1
		6,14,7,15	as above	13,29,15,31	as above
		12,13,14,15	011xx	14,15,30,31	x111x
				14,30,15,31	as above
				28,30,29,31	111xx

Step 4

Create minterm eights. Quads (12,13,14,15) and (28,29,30,31) combine at this stage – binary code x11xx. All other quads are implicants.

Last step

Generate table of prime and redundant implicants. The three darker implicants are redundant. Hence $Q = \overline{B}.\overline{C}.\overline{D}.E + \overline{A}.C.\overline{E} + \overline{A}.C.D + B.C$

Fig. 3.41 *Step 4 of the Quine–McCluskey method completed*

implicants decimal	binary	original minterms 1	4	6	7	12	13	14	15	17	28	29	30	31
1,17	x0001	✓								✓				
4,6	001x0		✓	✓										
4,12,6,14	0x1x1		✓	✓		✓		✓						
6,7,14,15	0x11x			✓	✓			✓	✓					
13,15,29,31	x11x1						✓		✓			✓		✓
14,15,30,31	x111x							✓	✓				✓	✓
12...15,28...31	x11xx					✓	✓	✓	✓		✓	✓	✓	✓

4 'Off-the-shelf' combinational logic circuits

Introduction

In the last chapter you discovered how to solve logic problems of a combinational nature – ones where it is possible to say what the output should be given the current state of all the relevant inputs. (The other type of logic – sequential – will be introduced in the next chapter.)

Some combinational problems (such as the problem of driving a seven-segment display) come up over and over again, so the chip manufacturers have designed ready-made solutions to them. The emergence of programmable devices has provided a different, more flexible way of tackling these problems, with one device having the potential to solve a huge number of different problems, so the market for pre-designed chips is reducing. The same requirements still occur, however, and in this chapter you will be introduced to them, find out which 'off-the-shelf' chips are available to satisfy them, and see the way that the XPLA software deals with them.

The chapter covers:

- multiplexers and demultiplexers
- encoders and decoders
- adders and subtractors
- the use of read-only memory (ROM) as combinational logic (multiplier)
- Electronics Workbench and XPLA implementation of all these devices
- an extended assignment

The complexity of these devices is an order of magnitude greater than the basic gates themselves, and they are categorised as 'medium-scale integration' (MSI) devices. While the SSI (small-scale integration) circuits of the basic gates may comprise up to about 10 gates per chip, these MSI devices have up to 100. While on the subject, taking the next ten-fold step up in complexity – up to 1000 gates – takes us to the realm of LSI (large-scale integration), and circuits like microprocessors are defined as VLSI (very large scale integration – anything above 1000 gates).

Multiplexers

Multiplexing means taking several different signals and sending them all down the same line. First the first signal is sent, then the second, then the third and so on until all the signals that need to be transmitted have had a brief opportunity to gain access to the line. Then a bit more of the first signal is sent, then the second, and so on. In data communications systems this is known as TDM – time-division multiplexing.

The device that selects the different input signals is known as a multiplexer. A mechanical version would be a multi-way, single-pole switch since this would be able to route one of many inputs through to a common output.

The 74××151 is a digital version, able to deal with eight signal inputs. It has an additional three-bit input that you use to select the required signal input, there's an enable input that enables the whole device, and the output is available in both true and complement form. (The ×× part of the 74××151 device number represents LS, HC, HCT etc., i.e. the various technologies used to manufacture the different logic families.) The 'traditional' and IEC logic symbols for the 75××151 are given in Figure 4.1.

Fig. 4.1 *Traditional and IEC symbols for the 74××151 8-input multiplexer*

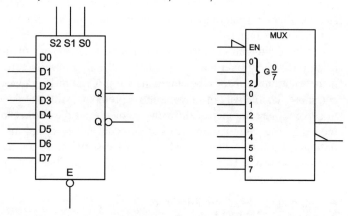

In the traditional symbol the **Select** inputs are labelled S2..S0 while the **Data** inputs are D7..D0. The **Enable** input is active-LOW. Note that the signal names are shown inside the symbol border, so inverted ones do not need a bar – the little circles already indicate signal inversion.

Provided the enable signal is active (i.e. LOW) then, if, for example, S2, S1 and S0 were set to 0,1,1 respectively, data input D3 would effectively be connected to the Q output. If the enable is inactive (HIGH) then none of the inputs is connected to the outputs; Q just sits there, LOW.

The IEC symbol shows the same information, but the three-bit select input is labelled G, with the $\frac{0}{7}$ symbol indicating the range of possible values for this input. The numbering of the other inputs indicates that they are selected according to the G value.

The 74××153 is a 'dual 4-input multiplexer': it's like a two-pole 4-way switch. The IEC symbol is given below.

Fig. 4.2 *Labelled IEC logic symbol for 74xx153 dual 4-input multiplexer*

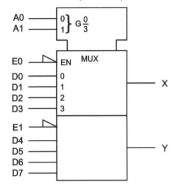

Note how the select inputs are shown as common to both multiplexers. Also, by convention, the information in the second, lower multiplexer is omitted since it is simply a duplicate of that in the first.

PAPER EXERCISE 4.1

List the connections required so that the data at input D2 appears on the X output. How would you get the data at D7 to appear on output Y at the same time?

Applications of multiplexers

As well as being used as described at the beginning of the section to route different signals one at a time through to an output line, multiplexers can be used to implement truth tables. Consider the circuit given in Figure 4.3.

Fig. 4.3 *Multiplexer used to implement a 3-input truth table*

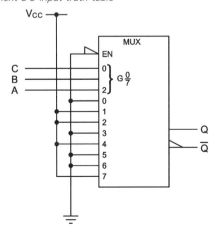

What does this do? Well, if the ABC input is 1, 2, 4 or 7 then the Q output will be HIGH, otherwise it will be LOW. This is the even parity generator function encountered in Chapter 3: the number of 1s on the three inputs plus the Q output is always even. $Q = \Sigma(1,2,4,7)$. (The $\overline{Q}$ output generates odd parity.) This scheme can easily be adapted to implement any three-input truth table simply by data inputs HIGH and LOW according to the truth table.

PAPER EXERCISE 4.2

How would you connect up the data inputs so that the Q output would indicate if the majority of the ABC inputs were HIGH?

With a bit more design effort, the circuit can be adapted to implement any four-input truth table as well. Consider the problem of deciding whether a 4-bit input forms a number that is divisible by 3. The truth table is shown below in Figure 4.4, and the circuit to implement it in Figure 4.5.

Look carefully at the truth table. The numbers down the left side show the value of the ABC part of the input number, A being the MSB. You can see that when ABC is 0 or 2 or 5 then the Q output wants to be 0, irrespective of the value of D. When it's 1 or 4 or 7 the Q output is the same as the D input. Finally, when it's 3 or 6 the Q output needs to be the inverse of the D input. The circuit diagram implements these statements.

Fig. 4.4 *Truth table for divisible-by-three detector*

	inputs				output
	A	B	C	D	Q
0	0	0	0	0	0
	0	0	0	1	0
1	0	0	1	0	0
	0	0	1	1	1
2	0	1	0	0	0
	0	1	0	1	0
3	0	1	1	0	1
	0	1	1	1	0
4	1	0	0	0	0
	1	0	0	1	1
5	1	0	1	0	0
	1	0	1	1	0
6	1	1	0	0	1
	1	1	0	1	0
7	1	1	1	0	0
	1	1	1	1	1

Fig. 4.5 *Circuit to implement truth table of Figure 4.4*

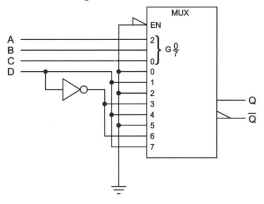

Using this idea, devise a circuit using a 74HC151 to detect if a 4-bit input represents a prime number. (0 and 1 are defined as not prime.)

PHDL implementation of multiplexers

PHDL code to define a system that would function along the lines of the 74xx151 is
given in Figure 4.6.

Fig. 4.6 *PHDL implementation of 8-to-1 multiplexer*

```
MODULE  mpx8to1
TITLE    '8 to 1 multiplexer (cf. 74xx151)'

DECLARATIONS
D7..D0,  S2..S0,  N_E  pin;
Q,  N_Q                pin;

S  =  [S2..S0];

EQUATIONS

when N_E  ==  0 then
  {
  when  S  ==  0 then  Q  =  D0;
  when  S  ==  1 then  Q  =  D1;
  when  S  ==  2 then  Q  =  D2;
  when  S  ==  3 then  Q  =  D3;
  when  S  ==  4 then  Q  =  D4;
  when  S  ==  5 then  Q  =  D5;
  when  S  ==  6 then  Q  =  D6;
  when  S  ==  7 then  Q  =  D7;
  }
N_Q  =  !Q;

END
```

The listing uses the `when...then...` syntax to define the required behaviour. Note how the condition (given just after the `when`) uses the double-equals sign to make the test, but the single-equals is used as normal for assigning the relevant data input signal to the output.

This example uses a 'nested' structure to achieve the desired behaviour as regards the active-LOW enable signal, `N_E`. Curly braces { } enclose the section of code that is to apply when the enable signal is active. Indentation is also used to emphasise the structure.

`when...then...` is often followed by an `else...` section. In the present example it could be used to specify what happens when the enable signal is not active, thus:

```
when N_E == 0 then
  {
  when S == 0 then Q = D0;
  when S == 1 then Q = D1;
  when S == 2 then Q = D2;
  when S == 3 then Q = D3;
  when S == 4 then Q = D4;
  when S == 5 then Q = D5;
  when S == 6 then Q = D6;
  when S == 7 then Q = D7;
  }
else Q = 0;
```

Although this doesn't actually add anything to the definition of the way the system will behave, it's quite useful, just to emphasise what happens when the enable signal is inactive.

The code produced when the module is compiled is shown below:

```
Q =!N_E & S0 & S1 & S2 & D7
 #   !N_E & !S0 & S1 & S2 & D6
 #   !N_E & S0 & !S1 & S2 & D5
 #   !N_E & !S0 & !S1 & S2 & D4
 #   !N_E & S0 & S1 & !S2 & D3
 #   !N_E & !S0 & S1 & !S2 & D2
 #   !N_E & S0 & !S1 & !S2 & D1
 #   !N_E & !S0 & !S1 & !S2 & D0;
```

You should be able to see that this will produce the required behaviour, and could be used as the source code. The `when...then...` syntax is rather easier to appreciate, however, and less prone to typing errors.

Demultiplexers

As you might expect from the name, these do the opposite job to the one the multiplexer does. A demultiplexer unravels the mixed up (multiplexed) signals present on a line and feeds them through to separate outputs. At least, it is capable of doing so, provided something knows when a new signal appears on the input so that the information is switched to the appropriate output at the correct time. The IEC symbol for the 74××238 demultiplexer is shown in Figure 4.7.

Fig. 4.7 *Symbol for 74××238 demultiplexer*

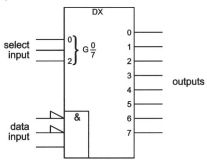

The symbol indicates that the data input is routed to one of the eight output lines, depending on the binary number present at the select input. The data input itself is formed by ANDing three signals together. If you only need a single data input line, the unused ones are taken to the state that allows the 'real' input through the AND gate. The two inverted inputs would be taken LOW, for instance, if the non-inverting data input was the one carrying the information that needed demultiplexing.

PHDL code for a demultiplexer

Fig. 4.8 *PHDL code to implement the function of a 74××238*

```
MODULE   dmpx
TITLE     '8 output demultiplexer (cf. 74xx238)'

DECLARATIONS
N_D1,N_D2,D3,S2..S0  pin;
Q7..Q0               pin;

S = [S2..S0];
D = !N_D1 & !N_D2 & D3;

EQUATIONS

when  S  ==  0  then  Q0  =  D;
when  S  ==  1  then  Q1  =  D;
when  S  ==  2  then  Q2  =  D;
when  S  ==  3  then  Q3  =  D;
when  S  ==  4  then  Q4  =  D;
when  S  ==  5  then  Q5  =  D;
when  S  ==  6  then  Q6  =  D;
when  S  ==  7  then  Q7  =  D;

END
```

The code is quite straightforward. One point worth mentioning is the definition within the **DECLARATIONS** section that the symbol D is to be expanded to mean !N_D1 & !N_D2 & D3 whenever it is encountered in the rest of the code. This allows the code itself to be written quite neatly.

When compiled, the XPLA software generates:

```
Q0 = !S0 & !S1 & !S2 & !N_D1 & !N_D2 & D3;
Q1 = S0 & !S1 & !S2 & !N_D1 & !N_D2 & D3;
Q2 = !S0 & S1 & !S2 & !N_D1 & !N_D2 & D3;
Q3 = S0 & S1 & !S2 & !N_D1 & !N_D2 & D3;
Q4 = !S0 & !S1 & S2 & !N_D1 & !N_D2 & D3;
Q5 = S0 & !S1 & S2 & !N_D1 & !N_D2 & D3;
Q6 = !S0 & S1 & S2 & !N_D1 & !N_D2 & D3;
Q7 = S0 & S1 & S2 & !N_D1 & !N_D2 & D3;
```

Decoders

The 74××238 device just discussed is described in the data books not just as a demultiplexer, but as a decoder/demultiplexer. The same device does two different jobs, depending on how you think about it. If you think of it as a decoder you draw the IEC symbol thus:

Fig. 4.9 *74××238 thought of as a decoder*

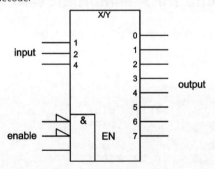

Here, the input is indicated to be a binary-weighted (1,2,4) code (X) while the output (Y) is an active-HIGH 1-out-of-8 code. The whole device is enabled when the three enable inputs are LOW, LOW, HIGH appropriately. When the device is enabled, the output that goes HIGH is determined by the 3-bit number at the input. If the device is not enabled, none of the outputs goes HIGH.

PHDL code for a decoder

Fig. 4.10 *PHDL code for the 74xx238 when considered as a decoder*

```
MODULE   decoder
TITLE    '3-to-8 decoder (cf. 74xx238)'

DECLARATIONS
N_E1,N_E2,E3,D2..D0  pin;
Q7..Q0               pin;

D = [D2..D0]; Q = [Q7..Q0];
E = !N_E1 & !N_E2 & E3;

EQUATIONS

when E then
  {
  when D == 0 then Q0 = 1;
  when D == 1 then Q1 = 1;
  when D == 2 then Q2 = 1;
  when D == 3 then Q3 = 1;
  when D == 4 then Q4 = 1;
  when D == 5 then Q5 = 1;
  when D == 6 then Q6 = 1;
  when D == 7 then Q7 = 1;
  }
else Q = 0;

END
```

This is similar to the previous code, but with different names for the various signals, to reflect the different way they are being regarded, and a slightly different structure to the equations. When compiled, the software produces exactly the same equations (apart from signal names) as before.

Applications of decoders

The 3-bit binary to 1-of-8 decoder is used extensively for selecting one device at a time from a range of possible devices. As it happens, most devices have an active-LOW enable and so the 74×x138 (which has active-LOW outputs but is otherwise identical to the 74×x238) is used extensively for this purpose. For example, in many computer systems it is used to activate one memory chip or input/output device at a time according to the address generated by the CPU. Figure 4.11 shows the type of thing.

The 8032 microcontroller can select which of the eight chips A to H that it wants to communicate with by setting up an appropriate address on its Port 2. It can then send data to the chosen chip, or read data from it via the 8-bit data bus connected to Port 0. For instance, to activate chip B it would send the binary number 001× ×××× to P2, where the ×s are 'don't care' values. In binary, any number from 0010 0000 to 0011 1111 would work. In hex this would be the range 20 up to 3F. Chip B would be said to occupy locations 20 to 3F on the memory map for the peripherals for this system.

Fig. 4.11 *Use of 74HC138 as an address decoder*

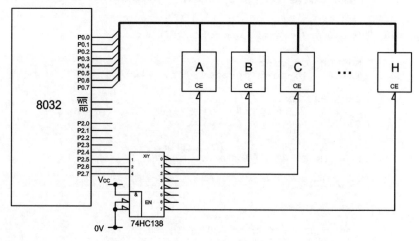

Calculate which area of the memory map chip H would occupy.

Bidirectional switch/multiplexer/demultiplexer

The 74xx151 multiplexer and the 74xx238 demultiplexer have defined inputs and outputs, but there are devices which will work either way around; just like a mechanical switch they will allow signals to flow through them in either direction. Such a device is the 4051 eight-channel analogue switch/multiplexer/demultiplexer. It is called analogue because it just connects a common input/output line to one of eight independent input/output lines. There are no particular threshold voltages, just a channel of about 80Ω between the two, so analogue signals could be accommodated just as well as digital. The 3-bit input signal that selects the channel is digital, however, as is the active-LOW chip-enable. When the chip is not enabled, none of the channels is connected.

Encoders

Encoders do the opposite job to decoders. A *decoder* takes an n-bit binary-coded input and generates an active signal on one of its 2^n outputs. An *encoder*, therefore, generates an n-bit binary output code depending on which of its 2^n inputs is active. An example is the 4532 eight-input priority encoder, whose IEC symbol is shown in Figure 4.12.

Fig. 4.12 *4532 8-input priority encoder*

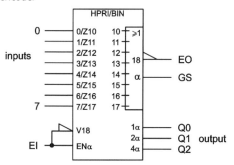

This is an example of how a symbol drawn up using the IEC standard conveys quite complex actions. Deciphering this information is a bit like working on a cryptic crossword puzzle clue – every piece of information means something.

The encoding part is fairly straightforward: the eight inputs are encoded to give a binary-weighted output Q2..Q0. The 'general qualifier' for the entire symbol is given as HPRI/BIN, the HPRI part meaning 'Highest Priority' (and 'BIN' implies binary). This caters for the situation where more than one of the inputs is HIGH – the one with the highest priority is the one that is encoded. Thus, if both inputs 4 and 5 were HIGH, the output code would be 101 (i.e. 5).

The EI (enable input) has to be HIGH to enable the Q outputs. This information is imparted by means of the α label attached to the EI and Q connections. If EI is LOW, the Q outputs just stay LOW.

The rectangular box within the symbol represents an OR function – refer back to Figure 1.37 to remind yourself why $\geqslant 1$ means OR. The inputs to the OR rectangle come from the inputs to the whole device, this being indicated by the Z (interconnection) dependency numbering. The outputs from the OR box are qualified, so GS goes HIGH if any of the inputs are active (that's the OR bit), but the chip must also be enabled with a HIGH on EI (that's the α bit).

Finally, the EO (enable output) goes LOW if any of the inputs are HIGH, but it is also forced LOW if the EI is LOW. How come? A LOW on EI is converted to a HIGH within the symbol because of the polarity converter. This internal HIGH has an OR effect on the EO output because of the V (OR) dependency indicated between the two connections numbered 18. Finally, the polarity converter on the EO output converts the internal HIGH into an external LOW.

Despite the polarity converter on the EO output, the EO signal is really an active-high signal, and the EO function should be represented by a separate AND function. This is shown in Figure 4.13.

You should now be able to see the behaviour of the EO function more clearly. It goes HIGH provided all of the inputs are LOW (see all those little logic state inversion bubbles on the & rectangle?) and the EI is HIGH. The EI now acts in the same sense for all the outputs, so can be shown as an EN(able) for the entire device.

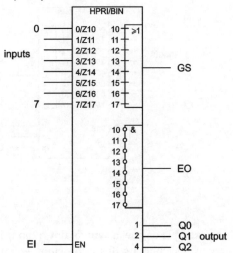

Fig. 4.13 *Alternative symbol for 4532 priority encoder*

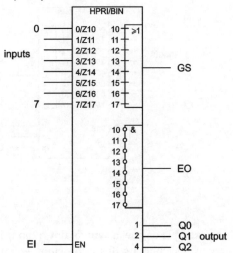

Using the information provided in Figure 4.13, see if you can complete the truth table for the 4532B. (Note: × = don't care – 1 or 0.)

Fig. 4.14 *Truth table for 4532B (to be completed)*

	inputs								outputs				
EI	7	6	5	4	3	2	1	0	Q2	Q1	Q0	GS	EO
0	×	×	×	×	×	×	×	×					
1	0	0	0	0	0	0	0	0					
1	0	0	0	0	0	0	0	1					
1	0	0	0	0	0	0	1	×					
1	0	0	0	0	0	1	×	×					
1	0	0	0	0	1	×	×	×					
1	0	0	0	1	×	×	×	×					
1	0	0	1	×	×	×	×	×					
1	0	1	×	×	×	×	×	×					
1	1	×	×	×	×	×	×	×					

The GS and EO signals are needed when you want to encode more than eight inputs. Figure 4.15 (apologies for the mix of IEC and traditional symbols!) shows how to expand to 16 inputs.

The figure shows how the EO output from the more significant of the two encoders (the lower one in the diagram) is used to enable the less significant, provided the input

Fig. 4.15 *Expanding two 8-bit priority encoders to cope with 16 inputs*

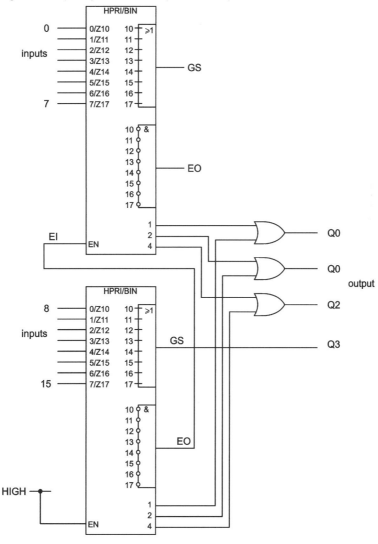

is less than 8. Suppose both inputs 7 and 8 are HIGH. The priority must be given to the 8, giving an output on Q3..Q0 of 1000. Since input 8 is HIGH, the EO from the bottom device will be LOW, disabling the top encoder. GS from lower device will be HIGH, so the required 1000 output will be generated.

For an input of 7, however, all eight inputs 8–15 are LOW, so the EO will go active, and the top encoder will come into play. It will generate 111 for Q2..Q0 while the GS from the lower device will be LOW, thus creating the correct 0111 4-bit output.

Design a 24-bit priority encoder circuit, using three 4532Bs and a 4075B triple 3-input OR. Run paper checks on your design assuming: (a) inputs 7, 8 and 17 are HIGH, (b) 7 and 8 are HIGH, (c) just input 7 is HIGH.

PHDL code for priority encoders

Fig. 4.16 *PHDL code to emulate a 4532B*

```
MODULE   encoder
TITLE    '8-to-3 priority encoder (cf. 4532)'

DECLARATIONS
EI,D7..D0      pin;
GS,Q2..Q0,EO   pin;

D = [D7..D0];  Q = [Q2..Q0];

EQUATIONS

when EI then
  {
  when D == 0 then EO = 1;
          else GS = 1;
  when D < 2 then Q = 0;
  else when D < 4 then Q = 1;
  else when D < 8 then Q = 2;
  else when D < ^h10 then Q = 3;
  else when D < ^h20 then Q = 4;
  else when D < ^h40 then Q = 5;
  else when D < ^h80 then Q = 6;
  else Q = 7;
  }
else Q = 0;

END
```

A new command is used in this example: testing to see if D is less than some value. These tests are equivalent to the rows in the truth table with the ×s in them. For instance, D < 8 covers 00000000 to 00000111, i.e. 000001××.

Listing the various tests in the order given, and using the ...else... syntax is important to achieve the required behaviour. Simulating this design using clock signals on D0, D1 . . . D7 with progressively halved frequencies indicates that the design should work satisfactorily.

As discussed above, the EO and GS functions are only used when more than one device is needed, when dealing with more than eight inputs. With PHDL, however, you can increase the bit-width of the input simply by declaring wider inputs, and extending the ...else... clauses as necessary, so the EO output is not important in itself.

Design and simulate a 10-input priority encoder.

Comparators

These compare two numbers. They tell you one of three things: either the two numbers are the same, or number A is bigger than number B, or number A is smaller than number B. The 74××85 deals with 4-bit numbers and has three output pins to tell you about the input data. As well as the two lots of 4-bit input pins the 74××85 has three more inputs for expansion purposes, used when you want to compare numbers with more than four bits. The idea is that you compare the four MSBs of the two numbers and if they are different you can make the decision about their relative magnitude straightaway. If the four MSBs are the same, however, then you have to look at the next four less significant bits, then the next four and so on until you've looked, if necessary, at all the bits of both numbers. The circuit in Figure 4.17 shows the idea. Note how the expansion inputs of the upper (less significant) device are connected to permanent HIGH and LOW voltages, but those of the lower are driven by the relevant outputs of the upper comparator.

Fig. 4.17 *Expanding two 74××85s to compare two 8-bit words*

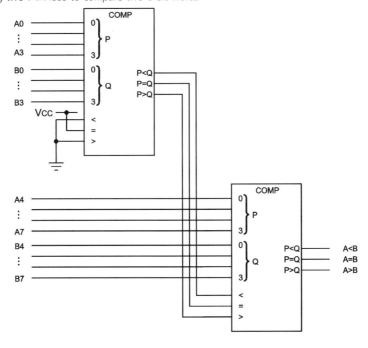

PHDL code for comparators

The high-level constructs available in the language make it easy to design comparators.

Fig. 4.18 *PHDL code for 4-bit comparator*

```
MODULE  comparator
TITLE    '4-bit (cf.  74xx85)'

DECLARATIONS
A3..A0,B3..B0,LT_I,EQ_I,GT_I  pin;
A_LT_B,A_EQ_B,A_GT_B          pin;

A = [A3..A0]; B = [B3..B0];

EQUATIONS

when A < B then A_LT_B = 1;
when A > B then A_GT_B = 1;

when A == B then
  {
  A_LT_B = LT_I;
  A_EQ_B = EQ_I;
  A_GT_B = GT_I;
  }

END
```

PRACTICAL EXERCISE 4.2

Enter the code in Figure 4.18, compile it and take a look at the optimised equations generated by the XPLA software. Be thankful that you've not had to design the comparator from scratch! ☐

To exercise the design on the simulator, fit it, then run the timing simulator. Set the LT_I and GT_I inputs LOW, and EQ_I HIGH. Set up binary-weighted clock signals on A0..A3,B0..B3 with A0 having a period of 50ns, A1 100ns, doubling the period for each signal until B3 is 6400ns. Start all of the clocks LOW, so you end up with a binary up count. Set the simulation to run until 8000ns, and arrange the signals in order, with A0 at the top. Run the simulation. ☐

You will find rather a lot of glitches, but apart from that, check that the outputs do what you would expect them to do. Think of the A input counting up sixteen times faster than the B. To begin with, while B has a small numerical value, the A_GT_B signal should be HIGH for most of the time, but towards the 6400ns point, as B gets up to 15, the A_LT_B signal should take over. Of course, when A momentarily reaches the same value as B, the A_EQ_B signal should go HIGH and the A_GT_B and A_LT_B signals should both be LOW. ☐

Although the optimised equations for A_LT_B and A_GT_B are somewhat complex, the equation for A_EQ_B is more straightforward if you look at it in the light of the exclusive-NOR function. The truth table for ex-NOR is shown below (Figure 4.19).

Fig. 4.19 *Truth table for exclusive-OR and exclusive-NOR*

inputs		output	output
A	B	ex-OR	ex-NOR
0	0	0	1
0	1	1	0
1	0	1	0
1	1	0	1

The exclusive-NOR can be thought of as testing two 1-bit inputs to see if they are the same. This is obviously going to be useful in the equality output signal of the comparator.

PAPER EXERCISE 4.7

Using four 2-input exclusive-NOR gates and a 4-input AND, design a circuit whose output goes HIGH if its two 4-bit inputs are equal.

Adders

Carrying out complex arithmetic on data is probably most easily achieved using micro-processors, or digital signal processors, but there are MSI chips available to add two numbers together. Before looking at them, however, we need to visit the exclusive-OR gate once more, and see how it can add two 1-bit numbers together. Look at the table in Figure 4.20.

Fig. 4.20 $S = A + B$

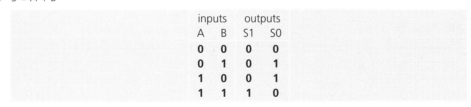

inputs		outputs	
A	B	S1	S0
0	0	0	0
0	1	0	1
1	0	0	1
1	1	1	0

The caption indicates that S is the arithmetic sum of A and B. (The + sign here means plus, not OR.) S1 is the MSB of the sum, and S0 the LSB. The first row reads '$0 + 0 = 0$'; the second and third show that $0 + 1 = 1$ while the last is $1 + 1 = 10$ (binary) $= 2$ (base ten). But you should recognise that S1 is just the AND of A and B, while S0 is the exclusive-OR of A and B. Thus, the circuit of Figure 4.21 will form the 2-bit sum of two 1-bit numbers.

Fig. 4.21 *Circuit to add two 1-bit numbers ('half-adder')*

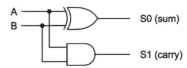

How can we add bigger numbers together? Well, consider the problem of adding 10111010 and 11111100: two 8-bit numbers. Figure 4.22 shows how to do it.

Fig. 4.22 *Adding two binary numbers*

	128 64 32 16 8 4 2 1
first number	10111010
second number	11111100
carries	1 1 1 1 1
answer	110110110

Column 1	$0 + 0 = 0$
Column 2	$1 + 0 = 1$
Column 4	$0 + 1 = 1$
Column 8	$1 + 1 = 0$, carry 1 into the next (16s) column
Column 16	$1 + 1 + 1 = 1$, carry 1 into next (32s) column
Column 32	$1 + 1 + 1 = 1$, carry 1 into next (64s) column
Column 64	$0 + 1 + 1 = 0$, carry 1 into next (128s) column
Column 128	$1 + 1 + 1 = 1$, carry 1 into next (256s) column

For any column, apart from the least significant, you may have three bits to add: one from the first number, one from the second, and a possible carry into that column from the one on its right. In other words, a general-purpose adding block needs to have a carry-in as well as a carry-out. If we can design one of these then they can be strung together to make an adder as wide as needed.

The truth table for such a 'full adder' is given in Figure 4.23:

Fig. 4.23 *Truth table for full adder*

inputs			outputs	
C_{in}	A	B	S	C_{out}
0	0	0	0	0
0	0	1	1	0
0	1	0	1	0
0	1	1	0	1
1	0	0	1	0
1	0	1	0	1
1	1	0	0	1
1	1	1	1	1

It turns out that these functions have been met before, though in different guises. The Sum column is just the same as an even parity generator (see Figures 3.11 and 3.15) and the C_{out} is the most-of-the-inputs-are-HIGH detector (see Figure 2.22), so those designs could be used to build a full adder.

An alternative is to use two half-adders plus an OR gate, as shown in Figure 4.24:

Fig. 4.24 *Full adder made from two half-adders (plus an OR)*

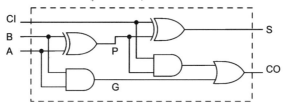

Fig. 4.25 *4-bit adder – Electronics Workbench implementation*

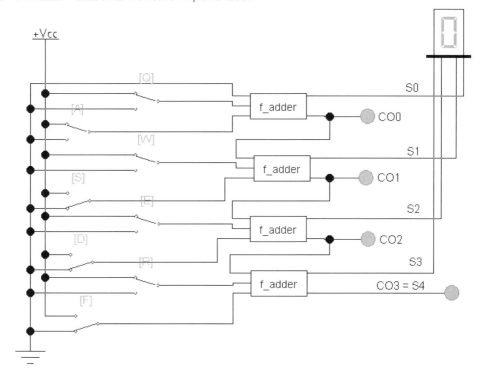

Stringing some of these together creates a four-bit adder – see Figure 4.25.

The circuit is provided on the CD as **fig4_25.ewb**. The characteristics of the digital components inside the full adder sub-circuits have been changed: click **Use circuit model** when opening this file (and don't save changes to the default digital library when closing). The propagation delays have been increased (to 0.1 s) to emphasise the length of time it takes for the final output to settle as the information ripples down from the top (least significant) adder to the bottom. Try setting the switches as shown in the figure (1111 + 0001 = 10000: 15 + 1 = 16 in decimal) and then switching switch A. The ripple is similar to the effect demonstrated in the previous chapter – see the Gray to binary converter circuit, Figure 3.19.

Fast adders are important functions so engineers have developed a way to overcome the ripple-through problem in adder circuits. It is called 'carry look ahead'. The technique requires the use of gates with more and more inputs as the numbers get wider (i.e. more bits are added) but the sum is computed with no greater delay.

Consider the signals P and G in the full adder, Figure 4.24. Using the symbol $\oplus$ to signify exclusive-OR, we may write $P = A \oplus B$, while $G = A.B$, and the equation $CO = G + P.CI$ shows how the CO (Carry Out) signal is generated from the A and B inputs and the CI (Carry In). But, as Figure 4.25 shows, the CO of one stage is the CI of the next most significant. Using subscripts to represent stages, 0 being the least significant, we may write:

$$CO_3 = G_3 + P_3.CO_2$$
$$CO_2 = G_2 + P_2.CO_1$$
$$CO_1 = G_1 + P_1.CO_0$$
$$CO_0 = G_0 \qquad \text{(LSB is just a half-adder, Figure 4.21)}$$

Similarly, $S_3 = P_3 \oplus CO_2$ and so on. Nothing new so far, apart from writing everything down in Boolean algebra. But it is now easy to see that

$$CO_1 = G_1 + P_1.G_0$$
$$CO_2 = G_2 + P_2.(G_1 + P_1.G_0) = G_2 + P_2G_1 + P_2.P_1.G_0$$
$$CO_3 = G_3 + P_3.(G_2 + P_2G_1 + P_2.P_1.G_0)$$
$$\qquad = G_3 + P_3.G_2 + P_3.P_2.G_1 + P_3.P_2.P_1.G_0$$

Fig. 4.26 *4-bit adder with carry look-ahead*

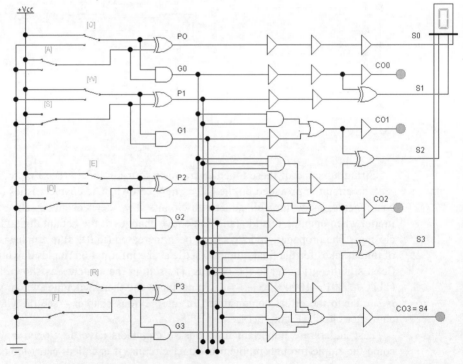

What does this mean in terms of gates? Well, 'multiplying out' the brackets removes them, which means that the gates get wider, but propagation delay is removed. (Compare Figure 2.3.) Each of the CO signals can be generated with just three gate delays, and the total computation takes four, no matter how many bits are added. Compare this to the ripple-through system – the output takes $1 + 2n$ gate delays, where n is the bit-width of the numbers being added.

In the Electronics Workbench version of the circuit some extra buffers have been inserted so that all signals take the same time to propagate through from the input to the output – four gate delays. It means that the outputs all change at exactly the same time as each other. Run the simulation (**fig4_26.ewb**), again choosing **Use circuit model** when the message about **Models Clash** appears (and **No** when asked if you wish to save the changes made to the default digital library when you come to exit the circuit). Compare the behaviour of this circuit to **fig4_25**. No ripple-through, yet the gate delays are the same in the two circuits. ☐

PRACTICAL EXERCISE 4.3

Extend the circuit to add two 5-bit numbers. First, write down the Boolean expression for CO_4 by studying the expressions for CO_3, CO_2 and CO_1, then implement it in Electronics Workbench. S_4 becomes the exclusive-OR of P_4 and CO_3 of course. If you like them, throw in some buffers to equalise all signal path delays, and check that you can add 31 and 1 to get 32 ($11111 + 00001 = 100000$ in binary, $1F + 1 = 20$ in hex) within four gate delays.

Subtractors

Instead of thinking in terms of subtracting number B from number A, the way to tackle this problem is to make B negative, then *add* it to A. We already know how to add numbers, so the problem has turned into one of generating negative numbers from positive ones.

Before tackling this task, we need to establish how to *represent* negative numbers in binary arithmetic.

Imagine you have just purchased a brand new car and, being a little eccentric, decide to drive it home backwards. What will the milometer do? Well, it will probably have a few positive miles on the clock to start with, so these will reduce down to zero, and then all the 9s will appear, then 999998, 999997 etc. The number 999999 could be regarded as −1, 999998 as −2, and so on. This idea is carried over into the binary number system, with 11111111 representing −1, 11111110 = −2, 11111101 = −3, etc. Isn't this a little confusing? How do you know if 11111111 means +255 or −1? The answer is, you don't know, just as you don't know, by simply looking at the milometer, whether the car containing it has gone forwards 999999 miles, or backwards just 1.

If, in a digital electronic system, numbers are represented as 8-bit quantities, and it is anticipated that negative numbers will need to be represented, then the numbers from 00000000 up to 01111111 (0 to 127) are regarded as positive, but the numbers 11111111 down to 10000000 (−1 down to −128) are assumed to be negative. If you don't expect negative numbers, then all the values from 00000000 up to 11111111 (0 to 255) are taken as positive.

This system is called 2s complement arithmetic. You can tell if a number is negative by looking at the MSB: if it's 1 then the number is negative. To form a negative number using 2s complement arithmetic, each bit of the positive number is inverted then 1 is added to the result. Thus, in an 8-bit system, +1 is 00000001. Invert each bit: 11111110. Now add 1: 11111111. This agrees with the previous definition of −1.

PAPER EXERCISE 4.8

What is the 8-bit, 2s complement representation of −63? What is the 10-bit, 2s complement representation of −63?

To evaluate a 2s complement number, assign all the bits their normal values (1, 2, 4, 8 . . .) but take the MSB as the negative of its normal weighting. Thus, 11111111 is worth $1 + 2 + 4 + 8 + 16 + 32 + 64 - 128 = -1$.

Now that a way of representing negative numbers has been defined, the problem of subtracting B from A can be dealt with. Simply invert each bit of number B, then add it to A, and add in a 1 as well. Remembering that exclusive-OR gates can act as conditional inverters the circuit below (Figure 4.26) can be used either to add B to A, or subtract B from A.

Fig. 4.27 *4-bit adder/subtractor*

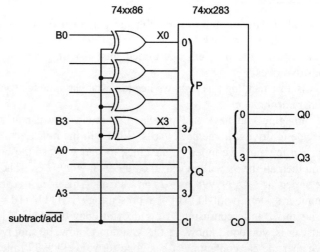

The circuit uses two standard ICs: the 74××86 quad exclusive-OR and the 74××283 4-bit full adder. When the subtract/add signal is LOW the B values are fed through unaltered, and the Q output is the sum of A and B. When it's HIGH, however, the exclusive-OR gates invert the B inputs, a 1 is added in via the CI (carry in) connection of the '283, and the Q output will be A − B.

PAPER EXERCISE 4.9

Does it really work? In 4-bit 2s complement arithmetic the range of numbers is from −8 to +7 (1000 to 0111). Bearing this in mind, complete the following table, Figure 4.28. Remember that the '283 doesn't know that you are working in 2s complement: it will simply add the values at A, X and CI together (i.e. columns 4, 8 and 1) and generate an answer (column 9). This is a 5-bit result, of course, and will be presented on its CO and Σ outputs. You, with your view of the whole of Figure 4.27, will interpret the A and B inputs and the Q output as 2s complement numbers.

Fig. 4.28 *Adding and subtracting 4-bit 2s complement numbers*

	CI	A			B		X		Q		
	sub/add	your view	bin	chip view	your view	bin	bin	chip view	chip view	bin	your view
1	0	3	0011	3	2	0010	0010	2	5	0101	5
2	1	3	0010	3	2	0010	1101	13	17	0001	1
3	0	−1	1111	15	1	0001	0001	1	16	0000	0
4	0	3	0011	3	6	0110	0110	6	9	1001	−7
5	0	−1			−1						
6	1	−1			−2						
7	1	−3			7						
8	0	7			−3						
9	1	4			−3						
10	1	−5			2						
	1	2	3	4	5	6	7	8	9	10	11

Note that the CO result is not shown on the table, but would be HIGH whenever the value in column 9 is 16 or greater.

You should find that everything works, provided you don't try to generate an output outside the range −8 to +7.

In row 1, the numbers 3 and 2 have been added together to give 5.

Row 2 shows 2 being subtracted from 3 to give 1. The chip reckons 3, 13 and 1 have been added together to give 17, but that's 10001 and the first of those 1s (the CO) is ignored.

Row 3 shows −1 and +1 being added to give 0 (or, from the chip's point of view, 15 and 1 being added to give 16).

In row 4 there is a problem: here we are trying to add 3 and 6 together. The chip dutifully generates the number 9, but in 2s complement interpretation 1001 means −7. The technical term for such an error is 'overflow'.

Fig. 4.29 *PHDL code for 'ripple-through' 4-bit adder*

```
MODULE   adder
TITLE    '4-bit adder'

DECLARATIONS
A3..A0      pin;                        "input
B3..B0      pin;                        "input
S4..S0      pin;                        "sum output
CO2..CO0    node istype 'keep';         "internal carries
P3..P0      node istype 'keep';         "internal P signals
G3..G0      node istype 'keep';         "internal G signals
full_adder macro (CI,A,B,P,G,S,CO)
"  direct implementation of Figure 4.24
   {
   ?P  = ?A  $  ?B;
   ?G  = ?A  &  ?B;
   ?S  = ?P  $  ?CI;
   ?CO = ?G  #  (?P & ?CI);
   };

EQUATIONS

"  direct implementation of Figure 4.25
full_adder(0,  A0,B0,P0,G0,S0,CO0);
full_adder(CO0,A1,B1,P1,G1,S1,CO1);
full_adder(CO1,A2,B2,P2,G2,S2,CO2);
full_adder(CO2,A3,B3,P3,G3,S3,S4 );

END
```

PHDL implementation of adders and subtractors

The PHDL equivalent of Figure 4.25 – the 'ripple-through' type adder – is shown in Figure 4.29. A 'macro' has been used to define a full adder, which has then been used four times to create the 4-bit adder.

A macro definition is placed within the **DEFINITIONS** section of the design. It consists of the keyword **macro** preceded by the name you wish to use when referring to it – **full_adder** in this case. Following the **macro** keyword is the list of 'formal parameters' – the list of input, internal and output signals that are used by the macro sub-design. These formal parameters should not be declared anywhere else in the design – they are just local to the macro definition. The behaviour of the macro is specified in the equations that follow, encapsulated by the { } braces. Note that the name of each signal is preceded by a question mark (?) each time it is used within the macro. The macro definition is completed with a ; after the closing }.

When the macro gets used in the **EQUATIONS** section of the design, the list of parameters should be the list of actual signals that you want the macro to work on in each instance. These 'actual parameter' signals *do* need to be declared properly in the **DECLARATIONS** section of the design.

Note that the P, G and CO signals have been declared as 'nodes' rather than pins. This means that they are internal signals (nodes) that do not need to be connected to the outside world via pins. In addition, these nodes have the property `keep` assigned to them by means of the **istype** command. You will see what effect this has in due course.

The code is provided on the CD as `adder.phd`. Run the XPLA software, either create a new project or remove any existing source code from your current project, and import `adder.phd`. ☐

Compile the design, set the device to **xcr5032c-10pc44c**, fit, and run a timing simulation. ☐

Set the **Simulate Until** value to 400ns, use the **Change Value** facility to set all four B signals to '1', and all four A signals to '0'. Use the **Events** + facility to add a rising edge on A0 at about 100ns, then a falling edge at 200ns. Run the simulation. You should find the sum signals change from 15 to 16 and back again (01111 to 10000 and back), but with a similar ripple-through effect as observed with the Electronics Workbench implementation. See Figure 4.30. ☐

Fig. 4.30 *XPLA simulation of ripple-through 4-bit adder*

Use the **Set Marker** facility to measure how long it takes for the output to settle after the input changes state. ☐

Return to the XPLA user interface (Project Panel), double-click on the **.ph1** (optimised equations) output file and examine the format of the equations.

You should be able to make sense of them bearing in mind the circuits that have been implemented, namely Figures 4.24 and 4.25. The exclusive-OR functions such as `S1 = P1 $ CO0;` have been expanded into equations like `S1 = P1 & !CO0 # !P1`

& CO0; but otherwise the equations very much reflect the circuits. Make a note of the level of the various equations (LVL). □

Close the optimised equations file and open the source code. Edit the file by removing the three istype 'keep' statements (but leave the node keywords), save, and return to the **Project Panel**. Click the **Properties** button and set the **Max P-term** per equation value to 36. Hide the **Properties** window, compile, fit and run a timing simulation. You should find that the design now generates an answer to the problem $15 + 1 = ?$ in just 12ns. □

How has it managed to do this? (By way of comparison, the 74HC283 takes twice as long.) The answer is that the design has been 'flattened'. This is the same process of removing brackets that was employed in the 'carry look-ahead' technique discussed above. If you take a look at the **.ph1** file you will find that all the equations have a level of 1 (LVL = 1) which means that the output is derived directly from the input signals, rather than from some intermediate signal such as the P, G or CO terms. (When the 'keep' parameter was attached, the compiler was forced to keep the different level signals, building up to level 5 for S3 and S4.)

You will also notice that the equations have become very much 'wider', i.e. contain more product terms (PT). This was also the case with the carry look-ahead technique where a 4-input OR gate was needed for S3 – see Figure 4.26 above. The XPLA software has taken the technique to the extreme, totally removisng *all* brackets, thereby reducing the level to just 1, but having to employ a 36-input OR for S3. (The FI reference in the equations is to **Fan In**, i.e. how many signals are used in the equation.)

Armed with your Boolean algebra knowledge from chapter 2, you should be able to see what the XPLA software has done. Try unravelling S1. The circuitry equivalent to the first two macros is shown in Figure 4.31 (which is the same as the top half of Figure 4.25, but with the insides of the sub-circuits drawn).

Fig. 4.31 *2-bit adder built from two full-adders*

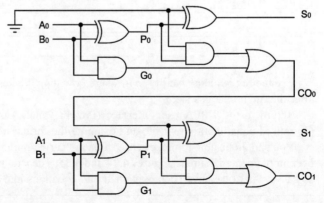

Here's how to start:

$$S_1 = P_1 \oplus CO_0 \quad = P_1.\overline{CO_1} + \overline{P_1}.CO_0$$
$$P_1 = A_1 \oplus B_1 \quad = A_1.\overline{B_1} + \overline{A_1}.B_1$$
$$CO_0 = G_0 + P_0.0 \quad = G_0$$
$$G_0 = A_0.B_0$$

Now substitute lower equations into higher ones:

$$CO_0 = A_0.B_0$$
$$S_1 = (A_1.\overline{B_1} + \overline{A_1}.B_1).\overline{A_0.B_0} + \overline{(A_1.\overline{B_1} + \overline{A_1}.B_1)}.A_0.B_0$$

Now use De Morgan to break the bars, then just multiply everything out. You should get exactly the same as the optimised equation for S1.

The code of Figure 4.29 is hierarchical – the full adder macro defines the behaviour of the circuit at a low level, then the macro can be used as a component at a higher level. This idea can be taken further. The description of the one-bit full adder can be written as a separate **.phd** file, which can then be utilised by other ('higher') **.phd** design files. This method of working is very important for large designs, allowing different members of a design team to work on different parts of the design, and then the whole lot can be integrated. It also allows designers to build up a library of design files that can be incorporated into future systems. Figures 4.32 and 4.33 show how it works.

There's nothing unusual about Figure 4.32: it's a straightforward PHDL stand-alone file. Figure 4.33 makes use of it by means of the **INTERFACE** and **FUNCTIONAL_BLOCK** keywords.

The **INTERFACE** keyword points to the **.phd** file with the name specified; thus Figure 4.32 has to be saved as `adder1.phd`, and it has to be in the same directory as the file that uses it. The list of inputs and outputs reflects the inputs and outputs of `adder1`, and the names of the connections need to be the same as those used in the original file.

Fig. 4.32 *PHDL code for 1-bit adder*

```
MODULE   adder1
TITLE    'One-bit full adder'

DECLARATIONS
A,B,CI,S,CO  pin;    "inputs and outputs
P,G              node;  "internal nodes

EQUATIONS

" direct implementation of Figure 4.24

  P  = A $ B;
  G  = A & B;
  S  = P $ CI;
  CO = G # (P & CI);

END
```

Fig. 4.33 *PHDL code showing how a 4-bit adder can be built using the code of Figure 4.32*

```
MODULE   adder4
TITLE    '4-bit adder'

DECLARATIONS
A3..A0   pin;    "input
B3..B0   pin;    "input
S4..S0   pin;    "sum output

adder1 INTERFACE (A,B,CI->S,CO);

adder1_0 FUNCTIONAL_BLOCK adder1;
adder1_1 FUNCTIONAL_BLOCK adder1;
adder1_2 FUNCTIONAL_BLOCK adder1;
adder1_3 FUNCTIONAL_BLOCK adder1;

EQUATIONS

" direct implementation of Figure 4.25

adder1_0.CI = 0;
adder1_0.A = A0;
adder1_0.B = B0;
S0 = adder1_0.S;

adder1_1.CI = adder1_0.CO;
adder1_1.A = A1;
adder1_1.B = B1;
S1 = adder1_1.S;

adder1_2.CI = adder1_1.CO;
adder1_2.A = A2;
adder1_2.B = B2;
S2 = adder1_2.S;

adder1_3.CI = adder1_2.CO;
adder1_3.A = A3;
adder1_3.B = B3;
S3 = adder1_3.S;

S4 = adder1_3.CO;

END
```

The **FUNCTIONAL_BLOCK** keyword is used to declare an instance of the sub-module. Here four modules have been so 'instantiated', named **adder1_0**, **adder1_1**, **adder1_2** and **adder1_3**.

The EQUATIONS section (in Figure 4.33) can now be used to make the appropriate connections to the sub-modules, using dot-extensions to specify the relevant input or output of each sub-module. Thus the first line of the section shows that the **Carry-In** connection of sub-module adder1_0 is connected to 0, and the last line shows that the MSB of the sum (S4) is generated by the **Carry-Out** connection of adder1_3. Refer back to Figure 4.25 to check the rest of the connections.   □

Remove any source files from the current XPLA project, and import the files adder1.phd and adder4.phd. Right-click on the adder4.phd file and make it the top file, using the **Assign Top File** facility from the pop-up menu. Now compile the design, and check the optimised equations. You should find the two input files (adder1.phd and adder4.phd) have been combined into one, and exactly the same equations generated as before, when the listing of Figure 4.29 was compiled.   □

If you think that the XPLA software is clever at Boolean algebra, you will be even more impressed with its ability to compile designs from high-level statements. Instead of having to worry about how to add numbers together, you, as a designer, can ask the software to do it. You simply use the + sign to add (and the – sign to subtract).

Fig. 4.34 *XPLA use of + syntax to add*

```
MODULE   adder
TITLE    '4-bit adder: high-level implementation'

DECLARATIONS
A3..A0, B3..B0  pin;
S4..S0          pin;
A = [A3..A0];
B = [B3..B0];
S = [S4..S0];

EQUATIONS

S = A + B;

END
```

Try this out. Check that the compiler properties are still set so that 36-wide OR gates are allowed, compile, and check the optimised equations. You should again find the same ones. Fit and check the timing. You should find that it adds 15 and 1 within 12ns.

Multipliers

Having spent some time looking at the arithmetic functions of adding and subtracting, how about multiplying? Not so easy! You can't get a multiplier in the 74 series, and you can't write S = A * B in PHDL and get it to compile. 'Clever' designs for multipliers are embedded within microprocessors and digital signal-processing chips, but a 'stupid' design is to employ a 'look-up table'.

How do *you* multiply 6 by 7? Haven't you simply *learnt* the answer? Isn't it buried in your memory somewhere, ready to be looked up when needed? The look-up table approach is the same. You get a memory chip, put all the answers to all the possible questions into it, then just look up the answers when needed.

How much memory would you need? To multiply two 4-bit numbers, there are just 256 different problems, ranging from 0×0 to 15×15, with the biggest answer requiring 8 bits to store it. A memory capable of storing 256 bytes would thus be big enough to hold the required look-up table.

What sort of memory would you need? In order to discuss this some background into memory types is now given.

A look-up table would need to be non-volatile, i.e. made from memory that wouldn't lose its information when power was turned off. Now, in the past non-volatile memory was impossible to write to, so the term 'read-only memory' (ROM) was coined. Nowadays you *can* write to some sorts of non-volatile memory, but it is still generally referred to as ROM. Of course, information has to be written into the ROM at some point, and different types of ROM were developed to cater for differing needs in this respect. Mask-programmed ROM has its information built into it at the mask stage, during chip manufacture. This is OK as long as you are a big company, expecting to purchase tens of thousands of a particular ROM requiring the same information.

Smaller production runs make use of Programmable ROM, PROM. This is capable of being programmed by the equipment manufacturer as opposed to the chip manufacturer. Generally speaking, once a PROM has been programmed it cannot be altered. This can be inconvenient, especially at the development stages of a product, so Erasable PROMs (EPROMs) were developed. These are packaged in ceramic blocks that have windows that are transparent to UV light, and the memory is erased by exposing the silicon chip to bright UV light for ten minutes, or so. This ceramic/quartz glass window packaging tends to be more expensive than the silicon chip inside, so one-time programmable PROMs were developed that had exactly the same internal technology, but cheaper plastic packaging without the quartz window. PROMs, EPROMs and OTP PROMs have to be taken to special programming machines to have their memory programmed ('blown'). Designers then came up with the idea of having non-volatile memory that could be altered while in the destination circuit. This is useful where calibration tweaks need to be made, possibly automatically, or where configuration data needs to be altered. EEPROM (Electrically Erasable PROM) and flash-programmable memory were thus developed. Writing to these devices takes a relatively long time, but this is no great drawback since they are only altered occasionally (perhaps each time power is applied, or when the user requires different functionality). With EEPROM individual memory locations can be altered, while flash generally requires whole chunks to be erased before being re-written. When writing to the Atmel 28C16 EEPROM, for instance, a memory write takes 1ms, but a read is completed within in 150ns. With the 29C256 flash memory chip you load 64 bytes into a buffer (temporary holding device), then wait for them to be written automatically to permanent memory, the whole operation taking 10ms to complete. Reading (a single byte) from the chip, however, takes just 70ns.

The other broad category of memory is RAM, which can be written just as quickly as it can be read – fast versions take just tens of ns. The drawback is that it is volatile – the contents 'evaporate' when power is removed. So-called 'non-volatile RAM' consists of ordinary RAM but with a battery backup. When power is removed from the instrument, the RAM chips go into shutdown mode, consuming only a minuscule amount of power from the (generally lithium) battery, but preserving the contents of their memory. The acronym RAM stands, as everybody knows, for Random Access Memory, meaning that items in memory can be accessed in any required order. The term was coined to contrast this mechanism with the way some memory systems (like tape)

Fig. 4.35 *A memory system comprising 256 8-bit locations*

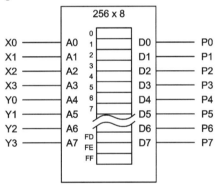

require serial access to data. Nowadays almost all memory systems allow their contents to be accessed randomly, and the term RAM is used to imply that the memory is writable but volatile.

Getting back to the suggestion that some sort of ROM (i.e. non-volatile memory) chip could hold a look-up table for the multiply function, the details are shown in Figure 4.35.

The memory consists of 256 locations, each location having an *address*, ranging from 0 to 255 (0 to FF in hex), and containing an 8-bit number. The eight connections on the left of the rectangle are *address lines*: they are used to specify which of the 256 memory locations are to be activated. The eight connections on the right are for *data*: in a RAM data could enter or leave by these connections, but for ROM they are output only. As it happens, this memory system has eight address lines as well as eight data lines. Having equal numbers of address and data lines is not generally the case, of course: a 512 by 4 memory would have nine address lines (since $2^9 = 512$) and four data connections. In addition to all these memory locations, a memory chip needs an on-chip decoder to allow the address input to activate the correct location. The decoder discussed earlier in this chapter was a 3-to-8 decoder; our 256-location memory would need an 8-to-256 decoder.

This is a general description that applies to any ROM. To turn this system into a 4-bit multiplier we simply ensure that the contents of each of the 256 locations are the product of the X and Y numbers. Thus, using hex numbering, memory locations 00 to 0F all contain 00 as do locations 10, 20, 30 . . . F0 since each of these is the product of 0 and some other number. Location 11 contains 01 ($1 \times 1 = 01$), 12 contains 02, 22 contains 04, 33 contains 09, 34 contains 0C, 44 contains 10, FE contains D2 ($15 \times 14 = 210$) and FF contains E1 ($15 \times 15 = 225$). Every location contains the result of multiplying the two nibbles of its address together. You just work out what all these multiplications are, use an appropriate programmer to blow the data into the chip, and there's your 4 by 4 multiplier.

How about an 8×8 multiplier? You would need 16 address lines, of course, for the two 8-bit multiplicands, implying a memory with 2^{16} (65536 or '64k') locations. Also, each location would need to be 16 bits wide, to hold the 16-bit product of the two input numbers. Now, memory chips tend to come with 8-bit wide locations, so two $64k \times 8$ chips will be needed, one to hold the low byte of the answer, and the other to hold the high byte. Figure 4.36 shows the idea.

Fig. 4.36 *64k × 16 memory system*

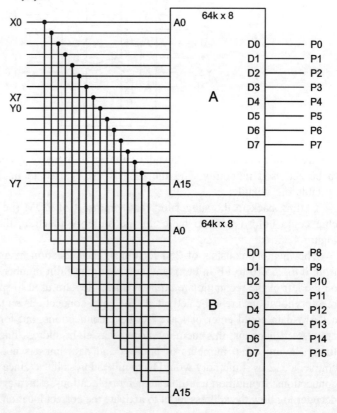

Devising the contents of each memory location for this system is a similar process to that used before. Simply work out the product of the two bytes making up each 16-bit address, and place the lowest eight bits of that product in chip A, and the top eight bits in chip B. Thus in memory locations 0000 to 00FF, and in location 0100 (the first 257 locations) each chip will contain 00 since each one of those calculations involves multiplying by 0. Location 0101 of chip B will also contain 00, but chip A will contain 01 (since $01 \times 01 = 00\ 01$). Location FFFF of chip B will contain FE, while chip A contains 01 (FF $\times$ FF = FE 01, or $255 \times 255 = 65,025$). Only 130,813 more calculations to consider. Still, once programmed, the system would be able to produce each answer quite quickly, e.g. 150ns if using EPROMs.

There is one final point to make about memory chips and that is how their size is measured. If you are used to talking about computer memories, you would say each chip in the 8×8 multiplier was 64k. However, the size of chips is given in *bits* rather than bytes so you would need ones with a capacity of 514,288 bits, organised as 65,536 words $\times$ 8 bits.

Summary

This chapter has covered all of the categories of MSI combinational logic available in the 74 series. They have been described as 'off-the-shelf' since they are available as pre-designed standard parts, ready to be purchased from IC distributors. You have seen how they can all be implemented using a programmable logic device such as the **xcr5032** and you should appreciate how much design effort high-level constructs in languages such as PHDL can save. For instance, adders with extensive carry look-ahead can be created simply by using statements such as Q = A + B.

Some applications of some of the devices have been indicated, but a proper appreciation of their use only comes during project design. You may find it helpful to return to this chapter when trying to solve some combinational logic problem in a future design to remind yourself what, for instance, a multiplexer does, or how a priority encoder can be expanded. Of course, programmable logic chips can have a mixture of functions created inside them, saving on the number of chips required in a design, and saving development and production effort. Simulation of combinational logic designs using programs such as Electronics Workbench or the XPLA simulator help to verify that designs will behave as required, and the XPLA simulator is good at picking up more subtle problems such as glitches.

You have now learnt all the essential concepts in combinational logic. The next chapter introduces sequential systems.

Introduction

The demonstration board accompanying this book contains, among other things, an oscillator, a ten-LED bar graph array and some slide switches. The aim of this assignment is to design a way to route the clock signal from the oscillator to any one of the ten LEDs under control from the slide switches.

Much of this chapter has been taken up with discussing MSI ICs so you are asked to design a similar system using such ICs and then compare the two approaches.

Task 1

Using the XPLA system and PHDL, design a system that routes the signal from the 555 timer output through to one of the ten LEDs of the bar graph array, using switches 1, 2, 3 and 4a to control which LED receives the clock signal. The control should be binary coded, i.e. the LED that gets connected is the one corresponding to the binary number on the switches, taking SW1 as the MSB of the switches, and numbering the LEDs 0 to 9 left to right.

Task 2

Simulate the design, fit, download and test.

Task 3

Re-design the system so that the control is Gray rather than binary; fit, download and test.

Task 4

Design two similar systems using MSI chips from the 74HC series. Check the details of the operation of any chips from the manufacturers' data books, or look up data sheets on the manufacturers' websites. Include pin numbers on your circuit diagram and use IEC symbols where appropriate. You do not need to build your design but if you have access to Electronics Workbench you may wish to simulate it to verify likely behaviour.

Task 5

Write a report on this assignment. You should describe what you have done, include PHDL listings for the designs of tasks 1 and 3, a printout of the simulated waveforms for task 2, circuit diagrams for the two designs of task 4, and copies of any relevant manufacturers' data sheets. Compare the two approaches to the design, i.e. CPLD and individual ICs, discussing the pros and cons of each, taking into account cost, time to design, time to manufacture and other technical matters, such as device packages (through-hole or surface mount).

Coverage

This assignment covers all four of the assessment criteria of Outcome 1 of the Edexcel \ BTEC H-level unit Combinational and Sequential Logic and all four assessment criteria for Outcome 2.

Grading criteria

Pass

- 'interpret manufacturers' literature to select appropriate combinational logic devices for specific purposes' (complete task 4 satisfactorily for the binary coded system)
- 'compare the characteristics of similar devices using different technologies' (complete task 5 satisfactorily)
- 'compare the functionality achieved by modern LSI and VLSI devices with traditional techniques' (complete task 5 satisfactorily)
- 'explain the constraints placed upon system designers by modern device packaging' (complete task 5 satisfactorily)
- 'design combinational logic circuits to meet a given specification' (complete tasks 1 and 2 satisfactorily)
- 'use computer simulation to verify logic designs' (complete task 2 satisfactorily)
- 'construct and test combinational circuits' (complete task 2 satisfactorily)
- 'use programmable logic devices to minimise component count in combinational logic circuits' (complete tasks 1 and 2 satisfactorily)

Merit

- 'use a range of methods and techniques to collect, analyse and process information/ data' (use XPLA and Electronics Workbench simulators)
- 'apply and analyse detailed knowledge and skills, using relevant theories and techniques' (circuit diagrams for task 4 drawn mainly accurately and using appropriate conventions)
- 'coherently present and communicate work using technical language accurately' (task 5)

Distinction

- 'check validity when collecting, analysing and processing complex information/ data' (discuss validity of information presented by XPLA and Electronics Workbench simulators)
- 'evaluate and synthesise relevant theories and techniques to generate and justify conclusions' (not applicable to this assignment)
- 'show an individual approach in presenting and communicating work coherently, using technical language fluently' (task 5)

Paper exercise 4.1

To connect input D2 to the X output, take E0 LOW (to enable the top multiplexer) and connect A1 and A0 HIGH and LOW respectively (to select input D2).

To connect D7 through to the Y output E1 would need to be LOW and A1 and A0 both HIGH. It's not possible to connect D2 to X and D7 to Y simultaneously.

Paper exercise 4.2

The Q output needs to go HIGH if the ABC input is 011, 101, 110 or 111, i.e. $Q = \Sigma(3,5,6,7)$. Thus connect data inputs 3, 5, 6 and 7 HIGH and the others LOW. The EN input would also need to be active (LOW).

Paper exercise 4.3

The truth table is shown in Figure 4.37.

Fig. 4.37 *Truth table for 4-bit prime number detector*

		A	B	C	D	Q
	0	0	0	0	0	0
		0	0	0	1	0
	1	0	0	1	0	1
		0	0	1	1	1
	2	0	1	0	0	0
		0	1	0	1	1
	3	0	1	1	0	0
		0	1	1	1	1
	4	1	0	0	0	0
		1	0	0	1	0
	5	1	0	1	0	0
		1	0	1	1	1
	6	1	1	0	0	0
		1	1	0	1	1
	7	1	1	1	0	0
		1	1	1	1	0

(Header: inputs — A B C D; output — Q)

When the ABC input state is 0, 4 or 7 the Q output is LOW, irrespective of the D input. When ABC is 1 the Q output is HIGH, irrespective of the D input. When ABC is 2, 3 or 5 the Q output is the same as the D input. The circuit below (Figure 4.38) implements these statements.

Fig. 4.38 *Circuit to detect if the 4-bit input (A = MSB) is prime*

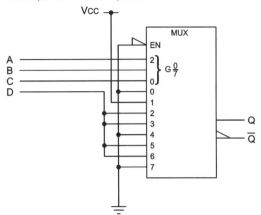

Paper exercise 4.4

Chip H would be activated whenever Port 2 had 111 as its three MSB's. Thus, in binary, chip H would occupy the range 1110 0000 to 1111 1111. In hex this would be E0 to FF.

Paper exercise 4.5

Note that the symbol itself doesn't really define what the Q outputs should do if the device is enabled, but *none* of the inputs is HIGH – see row 2. The data book for the 4532B includes the function table below, however (Figure 4.39).

Although the Q outputs remain unchanged between rows 2 and 3, the GS and EO signals do change state. On row 2 all of the inputs are LOW, so satisfying the requirement for EO to go HIGH. On all the subsequent rows at least one of the inputs is HIGH, satisfying the requirement for GS to go HIGH.

Fig. 4.39 *Truth table for 4532B completed*

	inputs									outputs				
EI	7	6	5	4	3	2	1	0	Q2	Q1	Q0	GS	EO
0	×	×	×	×	×	×	×	×	0	0	0	0	0
1	0	0	0	0	0	0	0	0	0	0	0	0	1
1	0	0	0	0	0	0	0	1	0	0	0	1	0
1	0	0	0	0	0	0	1	×	0	0	1	1	0
1	0	0	0	0	0	1	×	×	0	1	0	1	0
1	0	0	0	0	1	×	×	×	0	1	1	1	0
1	0	0	0	1	×	×	×	×	1	0	0	1	0
1	0	0	1	×	×	×	×	×	1	0	1	1	0
1	0	1	×	×	×	×	×	×	1	1	0	1	0
1	1	×	×	×	×	×	×	×	1	1	1	1	0

Paper exercise 4.6

The design for a 24-input priority encoder is shown in Figure 4.40.

Inputs 7, 8 and 17 HIGH: bottom encoder will generate 1 on Q4 and 010 on Q2-Q1-Q0. Other encoders will be disabled, so Q3 will be 0, hence output will be 10010, as required. For 7 and 8 HIGH, bottom encoder will generate 0 on Q4, but 1 on its EO, so middle encoder will take control. 01000 will be output. If just input 7 is HIGH, both middle and bottom encoders will generate 0s on their GS outputs, both will generate 1s on their EO outputs, top encoder will be active, generating 00111 output as required.

Fig. 4.40 *24-input priority encoder*

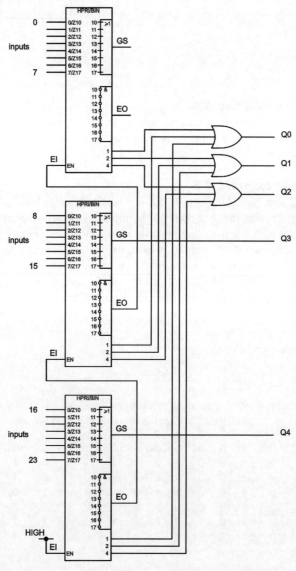

Practical exercise 4.1

Figures 4.41 and 4.42 show the PHDL and .scl files.

Fig. 4.41 *PHDL code for 10-input priority encoder*

```
MODULE    encoder
TITLE     '10-to-4 priority encoder, with enable input and
          strobe out'

DECLARATIONS
EI,D9..D0   pin;
GS,Q3..Q0   pin;

D = [D9..D0];  Q = [Q3..Q0];

EQUATIONS

when EI then
  {
  when D != 0 then GS = 1;
  when D < 2 then Q = 0;
  else when D < 4 then Q = 1;
  else when D < 8 then Q = 2;
  else when D < ^h10 then Q = 3;
  else when D < ^h20 then Q = 4;
  else when D < ^h40 then Q = 5;
  else when D < ^h80 then Q = 6;
  else when D < ^h100 then Q = 7;
  else when D < ^h200 then Q = 8;
  else Q = 9;
  }
else Q = 0;

END
```

Fig. 4.42 *.scl file suitable for simulation of priority encoder*

```
*   C:\xplawork\pencoder10.scl
*   Tue Jan 11 21:26:03 2000
*   XPLA-Sim (2.1d)

*   These Signals Will Be Viewable After Running The Simulator

P D9, D8, D7, D6, D5, D4, D3, D2, D1, D0, EI, GS, Q3, Q2, Q1, Q0

*   These Are The Initializations.

IT 1 (VCC)

*   These Are The Signal Transitions For The Simulation

S 0 (  50,  100,  ETC) D0
S 0 ( 100,  200,  ETC) D1
S 0 ( 200,  400,  ETC) D2
S 0 ( 400,  800,  ETC) D3
S 0 ( 800, 1600,  ETC) D4
S 0 ( 1600, 3200, ETC) D5
S 0 ( 3200, 6400, ETC) D6
S 0 ( 6400, 12800, ETC) D7
S 0 ( 12800, 25600, ETC) D8
S 0 ( 25600, 51200, ETC) D9
ST 1 (EI)
SU TIME = *+100000
*                        SU TIME = 100000

F
```

Paper exercise 4.7

Figure 4.43 shows the design of a 4-bit equality indicator.

Fig. 4.43 *Circuit diagram for 4-bit equality indicator*

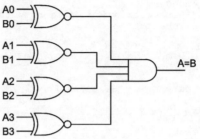

The exercise didn't ask you to design one, but a PHDL solution would be simply:

    when (A==B) then A_EQ_B = 1;

An alternative syntax is:

    A_EQ_B = (A==B);

Practical exercise 4.3

The pen and paper part of this exercise is given below.

$$CO_4 = G_4 + P_4.CO_3$$
$$CO_3 = G_3 + P_3.CO_2$$
$$CO_2 = G_2 + P_2.CO_1$$
$$CO_1 = G_1 + P_1.CO_0$$
$$CO_0 = G_0$$

Hence:

$$CO_1 = G_1 + P_1.G_0$$
$$CO_2 = G_2 + P_2.(G_1 + P_1.G_0) = G_2 + P_2G_1 + P_2.P_1.G_0$$
$$CO_3 = G_3 + P_3.(G_2 + P_2G_1 + P_2.P_1.G_0)$$
$$= G_3 + P_3.G_2 + P_3.P_2.G_1 + P_3.P_2.P_1.G_0$$
$$CO_4 = G_4 + P_4.(G_3 + P_3.G_2 + P_3.P_2.G_1 + P_3.P_2.P_1.G_0)$$
$$= G_4 + P_4.G_3 + P_4.P_3.G_2 + P_4.P_3.P_2.G_1 + P_4.P_3.P_2.P_1.G_0$$

$$S_5 = CO_4$$
$$S_4 = P_4 \oplus CO_3$$
$$S_3 = P_3 \oplus CO_2$$
$$S_2 = P_2 \oplus CO_1$$
$$S_1 = P_1 \oplus CO_0$$

The Electronics Workbench circuit consists of **fig4_26.ewb** but S_4 implemented as $P_4 \oplus CO_3$ and with an extra stage at the bottom for CO_4 (= S_5).

Paper exercise 4.8

In 8-bit arithmetic +63 = 0011 1111, so −63 = 1100 0000 + 1 = 1100 0001. In 10-bit arithmetic +63 = 00 0011 1111, so −63 = 11 1100 0000 + 1 = 11 1100 0001.

Note that the 8-bit and 10-bit representations of −63 are the same except for extra 1s on the front. This way of extending negative numbers when changing to larger bit widths is referred to as 'sign-extension'.

Paper exercise 4.9

Figure 4.44 shows the completed table. Note that all the results are valid except rows 4 and 7. In both these rows the correct answers (+9 and −10 respectively) are outside the range accommodated by 4-bit 2s complement arithmetic.

Fig. 4.44 *Adding and subtracting 4-bit numbers using 2s complement arithmetic*

	CI	A			B			X		Q		
	sub/ add	your view	bin	chip view	your view	bin	bin	chip view	chip view	bin	your view
1	0	3	0011	3	2	0010	0010	2	5	0101	5
2	1	3	0010	3	2	0010	1101	13	17	0001	1
3	0	−1	1111	15	1	0001	0001	1	16	0000	0
4	0	3	0011	3	6	0110	0110	6	9	1001	−7
5	0	−1	1111	15	−1	1111	1111	15	30	1110	−2
6	1	−1	1111	15	−2	1110	0001	1	17	0001	1
7	1	−3	1101	13	7	0111	1000	8	22	0110	6
8	0	7	0111	7	−3	1101	1101	13	20	0100	4
9	1	4	0100	4	−3	1101	0010	2	7	0111	7
10	1	−5	1011	11	2	0010	1101	13	25	1001	−7
	1	2	3	4	5	6	7	8	9	10	11

5 Flip-flops and sequential logic

Introduction

In the previous chapters some fairly complex circuits have been examined, and you now know how to send signals along different routes using multiplexers, and how to check for parity, and how to add and subtract numbers. None of the circuits possesses any sense of sequential ordering, however. They all just react instantaneously (well, within a few nanoseconds) to the inputs presented to them. You could not make a counter from such devices. Nor could you make a computer, or develop digital communication systems, or play electronic games.

The extra ingredient needed is *memory*. A 'flip-flop' is the basic logic circuit that possesses memory. It can't remember very much – just which of two possible logic states it is in – but string a few together and you get quite powerful blocks from which to build sequential logic systems.

This chapter covers:

- the different types of flip-flop (RS, JK, the D- and T-types)
- counters (ripple-through and synchronous)
- data registers (for storing data)
- shift registers (for manipulating data)
- numerous simulations using Electronics Workbench
- practical work with the XPLA system and the CPLD target board
- two extended assignments

RS flip-flop (SR flip-flop)

This circuit simply remembers whether it has been 'set' or 'reset' – the R and S of the flip-flop's names refers to this action. The term 'set' means that the circuit's output is HIGH, 'reset' means it's LOW. An RS flip-flop can thus act as a memory cell for a single binary digit, storing either a 1 (HIGH) or a 0 (LOW).

The circuit has two inputs. One of these is used for setting the flip-flop (i.e. storing a 1), the other for resetting it (storing a 0). Figure 5.1 shows one version of an RS flip-flop.

Fig. 5.1 *RS flip-flop, NOR-gate version*

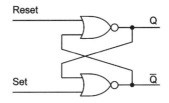

If you try to analyse what the circuit will do by considering 1s and 0s at the input, you get so far, but then encounter a rather peculiar situation. Starting with both inputs HIGH, you deduce that both the Q and $\overline{Q}$ outputs will be LOW, simply from the '1 in forces 0 out' behaviour of a NOR gate.

If Reset is HIGH, but Set is LOW, you still get a LOW on the Q output. The lower NOR will now have both inputs LOW, so will give a HIGH output on $\overline{Q}$. Swapping over the inputs, so that the Reset is LOW but the Set is HIGH, swaps the outputs over: HIGH on Q, LOW on $\overline{Q}$.

The peculiar situation arises if both Reset and Set are LOW. There are no 'forcing 1s' to get you started. You can guess that output Q will be HIGH. From that you deduce that the $\overline{Q}$ output will be LOW, since there is now a forcing 1 on the lower NOR. The two LOWs on the top NOR will indeed give a HIGH on Q, so you conclude that your guess was correct. However, you can also convince yourself that the opposite situation is the correct one, with Q LOW and $\overline{Q}$ HIGH. The top NOR now has the forcing 1 on its input, forcing Q LOW, and the lower NOR has two LOWs giving $\overline{Q}$ HIGH.

What's going on? Well, both situations are indeed possible, stable states for this circuit. You could say that the circuit is simply remembering what state it's in.

To recap, the operation of the circuit is as follows:

- If both inputs are (inactive) LOW the circuit just sits there, with the Q output either HIGH or LOW – the circuit is either set or reset.
- Normally, the $\overline{Q}$ output is in the opposite state to the Q output.
- If the Set input is taken HIGH the Q output is forced HIGH.
- If the Reset input is taken HIGH the Q output is forced LOW.
- If you take both the Set *and* Reset inputs HIGH at the same time, then both outputs go LOW. This is not normally a useful thing to do.

Sometimes you will see this last operation described as 'impossible', or 'not allowed'. It is, as we have seen, perfectly possible and does no harm. However, if you take the circuit straight from this both-inputs-HIGH state to the both-inputs-LOW state then it is not possible to predict how the circuit will settle. In practice it will depend on which transistors happen to switch faster.

This action can be summarised using a function table – see Figure 5.2. Note that the darker cells in Figure 5.2 show the active signal. The last row shows both the Set and Reset attempting to be active. This is why it is described as 'not normally useful'.

There is another version of the RS flip-flop, built using NAND gates instead of NORs – see Figure 5.3.

Fig. 5.2 *NOR-gate RS flip-flop function table*

inputs		outputs		comment
S	R	Q	Q̄	
0	0	0 or 1	1 or 0	remembering
0	1	0	1	reset
1	0	1	0	set
1	1	0	0	not normally useful

Fig. 5.3 *RS flip-flop, NAND-gate version*

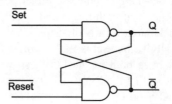

The Set and Reset inputs have swapped over, and the signal names have been written with bars over, to indicate that they act when they are LOW. Apart from these differences the action of the circuit is similar to the NOR-gate version:

- If both inputs are (inactive) HIGH the circuit remains set or reset.
- Normally, the Q̄ output is in the opposite state to the Q output.
- Taking S̄et LOW forces Q HIGH
- Taking R̄eset LOW forces Q LOW.
- Note: Taking S̄et *and* R̄eset LOW simultaneously forces both outputs HIGH.

This action is summarised in the function table Figure 5.4. Note that the input 0s are highlighted in Figure 5.4 since the inputs are active LOW.

Fig. 5.4 *NAND-gate RS flip-flop function table*

inputs		outputs		comment
S	R	Q	Q̄	
0	0	1	1	not normally useful
0	1	1	0	set
1	0	0	1	reset
1	1	0 or 1	1 or 0	remembering

5.1 In Figure 5.1 (the NOR-gate RS flip-flop) the Q output will definitely be HIGH if the Set and Reset inputs are respectively . . . ?
(a) 0,0   (b) 0,1   (c) 1,0   (d) 1,1

5.2 In Figure 5.1 the Q output is LOW. This means that the Set and Reset inputs are respectively (choose three) . . . ?
(a) 0,0   (b) 0,1   (c) 1,0   (d) 1,1

5.3 In Figure 5.3 (the NAND-gate RS flip-flop) the Q output will definitely be HIGH if the Set and Reset inputs are respectively (choose two) . . . ?
(a) 0,0   (b) 0,1   (c) 1,0   (d) 1,1

5.4 In Figure 5.3 the Q output is LOW. This means that the Set and Reset inputs are respectively (choose two) . . . ?
(a) 0,0   (b) 0,1   (c) 1,0   (d) 1,1

PRACTICAL EXERCISE 5.1

Electronics Workbench

Fig. 5.5 *NOR-gate RS flip-flop*

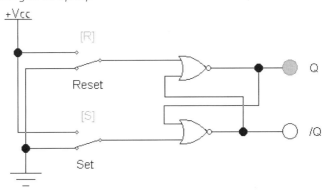

Run Electronics Workbench and open the file **fig5_5.ewb**. When the circuit is first simulated you may find that the outputs flicker. The circuit is in its remembering mode – neither the Reset nor the Set input is HIGH – but there is nothing for it to remember, so to speak.

Verify that toggling the Set switch HIGH then LOW (using the S key on the keyboard) makes the Q indicator light up, while pressing twice on R turns it off.   ☐

Also check that if both Set *and* Reset are HIGH both outputs go low.   ☐

Try pressing the R and S keys together to confuse the software! (In a real circuit this would not happen.)   ☐

Replace the NORs with NANDs and check that the circuit behaves in accordance with the table of Figure 5.4.   ☐

XPLA

The code in Figure 5.6 is a straightforward implementation of the NOR-gate version of the RS flip-flop.

Fig. 5.6 *PHDL code for a NOR-gate RS flip-flop*

```
Module  NOR_RS
Title   'RS flip-flop made from NOR gates'

Declarations
set,reset  pin  4,8;
Q,N_Q      pin  16,27;

Equations

Q  = !(reset # N_Q);
N_Q = !(set # Q);

End
```

After compiling, simulate the circuit. Set the **Simulate Until** value to 5000ns, and use the **Change Value** facility to set the SET signal HIGH and the RESET signal LOW. Now use the **Events +** button to add in the various edges to the SET and RESET signals, roughly as shown. Run the simulation once, to save the **.scl** file, then use the **File\Open Text File...** to edit the **.scl** file just created so that the edges are exactly as shown. Save the new **.scl** file, then use **File\Open...** to load the modified **.scl** file. □

Finally, run the simulation and verify that you get the waveforms shown in Figure 5.7. □

Fig. 5.7 *XPLA simulation of NOR-gate RS flip-flop*

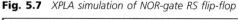
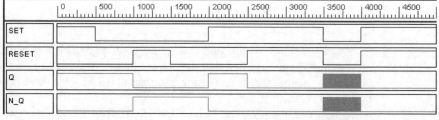

Choosing from the following descriptions, answer questions 5.5 to 5.8:

(a) remains set
(b) remains reset
(c) is actively set
(d) is actively reset

5.5 At 500ns the circuit ... (a), (b), (c) or (d)?

5.6 At 1000ns the circuit ... (a), (b), (c) or (d)?

5.7 At 1500ns the circuit ... (a), (b), (c) or (d)?

5.8 At 2000ns the circuit ... (a), (b), (c) or (d)?

PRACTICAL EXERCISE 5.1 (CONTINUED)

The funny stuff between 3500 and 4000ns is a high frequency oscillation, set up by the circuit not knowing what to do after both Set and Reset go simultaneously from active to inactive states.

The NAND version of the RS flip-flop can be described by changing the two equations to

```
Q   = !(set & NQ);
N_Q = !(reset & Q);
```

The remainder of the file can stay unchanged, and the same **.scl** file can be used to control the simulation. Save the **.phd** file, compile and simulate. □

You should get the waveforms shown in Figure 5.8:

Fig. 5.8 *XPLA simulation of NAND-gate RS flip-flop*

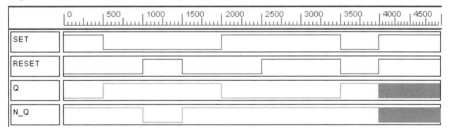

This gives similar results to the NOR version of the circuit except that the SET and RESET signals are now active-LOW. The flip-flop thus starts with the Q output LOW since the RESET signal is active at the beginning of the simulation. Now the software gets confused when the two inputs change simultaneously from both active to both inactive at 4000ns. □

Having simulated the design, fit it (make sure the correct device is targeted, i.e. **xcr5032c-10pc44c**) and download the JEDEC file to the target board. For the NAND version of the flip-flop set SW1 and SW3 up (in-active) and verify that switching SW1 down (then back up again) flips the flip-flop so that the left-hand LED lights up, and that SW3 'flops' the flip-flop so that the right-hand LED is illuminated. □

For the NOR version the switches should normally be down, with movements up and down again being required to flip the circuit from one state to the other. □

JK flip-flops

This flip-flop shown in Figure 5.9 is much more versatile than the RS.

Fig. 5.9 *JK flip-flop*

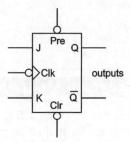

The internal operation of the circuit is not discussed here. What's important is gaining a familiarity with the overall behaviour of the device. The letters J and K don't actually stand for anything, by the way; they just roll off the tongue nicely, and haven't been used for anything else.

The two outputs respond to the Pre and Clr inputs as follows:

- Taking Pre(set) LOW forces the Q output HIGH (and $\overline{Q}$ LOW).
- Taking the Cl(ea)r LOW forces the Q output LOW (and $\overline{Q}$ HIGH).

This is just the same behaviour as a NAND-gate RS flip-flop, the Pre input being the Set and the Clr the Reset. Note the circles on these two inputs indicating active-LOW behaviour. The Pre and Clr inputs override anything else that's going on. Without knowledge of the internal circuitry it is not possible to say what will happen if both the Pre and Clr inputs are asserted simultaneously. If you really wanted to do this, you would have to check out the data sheet for the particular device you were using. The function table for the 74HC112, for instance, states that the Q would go HIGH and the $\overline{Q}$ LOW.

The J and K inputs work in conjunction with the Cl(oc)k input, which acts as a kind of 'trigger'. The circuit *ignores* the J and K inputs most of the time. It's only when the Clk signal changes state (that's what the wedge symbol implies next to the Clk connection) from HIGH to LOW in this negative-edge-triggered version (that's what the inversion bubble implies) that the outputs respond to the J and K inputs. They do so like this (see Figure 5.10)

Fig. 5.10 *Function table for JK flip-flop*

	inputs			outputs		comment
	J	K	Clk	Q_{n+1}	$\overline{Q}_{n+1}$	
1	0	0	↓	Q_n	$\overline{Q}_n$	no change
2	0	1	↓	0	1	transfer
3	1	0	↓	1	0	transfer
4	1	1	↓	$\overline{Q}_n$	Q_n	toggle

Note that Q_n refers to the state of the Q output just *before* the Clk goes LOW while Q_{n+1} signifies the state of the Q output immediately after. Similarly, $\overline{Q}_n$ and $\overline{Q}_{n+1}$ refer to the state of the $\overline{Q}$ output just before and just after the clock falling edge. ↓ refers to the falling edge of Clk. Studying the function table shows:

- Line 1: if the J and K inputs are both LOW when the Clk triggers the flip-flop then there is *no change* at the output: Q_{n+1} is the same as Q_n.
- Lines 2 and 3: if the J and K inputs are different (0,1 or 1,0) then the JK data gets *transferred* to the output when the Clk signal triggers the device.
- Line 4: if the J and K inputs are both HIGH then the outputs *toggle* when the Clk triggers the flip-flop. 'Toggle' means that each output flips into its opposite state. Q_{n+1} takes the state that $\overline{Q}_n$ was.

PRACTICAL EXERCISE 5.2

Electronics Workbench

Fig. 5.11   *Electronics Workbench JK flip-flop test*

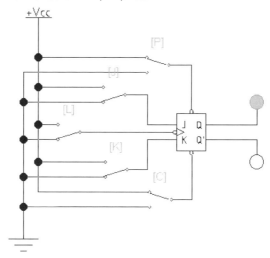

Verify the action of the circuit:

First, check out the P and C signals. You should find they Preset and Clear the circuit just like an active-LOW RS flip-flop. When done, leave them both dis-asserted (HIGH, in other words).   ☐

Next, with J and K both LOW, check that clicking the cLock switch has no effect. (See line 1 of the function table).   ☐

Next, ensure that the circuit is set (Q output HIGH), set J LOW and K HIGH. Now click the cLock until you get a HIGH-to-LOW transition at the Clk input of the flip-flop. Verify that the JK data is transferred to the output on the falling edge of the Clk. (Line 2 of the function table.) ☐

Keep clicking the cLock: verify that nothing more happens. ☐

Now change J to HIGH, K to LOW. Click the cLock until you get a falling edge. Verify that the new JK data is transferred to the output. (Line 3 of function table.) ☐

Finally, set both J and K HIGH. Verify that the circuit toggles each time the cLock goes LOW. (Line 4 of the function table.) ☐

XPLA

The code in Figure 5.12 is an implementation of the circuit.

Fig. 5.12 *PHDL code for JK flip-flop*

```
MODULE  jkff
TITLE   'jk flip-flop'
   "positive edge triggered, active-HIGH preset

DECLARATIONS
Clock,J,K,Pre  pin  43,4,8,14;
Q              pin  16 istype 'reg_jk';
N_Q            pin  27;
Clock_out      pin  20;


EQUATIONS

Q.clk = Clock;
Q.j  = J;
Q.k  = K;
Q.ap = Pre;
N_Q  = !Q;
Clock_out  = Clock;


END
```

The code in Figure 5.12 shows how to implement a JK flip-flop. There are a few differences between its behaviour and that of the 74HC112 discussed above. The clock acts on its *rising* edge (rather than falling) there is no Clear input, and the Preset is active-HIGH.

The code itself has a couple of new features. The first is the declaration that the Q signal is a `'reg_jk'` type. The keyword **istype** is used to attach this attribute to the Q signal.

The other new feature is the use of the 'dot-extension' to describe the particular pin of the flip-flop that is being connected. The first line of the **EQUATIONS** section specifies that the signal `Clock` is to be connected to the `.clk` pin of the Q flip-flop. The next two lines show how the `J` and `K` signals are connected to its `.j` and `.k` inputs. The fourth line uses `.ap` to signify the 'asynchronous preset' input of the flip-flop.

A complete list of the dot extensions can be found in the XPLA Help system. To find the list use the **XPLAUI Help \ Contents \ Help Topics \ Index**, type 'dot', then click on **Dot Extensions**. You will find that there are alternatives for some functions. Instead of `.ap`, for instance, you could type `.aset` or `.pr`. There is a dot extension for the Clear function (`.ar`, `.aclr`, or `.re`) but the hardware inside the CPLD doesn't support both Clear and Preset on the same flip-flop. The CPLD hardware is discussed more fully in Chapter 7.

PRACTICAL EXERCISE 5.3

Type in the code for the PHDL module, save, compile, fit (check correct **DEVICE**) and download to the target board. The clock for the flip-flop is derived from the 555 timer circuit on the demonstration board, and is displayed on one of the middle LEDs on the bar-graph display. Slow down the frequency of the timer to minimum, so that the LED flashes slowly. ☐

Set the J and K inputs (SW1 and SW3) both HIGH and verify that the Q (left-hand LED) and $\overline{Q}$ (right-hand LED) toggle on the rising edge of each clock pulse (i.e. when the middle LED turns on). ☐

The Preset is generated by the microswitch on the board. Verify that you can override the flip-flop action by pressing it, to force the Q output HIGH. ☐

Set the J and K switches so that they are different from each other. Verify that the data gets transferred to the LED's at the next rising edge of the clock. ☐

Finally, switch the J and K inputs both LOW and verify that the flip-flop just sits there in whatever state it happens to find itself. ☐

The preset is described as 'asynchronous'. This implies that it takes effect as soon as it is asserted. The alternative is to use 'synchronous' signals for setting or clearing the flip-flop. In this case the signal is synchronised to the clock. Try amending the PHDL code so that the signal from the microswitch is connected to the synchronous clear instead of the asynchronous preset of the flip-flop. Save, compile, fit, download and test. You should find that the effect of pushing the micro-switch is delayed until the next rising edge of the clock. Being a clear instead of a preset, the effect is to clear the Q output LOW, of course. ☐

QUESTIONS

5.9 A JK flip-flop has active-LOW Preset and Clear, and a positive-edge-triggered clock. Suppose all five inputs are held permanently HIGH. This means that the Q and $\overline{Q}$ outputs will . . . ?
(a) stay as 0,1 or 1,0
(b) definitely be 0,1
(c) definitely be 1,0
(d) toggle between 0,1 and 1,0

5.10 Now all the inputs are held HIGH except the Pre, which is LOW. This means that the Q and Q̄ outputs will . . . ?
(a) stay as 0,1 or 1,0
(b) definitely be 0,1
(c) definitely be 1,0
(d) toggle between 0,1 and 1,0

5.11 Now all the inputs are held HIGH except the Clk, which changes from HIGH to LOW. This means that the Q and Q̄ outputs will . . . ?
(a) stay as 0,1 or 1,0
(b) definitely be 0,1
(c) definitely be 1,0
(d) toggle between 0,1 and 1,0

5.12 Suppose all the inputs are held HIGH except the Clk, which changes from LOW to HIGH. This means that the Q and Q̄ outputs will . . . ?
(a) stay as 0,1 or 1,0
(b) definitely be 0,1
(c) definitely be 1,0
(d) toggle between 0,1 and 1,0

5.13 Finally, imagine all the inputs are held HIGH except the Clk, which changes from LOW to HIGH, and the K input is LOW. This means that the Q and Q̄ outputs will . . . ?
(a) stay as 0,1 or 1,0
(b) definitely be 0,1
(c) definitely be 1,0
(d) toggle between 0,1 and 1,0

D-type and T-type flip-flops

These flip-flops can each do half the things that a JK can do.

Fig. 5.13 *Function tables for D- and T-type flip-flops*

	inputs			outputs		comment
	J	K	Clk	Q_{n+1}	$\bar{Q}_{n+1}$	
T	0	0	↑	Q_n	$\bar{Q}_n$	no change
D	0	1	↑	0	1	transfer
D	1	0	↑	1	0	transfer
T	1	1	↑	$\bar{Q}_n$	Q_n	toggle

As the table in Figure 5.13 shows, the D-type is restricted to the two middle rows of the JK function table, while the T-type implements just the first and last rows.

Figure 5.14 indicates how the D-type behaves. Whatever logic level is present at its D ('Data') input gets transferred to its Q output on the rising edge of the Clk. The Q̄ is the complement of the Q output.

Fig. 5.14 *A D-type is like a JK with an inverter between J and K*

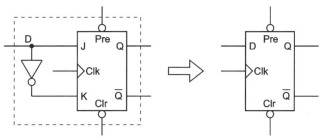

PAPER EXERCISE 5.1

Using a data book, website, or otherwise, find this function in the 74 series. ☐

Fig. 5.15 *A T-type is like a JK with its J and K inputs shorted*

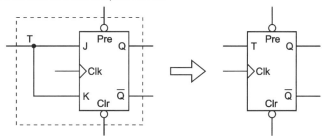

Figure 5.15 illustrates the behaviour of the T-type: if the T input is low, then the flip-flop does nothing, but if T is high it toggles at each positive edge of the clock.

PAPER EXERCISE 5.2

Using a data book, website, or otherwise, find this function in the 74 series. ☐

(Don't spend too long on this before referring to the answers.)

Applications of flip-flops

Most of the rest of this book is devoted to discussing applications of flip-flops. However, in the next few sections you will learn about some of the basic ways that flip-flops are used.

Switch de-bouncer

When you flick a switch the contacts bounce. They close, then they bounce open, then they close again, bounce, and so on. This may last for a few milliseconds. This can be a problem if the signal from the switch drives, for example, the clock of a flip-flop. If the flip-flop is in toggle mode, it may toggle several times each time the switch is switched, owing to the multiple edges generated by the bouncing.

If the switch is a change-over type, an RS flip-flop can eliminate this. (If it's a simple on-off type you have to 'smother' the bounces with RC smoothing circuits, etc., or just devise some means to wait for the bouncing to stop.) Figure 5.16 shows how the RS flip-flop ignores the bounces.

Fig. 5.16 *Switch de-bouncer*

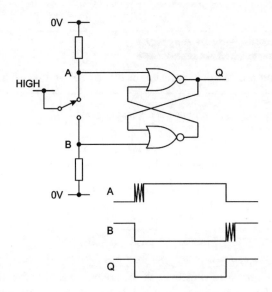

The bounce on signal A occurs when the switch is switched up. The contact closes and the signal goes HIGH, but then the contact bounces away momentarily, and the pull-down resistor pulls the signal back down to 0V. (Note that both resistors in the diagram are pull-downs.) The contact is then remade, signal A goes HIGH again, and so on, maybe for a dozen bounces. Similarly, signal B bounces when the contact is switched to the down position. Note that there is no bounce when the contact is opened. When the switch is moved away from the down position, for instance, signal B goes LOW and stays that way.

The circuit manages to get rid of the bounce glitches since the glitch just takes the circuit into the 'remembering', both-inputs-LOW, state, with the switch wiper touching *neither* of the fixed contacts.

PRACTICAL EXERCISE 5.4

The microswitch on the demonstration board is wired up like the switch in Figure 5.16. The two designs below (Figures 5.17 and 5.18) show how the switch can be connected to drive a T-type flip-flop firstly without, then with de-bouncing.

Fig. 5.17 *Clocking a T-type without de-bouncing*

```
MODULE  bouncer
TITLE     'un-de-bounced  clock  drives  T-type'

DECLARATIONS
A          pin  14;
toggle     pin  16  istype  'reg_t';
N_toggle   pin  27;

EQUATIONS

toggle.clk  =  A;
toggle.t  =  1;
N_toggle  =  !toggle;

END
```

Fig. 5.18 *Clocking a T-type with de-bounced switch*

```
MODULE  toggler
TITLE     'de-bounced  clock  drives  T-type'

DECLARATIONS
A,B        pin  14,11;
Q,N_Q      node;
toggle     pin  16  istype  'reg_t';
N_toggle   pin  27;

EQUATIONS

Q  =  !(A  #  N_Q);
N_Q  =  !(B  #  Q);
toggle.clk  =  Q;
toggle.t  =  1;
N_toggle  =  !toggle;

END
```

Both of these designs use a T-type flip-flop, named `toggle`, with the `.t` connection set permanently HIGH. In the first listing the `.clk` input to the flip-flop is taken straight from the switch via signal `A`. The second listing, on the other hand, uses both signals `A` and `B` from the microswitch to drive a NOR-gate RS flip-flop, with output signal nodes `Q` and `N_Q`. The `Q` signal is then used to clock the `toggle` flip-flop.

Try out both of these designs. Pressing the microswitch when the first design is implemented will sometimes result in a proper toggle, but often the action is just a bit of a flicker of the other LED. By contrast, the second design should always give a good, solid, reliable toggle! ☐

Amend the second design so that the toggle action takes place when the switch is pressed (rather than when it is released). ☐

Ripple-through binary counter

Fig. 5.19 *Ripple-through binary counter using 74xx112s*

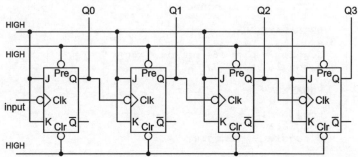

Figure 5.19 looks a little complex, but notice that all the Pre and Clr inputs are held HIGH, so they are *in*active and will have no effect on the circuit action.

The J and K inputs are also all HIGH. This means each flip-flop will toggle each time it gets a negative edge on its Clk input. The question is: *when* will each flip-flop receive such a signal?

The first (left-hand) one gets its Clk from the input signal, so Q0 will toggle each time the input goes LOW. See arrow a on Figure 5.20. The second flip-flop gets its Clk input from Q0, so Q1 will toggle each time Q0 goes LOW. See arrow b on Figure 5.20. Similarly, Q2 will toggle when Q1 goes LOW (see arrow c), and finally, Q3 will toggle when Q2 goes LOW (arrow d).

Fig. 5.20 *Waveforms within ripple-through binary counter*

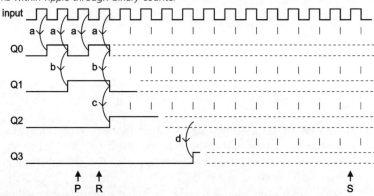

PAPER EXERCISE 5.3

Complete the waveforms in Figure 5.20. Make sure Q0 toggles each time the input signal goes LOW ('a' arrows), that Q1 toggles each time Q0 goes LOW ('b' arrows), that Q2 toggles each time Q1 goes low ('c' arrows) and Q3 toggles each time Q2 goes LOW ('d' arrows). □

5.14 At point P in Figure 5.20, the binary number formed by Q3 ... Q0 has the decimal value 2. At point R it is ... ?
   (a) 2   (b) 3   (c) 4   (d) 5

5.15 At point S it is ... ?
   (a) 11   (b) 15   (c) 30   (d) 37

5.16 After 1111 the ripple-through counter generates the number ... ?
   (a) 0000   (b) 1000   (c) 10000   (d) 11111

PRACTICAL EXERCISE 5.5

Electronics Workbench

Fig. 5.21 *Electronics Workbench version of ripple-though binary counter*

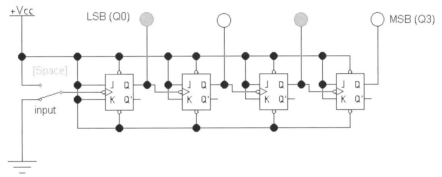

Run Electronics Workbench and open the file **fig5_21.ewb**. Click **Use circuit model** when **Models Clash** dialog box appears. (The propagation delay of the logic has been increased to show the ripple-through effect of the circuit. When exiting, say **No** when asked about saving changes to default digital Library.)

   Verify that the circuit counts up in binary as you operate the input switch.   ☐

   Note the ripple-through effect, particularly when changing from 7 to 8, or from 15 to 0.   ☐

   Try changing the connections so that the Q′ of each flip-flop clocks the next one, rather than using the Q. Leave the Q outputs connected to the output indicator probes, though. You should now find that the system counts from 0 down to 15, 14, 13 ...   ☐

   Draw out the waveforms for the circuit, in a similar fashion to those given in Figure 5.20. Each flip-flop toggles on the falling edge of the $\overline{Q}$ signal, which is equivalent to the *rising* edge of the Q. Thus, at the first (falling) edge of the input signal, and assuming all flip-flops are initially cleared, Q0 will toggle from 0 to 1. This rising edge will immediately toggle Q1, whose rising edge will toggle Q2, whose rising edge will toggle Q3.   ☐

XPLA

Figure 5.22 shows an implementation of the circuit.

Fig. 5.22 *PHDL code for ripple-through counter*

```
Module  rtbuc
Title   '4-bit ripple-through binary up counter'

Declarations
reset,clock  pin 14,43;
Q3..Q0       pin 20,21,24,25 istype 'reg_t';

Q = [Q3..Q0];

equations

!Q0.clk = clock;
!Q1.clk = Q0;
!Q2.clk = Q1;
!Q3.clk = Q2;

Q.ar = reset;
Q.t = ^b1111;   "this sets all four t inputs to 1

end
```

The listing is a more-or-less direct implementation of the circuit of Figure 5.19, except that T-type flip-flops have been used instead of JKs. (Remember that a JK flip-flop with its J and K inputs tied together acts in the same way as a T-type. See Figure 5.15.)

The T inputs have all been set HIGH using the statement `Q.t = ^b1111`. Having defined `Q` as `[Q3..Q0]`, this single line replaces the four lines of code:

```
Q3.t = 1;
Q2.t = 1;
Q1.t = 1;
Q0.t = 1;
```

Similarly, all four asynchronous resets to the four flip-flops are connected to the `reset` input (on pin 14) by the statement `Q.ar = reset;`

The `!`s in front of the `Q0.clk`, `Q1.clk`, `Q2.clk` and `Q3.clk` signals are needed to make the flip-flops *negative*-edge-triggered.

The pin numbers have been chosen bearing in mind the physical layout of the demonstration board. The `clock` signal is generated by the 555 timer circuit, and the `reset` by the microswitch. Note the pins used for the four output LEDs. This arrangement is needed to fit the design into the CPLD device. Although this is only a small design, it is unusual in that each flip-flop is clocked by a different signal, and this factor stretches the resources of the hardware to some extent.

Compile, fit and run a timing simulation of the design. Set the **Simulate Until** time to 2000ns, set up the **CLOCK** to 100ns cycle length starting at 0, change the value of the **RESET** to 1, with a negative edge event soon after 0ns. Verify the waveforms shown in Figure 5.23. □

Fig. 5.23 *Simulation of ripple-through counter*

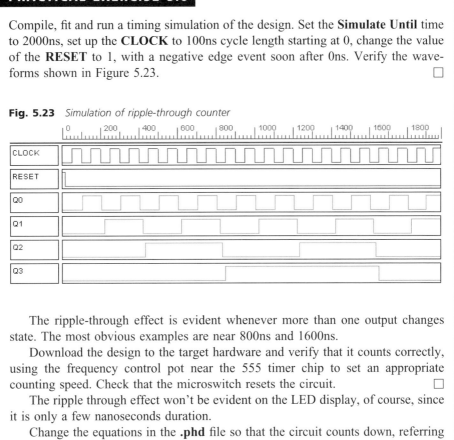

The ripple-through effect is evident whenever more than one output changes state. The most obvious examples are near 800ns and 1600ns.

Download the design to the target hardware and verify that it counts correctly, using the frequency control pot near the 555 timer chip to set an appropriate counting speed. Check that the microswitch resets the circuit. □

The ripple through effect won't be evident on the LED display, of course, since it is only a few nanoseconds duration.

Change the equations in the **.phd** file so that the circuit counts down, referring to the Electronics Workbench exercise above for details of how to do so. Save, compile, fit, simulate, download and test. □

Ripple-through BCD up counter

BCD stands for Binary-Coded Decimal. The requirement is that the circuit counts up to 9 then resets itself back to 0 on the next clock input, instead of counting right up to 15. The circuit shown in Figure 5.24 does this by generating a $\overline{\text{clear}}$ signal when the count reaches decimal 10 (note 10, not 9) which then almost instantly resets the count back to 0. Q3 and Q1 go HIGH on the count of 10 (binary 1010, but remember that the MSB is Q3, the far right output), which is why those signals feed the NAND gate to generate the active-LOW clear.

The invert-OR-invert gate allows for the circuit to be cleared by the input $\overline{\text{clear}}$ signal as well. (As the symbol indicates, an invert-OR-invert gate generates a LOW output when either (or both) its inputs are LOW. You will recall from Chapter 2 that this is the same as an AND gate.)

Fig. 5.24 *Reset-on-ten counter*

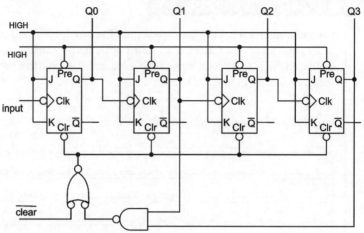

PRACTICAL EXERCISE 5.7

Electronics Workbench

Fig. 5.25 *Electronics Workbench BCD counter*

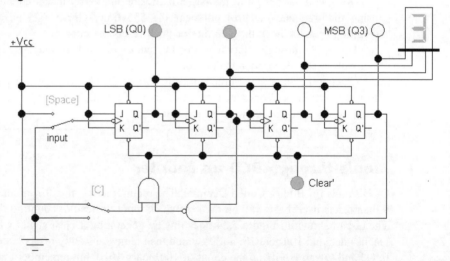

Run Electronics Workbench and open the file **fig5_25.ewb.** As before, the circuit has had the propagation delays increased to 50ms, so when you open it you will be asked about this. Choose **Use Circuit Models** from the **Models Clash** dialog box and when you quit this circuit, choose **No** when asked about saving changes made to **Digital Library Default**. □

The C switch may be used to clear the circuit at any time. It is active LOW, so should normally be left inactive up, as shown. The Clear' signal is also active-LOW, so the indicator probe attached to it is normally on. Note the use of the AND gate rather than the invert-OR-invert of Figure 5.24.

Verify that the circuit counts up from 0 to 9, briefly becomes 10 (A on the seven-segment display) then resets itself to 0. □

XPLA

Fig. 5.26 *PHDL code for BCD ripple-through counter*

```
Module  rtbuc9
Title   '4-bit ripple-through BCD up counter'

Declarations
reset,clock  pin 14,43;
Q3..Q0       pin 20,21,24,25 istype 'reg_t';

Q = [Q3..Q0];

equations

!Q0.clk = clock;
!Q1.clk = Q0;
!Q2.clk = Q1;
!Q3.clk = Q2;

Q.ar = (Q1 & Q3) # reset;
        "reset on decimal 10 (or external reset)

Q.t = ^b1111;

end
```

The only modification to the code for the binary counter is to alter the way the flip-flops are cleared. Edit the code from Figure 5.22, save, compile, fit and simulate the design. The simulation should use the same settings that you created for the binary counter. Verify that the waveforms shown below result. □

Fig. 5.27 *Simulation of BCD ripple-through counter*

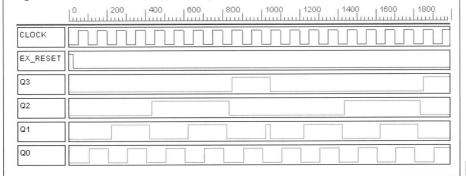

Ripple-through BCD down counter

Let's see if a BCD down counter can be designed along similar ideas. The requirement is for the counter to count down to 0, then go to 9 at the next input clock, rather than 15 as in the 'natural' binary version. If we allow the system to count down from 0 to 15, detect this situation and use it immediately to reset to 9, then the requirement should be met. Figure 5.28 implements these thoughts.

Fig. 5.28 *Design for a ripple-through BCD down counter*

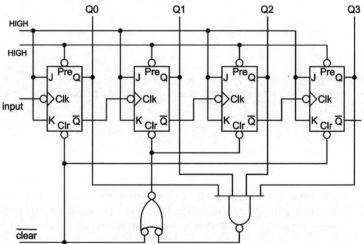

Figure 5.28 is the same as Figure 5.24 but modified in the following ways:

- $\bar{Q}$ to Clk instead of Q to Clk, so that the circuit counts down instead of up
- a 4-input NAND is used to detect the 1111 (15) state, instead of a 2-input NAND to detect 1010 (10)
- only the middle two flip-flops are automatically reset, to generate 1001 (9) instead of 0000 (0)
- external $\overline{clear}$ arrangement is slightly different, to accommodate the different requirements of the middle two flip-flops.

Electronics Workbench

Fig. 5.29 *Electronics Workbench implementation of Figure 5.28*

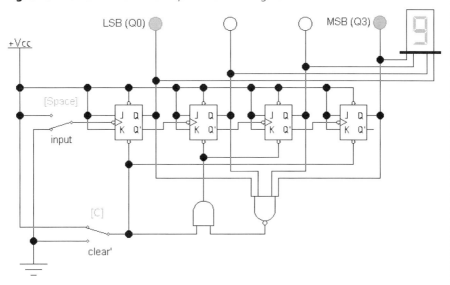

Run Electronics Workbench and open the file **fig5_29.ewb.** Propagation delays for the logic devices have been increased for this circuit so use the circuit model for the logic, and do not save the default model on exit.

Use the C key to clear the circuit. Leave the C key inactive HIGH then press the Space bar a couple of times. You should find that the circuit goes into the 1111 (F) state but then the two middle flip-flops get reset, ending up with 1001 (9) as required. So far, so good. You should find that the next up-down toggle of the input clock takes the circuit to 8, but something strange happens after that. This circuit goes to 1 instead of 7.

The reason is a little difficult to see, even with the delays slowed down to 50ms. You could try slowing things down even more, but the XPLA simulation of the next section is perhaps the best way to see what's going on.

XPLA

Figure 5.30: In this code the signal `int_reset` has been declared as a `node` in order to view it in the simulator. The clock signals are all connected up without inverters – this makes the counter count down instead of up.

Save the file, compile, fit and run the timing simulator. Set the **Simulate Until** figure to just 500ns, create a 100ns, start-at-0 clock, and a brief initial HIGH on the

Fig. 5.30 *PHDL code for a ripple-through BCD down counter*

```
Module  rtbdc9
Title   'Attempt at 4-bit ripple-through BCD down counter'


Declarations
reset,clock  pin 14,43;
Q3..Q0       pin 20,21,24,25 istype 'reg_t';
int_reset    node;


Q = [Q3..Q0];


equations


Q0.clk = clock;
Q1.clk = Q0;
Q2.clk = Q1;
Q3.clk = Q2;


int_reset = Q0 & Q1 & Q2 & Q3;
Q0.ar = reset;
Q3.ar = reset;
Q1.ar = int_reset # reset;
Q2.ar = int_reset # reset;


Q.t = ^b1111;


end
```

RESET. Create a bus from Q3 to Q0 and run the simulation. Verify that you get something similar to Figure 5.31. □

Soon (9ns) after the first rising edge of the CLOCK, the Q0 output toggles HIGH, which, after 15ns, causes Q1 to toggle HIGH which, after a further 15ns, toggles Q2 which, after yet another 15ns, toggles Q3. The Q bus visits states 1, 3 and 7 before reaching 15. When it does reach 15, the INT_RESET signal is generated, resetting Q1 and Q2 to give the bus a final value of 9.

This all takes so long, that there's not long to wait (just 21ns) for the next rising edge of CLOCK to arrive and toggle Q0 again. State 8 is reached.

The problems start at the next rising edge of CLOCK, which arrives at 250ns. Q0 duly toggles again, and the effect ripples down to Q1, Q2 and eventually to Q3. Unfortunately, during this sequence of events the bus visits state 15 on its way to state 7. This, of course, triggers INT_RESET, which resets Q1 and Q2. State 7 is rapidly knocked into state 1.

After state 1, the system counts down to 0, which is where we started.

Try downloading the design to the target board. You should find that the predictions of the simulator are borne out. The counter counts 0, 9, 8, 1, 0 . . . □

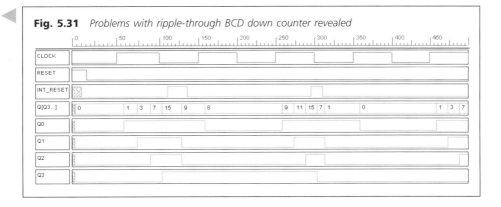

Fig. 5.31 *Problems with ripple-through BCD down counter revealed*

Synchronous and asynchronous systems

The ripple-through binary up and down counters counted OK, and the BCD up counter was satisfactory, but the initial design for the BCD down counter threw up some fairly subtle problems. It may be possible to overcome the problems by inserting buffers here and there to add compensating delays, but it would be a thoroughly nasty design!

The problems arise because the outputs change at different times from each other. This asynchronous behaviour of the outputs allows spurious states to exist that can cause severe headaches to designers. The general advice is that ripple-through (asynchronous) designs are examples *not* to follow!

Synchronous circuits are much nicer. There's no ripple-through effect, and consequently no spurious output states are created. All the flip-flops are clocked by the *same* signal, so all the flip-flops change state simultaneously, instantly creating the correct outputs.

(That's the theory, anyway. There are problems, clock 'skew' being the main one. This is the way different flip-flops will respond at slightly different times even to the same clock signal, especially if the clock has a slow edge. In PLD devices some effort has been expended to create 'low-skew' clock signals to get over this.)

The design of synchronous circuits will be dealt with in more detail in Chapter 6, but here is the synchronous version of the binary up counter.

Synchronous binary up counter

Compare this circuit to Figure 5.19, the ripple-through binary up counter. In that circuit all the JK connections were fixed HIGH, ensuring that every flip-flop always toggled when it got a clock edge of the correct polarity. To understand the circuit you had to work out just *when* each flip-flop would receive such an edge.

In Figure 5.32 you don't have to worry about when each flip-flop will receive a clock pulse: they all receive them all the time. What you need to work out is *what will each one do*?

Fig. 5.32 *Synchronous binary up counter*

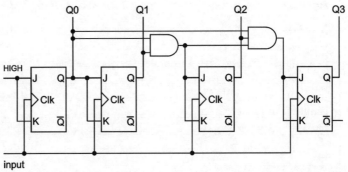

The answer for the first flip-flop (Q0) is that it will toggle each time, since its J and K inputs are both fixed HIGH. (See arrow a in Figure 5.33.)

The second flip-flop (Q1) is slightly more complicated. It will toggle if Q0 is HIGH (see arrow b) but remain unchanged if Q0 is LOW (see arrow x). (Remember a JK will toggle if its JK inputs are both HIGH, but remain unchanged if its inputs are both LOW.)

The 2-input AND gate that drives Q2's J and K inputs ensures that Q2 will toggle only when both Q0 AND Q1 are HIGH (see the two arrows at c).

Similarly, the 3-input AND allows Q3 to toggle only when Q0 AND Q1 AND Q2 are all HIGH.

Fig. 5.33 *Operation of the synchronous binary up counter*

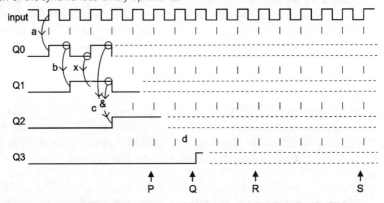

PAPER EXERCISE 5.4

Complete the waveforms in Fig. 5.33:

- First complete Q0, making sure it toggles each time the clock goes HIGH.
- Now complete Q1, toggling only when Q0 is HIGH, like arrow b.
- Now complete Q2, toggling only when Q0 AND Q1 are both HIGH, like c.

- Finally, complete Q3. It should toggle only when all three of the other Q signals are HIGH, such as d.

Concentrate on the states of the various signals just *before* each rising edge of the input clock in order to work out what a given signal will do immediately *after* the edge.

You should find that the overall behaviour of the Q3 Q2 Q1 Q0 outputs is to count up in binary. □

QUESTIONS

5.17 At the next rising edge of the clock after point P in Figure 5.33, Q1 toggles because . . . ?
(a) Q0 is LOW
(b) Q0 is HIGH
(c) Q0 and Q1 are both HIGH
(d) Q0, Q1 and Q2 are all HIGH

5.18 At the next rising edge of the clock after point Q, Q3 toggles because . . . ?
(a) Q0 is LOW
(b) Q0 is HIGH
(c) Q0 and Q1 are both HIGH
(d) Q0, Q1 and Q2 are all HIGH

5.19 At the next rising edge of the clock after point R, the Q1, Q2 and Q3 outputs remain unchanged because . . . ?
(a) Q0 is LOW
(b) Q0 is HIGH
(c) Q0 and Q1 are both HIGH
(d) Q0, Q1 and Q2 are all HIGH

5.20 At the next rising edge of the clock after point S, Q2 toggles because . . . ?
(a) Q0 is LOW
(b) Q0 is HIGH
(c) Q0 and Q1 are both HIGH
(d) Q0, Q1 and Q2 are all HIGH

PRACTICAL EXERCISE 5.9

Electronics Workbench
This works pretty well as expected, counting up in binary from 0000 to 1111, then resetting back to 0000, and so on. When you open it to simulate it choose **Use circuit model** from **Models Clash** dialog box, and don't save as default the digital library when you quit.

Fig. 5.34 *Electronics Workbench implementation of synchronous counter*

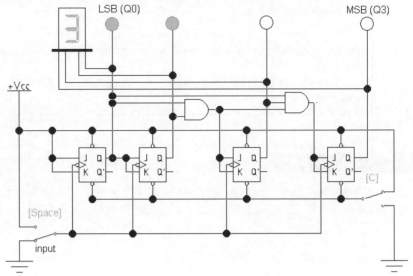

Note that there is still a noticeable propagation delay (set for this circuit to 0.2s) between the clock HIGH-to-LOW edge and the outputs changing. However, when they do change, all the outputs change together. □

XPLA

Figure 5.35: Note that all four flip-flops are clocked by the input signal: `Q.clk = clock;` Note also the way each `.t` input is driven from the AND of all the previous outputs.

Fig. 5.35 *PHDL code for synchronous up counter*

```
MODULE   sybuc
TITLE    '4-bit synchronous binary up counter'

DECLARATIONS
reset,clock  pin 14,43;
Q3..Q0       pin 16,17,18,19 istype 'reg_t';
Q = [Q3..Q0];

EQUATIONS

Q.clk = clock;
Q.ar  = reset;
Q0.t  = 1;
Q1.t  = Q0;
Q2.t  = Q0 & Q1;
Q3.t  = Q0 & Q1 & Q2;

END
```

Edit the previous code, save, compile, fit and run a timing simulation, setting the various simulation parameters appropriately so that you can see the full count sequence. You should see the familiar waveforms. The design works pretty well as expected, counting up in binary from 0000 to 1111, then resetting back to 0000, and so on. □

Zoom in at the 0111 to 1000 transition and use the **Set Marker** facility to measure the propagation delay from the rising edge of the clock to the outputs changing. Verify that this is 9ns. Verify also that the outputs all change together. □

If you wish to see this action in LEDs, download the file to the target board and verify the correct action. □

Synchronous down counter

A formal methodology for designing synchronous circuits will be dealt with in more detail in the next chapter, but it's possible to devise suitable counters by considering what each flip-flop is required to do at each edge of the clock. For the binary up counter, for instance, the algorithm is that any given flip-flop toggles only when all less-significant flip-flop outputs are HIGH. This leads to simple AND-gate circuitry to detect when all the relevant outputs are HIGH, to drive the JK (or T) input.

The first thing to do, then, is to draw out the required waveforms. Binary down counting is shown in Figure 5.36.

Fig. 5.36 *Waveforms for a binary down counter*

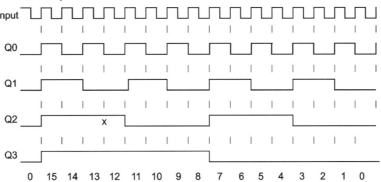

Upon examining the waveforms you can see that Q0 toggles at each rising edge of the clock, so its JK (or T) input can be held permanently HIGH. Q1 toggles when Q0 is LOW. This means that Q1's JK (T) input should be driven either by an inverter from Q0, or straight from $\overline{Q0}$.

Q2 toggles when both Q1 and Q0 are LOW. Note that if you just say Q2 toggles when Q1 is LOW, then Q2 will toggle at point x. Q2's JK (T) input should thus be driven by a 2-input AND gate with inputs from $\overline{Q1}$ and $\overline{Q0}$. Similarly, Q3 toggles when all less-significant outputs are LOW and its JK (T) input should be driven by a 3-input AND whose inputs are $\overline{Q2}$, $\overline{Q1}$ and $\overline{Q0}$.

Synchronous BCD up and down counters

First BCD up: Figure 5.37 gives the required waveforms. Q0 is still easy. It just needs
to toggle at each input rising edge, so slap in a HIGH on its JK (T) input and that should
work.

Fig. 5.37 *Waveforms for BCD up counting*

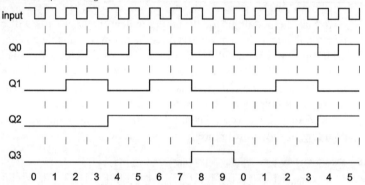

For the first few toggles, Q1 looks straightforward, but there's a problem at count 9.
How can it be prevented from toggling as the count goes from 9 back to 0? Q1 should
toggle at count 1, 3, 5 and 7, but not count 9. What's different about count 9 from the
others? Answer: Q3 is LOW for the others. The algorithm for Q1, then, is to toggle
when Q0 is HIGH AND Q3 is LOW.

Q2 can use the same algorithm as before: toggle when Q0 AND Q1 are HIGH.
Provided Q1 behaves properly, this should give the correct action for Q2.

The rule for Q3 can be 'Toggle when Q1 AND Q2 AND Q3 are all HIGH (to get
from 7 to 8) OR when Q0 AND Q3 are HIGH (for the 9 to 0 transition)'.

Fig. 5.38 *Synchronous version of BCD up counter*

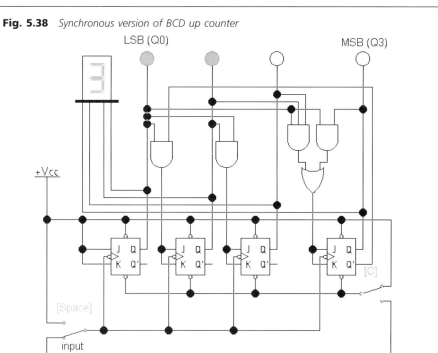

LSB (Q0)   MSB (Q3)

XPLA

Figure 5.39: The code directly reflects the algorithms discussed above. Enter the code, compile, fit and run the timing simulator. Verify that you get the waveforms shown in Figure 5.40. Note: correct operation and welcome absence of spikes! ☐

Fig. 5.39 *PHDL code for synchronous BCD up counter*

```
Module  sybuc9
Title   '4-bit  synchronous  BCD  up  counter'

Declarations
reset,clock  pin  14,43;
Q3..Q0       pin  16,17,18,19 istype 'reg_t';

Q = [Q3..Q0];

equations

Q.clk = clock;
Q.ar  = reset;
Q0.t  = 1;
Q1.t  = Q0  &  !Q3;
Q2.t  = Q0  &  Q1;
Q3.t  = (Q0  &  Q1  &  Q2)  #  (Q0  &  Q3);

end
```

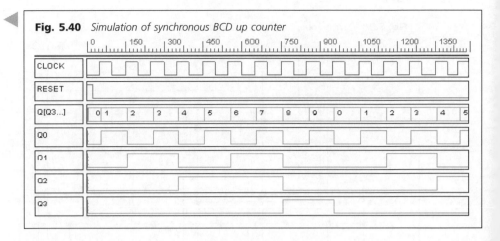

Fig. 5.40 *Simulation of synchronous BCD up counter*

Synchronous BCD down counter

The ripple-through version of a BCD down counter proved problematical; will a synchronous solution be any better? The required waveforms are shown in Figure 5.41.

Fig. 5.41 *Waveforms for BCD down counter*

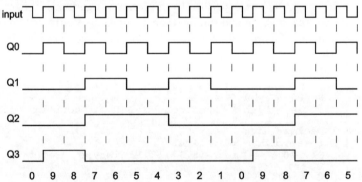

Now consider what each flip-flop should do at each positive edge of the input. Should it toggle, or should it stay unchanged?

Q0 toggles at each positive edge of the clock so tie its JK (T) inputs HIGH. It's difficult to spot obvious requirements for the remaining flip-flops. These are, in fact, combinational logic problems so let's use the tools of Chapter 3 to tackle them. Figure 5.42 below lists the possible count states, and whether each flip-flop should toggle (1 means 'yes', 0 = 'no', × = 'don't care').

Fig. 5.42 *Truth table defining toggling of outputs for BCD down counter*

count	current state				toggle?		
	Q3	Q2	Q1	Q0	Q1	Q2	Q3
0	0	0	0	0			1
1	0	0	0	1			0
2	0	0	1	0			0
3	0	0	1	1			0
4	0	1	0	0			0
5	0	1	0	1			0
6	0	1	1	0			0
7	0	1	1	1			0
8	1	0	0	0			1
9	1	0	0	1			0
	1	0	1	0	×	×	×
	1	0	1	1	×	×	×
	1	1	0	0	×	×	×
	1	1	0	1	×	×	×
	1	1	1	0	×	×	×
	1	1	1	1	×	×	×

PRACTICAL EXERCISE 5.12

Complete the entries in Figure 5.42 for Q1 and Q2. Q3 has been done for you and shows that it should toggle at the next clock edge if the count is currently 0 or 8; this information is drawn straight from the waveforms. The don't-care ×s assume that the counter will not reach any state above 9. □

Now draw up Karnaugh maps for each output and write down the minimised equations. Verify that they are the same as the ones used in the PHDL module in Figure 5.43. □

Fig. 5.43 *PHDL code for synchronous BCD down counter*

```
Module  sybdc9
Title   '4-bit synchronous BCD down counter'

Declarations
reset,clock  pin 14,43;
Q3..Q0       pin 16,17,18,19 istype 'reg_t';

Q = [Q3..Q0];

equations

Q.clk = clock;
Q.ar  = reset;

Q0.t = 1;
Q1.t = (Q3 & !Q0) # (Q2 & !Q0) # (Q1 & !Q0);
Q2.t = (Q3 & !Q0) # (Q2 & !Q1 & !Q0);
Q3.t = !Q2 & !Q1 & !Q0;

end
```

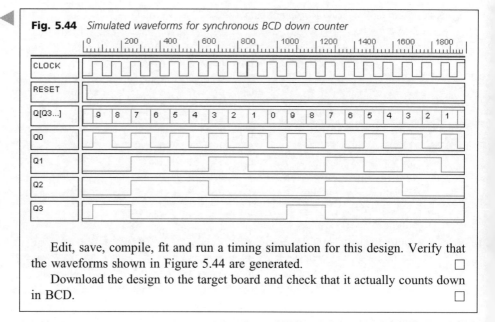

Fig. 5.44 *Simulated waveforms for synchronous BCD down counter*

Edit, save, compile, fit and run a timing simulation for this design. Verify that the waveforms shown in Figure 5.44 are generated. ☐

Download the design to the target board and check that it actually counts down in BCD. ☐

Shift registers

The subject of designing counters and other sequence generators will be revisited in Chapter 6, but the next circuit to consider in this chapter is the shift register. D-type or JK flip-flops can be used to build these circuits – here D-types.

Fig. 5.45 *Shift register built from D-type flip-flops*

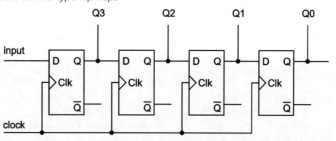

Remember that a D-type flip-flop simply transfers the data present at its D input pin to its Q output on the rising or falling edge of the clock signal. The resulting behaviour for the circuit of Figure 5.45 is for data to be transferred from one flip-flop to the next one on the right at each rising edge of the clock, with the first one getting its data from the input line.

After four clock pulses the data gets transported all the way from the input to the Q0 output. This is an example of serial to parallel conversion. Four bits of data have been accepted one after the other at its 'serial' input, and all four bits are now available simultaneously, i.e. in 'parallel'.

As well as accepting data in serial format, some shift registers have the facility to accept data in parallel. For the system of Figure 5.45 such a 'parallel load' would allow a 4-bit data word to preset/reset the individual flip-flops simultaneously to the appropriate setting. Having done so, the register can then be clocked a few times and the data will appear in serial format at the output of the final flip-flop. We now have parallel to serial conversion.

Note that the numbering of the outputs is arbitrary: Q3 is not necessarily any more significant than Q0. This contrasts with the counters we have just been examining, of course, where the weight of each output is an inherent factor in describing the circuit as a 'counter'.

If you think too hard about the shift register circuit you might start to wonder whether it would work correctly. Suppose the data is (1)-0-1-0-1 on the (input)-Q3-Q2-Q1-Q0 nodes. Taking Q2 as a typical element, it has a 0 on its input, provided by Q3, and a 1 on its output. At the next rising edge of the clock, the 0 will be transferred to its output. There should be no problem. The only worry is that just as Q2 is grabbing the 0 at its input, Q3 changes the 0 into a 1. Isn't Q2 going to get confused?

Well, no. Q3 doesn't actually change its output for a few nanoseconds after the clock edge, by which time Q2 has accepted the correct input data, so everything works fine. The parameters that control this behaviour are propagation delay, set-up time and hold time. Propagation delay has already been discussed: here it's the length of time taken between the clock rising edge and the output data changing. Set-up time is the time interval *before* the clock edge during which the input data must not change, and hold time is the interval *after* the edge when the data must be held steady.

For the shift register the critical thing is that the propagation delay must be longer than the hold time. For a 74HC74 dual D-type the worst hold time is 3ns, while the propagation delay is 16ns, so there should be no problem.

QUESTIONS

5.21 The shift register of Figure 5.45 contains the data 1011 on Q3, Q2, Q1, Q0. The signal present at the input is LOW. After the next rising edge of the clock the output data will be . . . ?
(a) 0101   (b) 1101   (c) 1011   (d) 1010

5.22 The shift register contains the binary equivalent of the decimal number 6, taking Q3 as the MSB. The signal present at the input is LOW. After the next rising edge of the clock the output data will be worth . . . ?
(a) 3   (b) 6   (c) 9   (d) 12

The IEC symbol for a shift register is able to imply the various functions within the symbol labelling system. By way of example, the symbol for the 74××194 is shown in Figure 5.46. This is a 4-bit shift register that has parallel-load facility, and both shift left and shift right capability.

It's a complex symbol, and some explanation is called for. You can tell it's a 4-bit shift register from the general qualifying symbol: SRG4. The numbers around the outside of the symbol are pin numbers. Pin 11 carries the clock input, the C name for

Fig. 5.46 *IEC symbol for 74xx194 shift register*

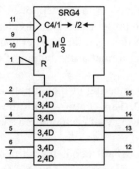

this input implying the Control function. The wedge shape indicates that this control is an edge-activated input. The number 4 on the clock and on all the inputs from pins 2 to 7 links these signals together, i.e. the clock controls all these inputs. Pin 1 is an active-LOW reset that resets all outputs LOW, irrespective of the clock. Pins 9 and 10 are the Mode control inputs, hence the M dependency labelling of these two signals. Pin 10 is the more significant, since it is labelled 1, while pin 9 is labelled 0. With a 2-bit mode control input, there are four possible operating modes; these modes are numbered 0 to 3, as implied by the $\frac{0}{3}$ label.

Mode 0 isn't specifically defined within the symbol, so the implication is that nothing happens in this situation: the clock input has no effect on the outputs, which just sit there, unchanged.

The label on the pin 2 input contains a 1, so this input must be effective in mode 1. The 1→ label attached to the clock input implies that in mode 1 the clock has a right-shift effect. Pin 2 is thus the serial data input during right-shifts.

Mode 2 works in similar fashion, except that the 2← label attached to the clock implies left shifting, and the fact that the pin 7 label contains a 2 shows that this is the serial data input during such shifts.

Finally, pins 3, 4, 5 and 6 each have a 3 in their label, implying that these inputs are effective in mode 3. These are the inputs used during a parallel load.

The only unresolved matter is which direction is right? By convention right is downwards: towards pin 12. Left is upwards: towards pin 15.

PRACTICAL EXERCISE 5.13

Electronics Workbench
Figure 5.47 shows a shift register in the state 0011. At the next rising edge of the clock another 0 would be shifted into the left flip-flop, since the input switch is connected LOW while the two existing 0s would shift one place right. The two existing 1s would also shift to the right, but the one presently on Q0 would 'fall off' and be lost. The result would be 0001.

Load the file (**fig5_47.ewb**) and try setting the input switch HIGH, then clock the shift register a few times. You should find that it 'fills up' with all 1s. Now take the input LOW, and watch the register empty as more clock pulses occur. □

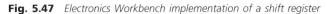

Fig. 5.47 *Electronics Workbench implementation of a shift register*

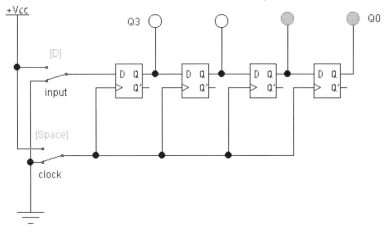

Now take the input HIGH, clock the register, take the input LOW, clock the register, input HIGH, clock, and finally leave the input HIGH and give the clock one last blip. You should find that you now have 1101 on the outputs. This is an example of converting a one-after-the-other 'serial' data input stream (1 . . . 0 . . . 1 . . . 1) into an all-available-together 'parallel' data output (1011, reading from Q0 to Q3) as discussed above. ☐

Now load the file **fig5_48.ewb**. This circuit uses the 74HC194 device of Figure 5.46. Note that Electronics Workbench uses its own convention for drawing symbols, rather than the IEC system – see Figure 5.48.

Fig. 5.48 *74HC194 shift register used as a ring counter*

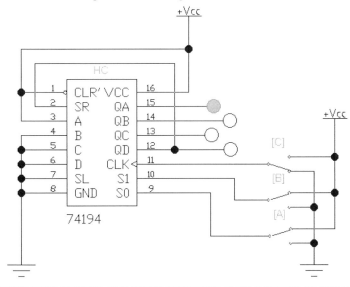

The four modes of operation are controlled by means of the inputs S1 and S0, which are set via keyboard keys B and A.

The data that is loaded during a parallel load comes from the four connections A, B, C and D. These are taken HIGH, LOW, LOW and LOW in Figure 5.48, so when the parallel load takes place outputs QA, QB, QC and QD will take on this binary pattern. Figure 5.48 shows this having just taken place.

As per the IEC symbol, shift right means shift down – towards QD – with new serial data being input via the SR connection. In Figure 5.48 the SR input has been connected to the QD output, so when data reaches the end of the register it automatically re-appears at the beginning. This configuration is known as a 'ring counter'.

Run Electronics Workbench and load the file. Set up parallel-load mode by setting S1 and S0 (switches B and A) both HIGH, give the clock switch a positive edge, and verify that the parallel data 1000 is loaded correctly, as shown in the figure. □

Now go to shift-right mode by setting S1 (B) LOW. Click the clock a few times and verify that the '1' moves towards the right, i.e. towards QD. Also verify that the connection from QD back to SR allows the '1' to circulate around the ring as long as you keep clocking the register. □

Mode 2 is left-shift mode. Set S1 (B) HIGH and S0 (A) LOW and verify that the '1' now moves left, i.e. towards QA on positive clock edges. By using the SL input, amend the circuit so that continuous circulation can take place in either direction. □

XPLA

The code in Figure 5.49 is a straightforward representation of Figure 5.45. A global reset has also been provided. Note how D-type flip-flops are specified by means of the `istype 'reg_d'` attribute, and how the `.d` connections are then used.

Enter the code, save, compile, fit and run a timing simulation. Set the **Simulate Until** figure to 1000ns, set up a 100ns cycle length, start-at-0 clock, a brief active-HIGH reset at the start of the simulation, and make the D_IN signal change from HIGH to LOW around about 500ns. Verify that the waveforms show the HIGH being clocked into all four flip-flops during the first four clock rising edges, and then the LOW propagating through once the D_IN signal itself goes LOW. See Figure 5.50. □

Download the design to the target board and check that data from SW1 is loaded into the shift register under control from the 555 timer clock. (Set the clock control pot to about mid position.) □

A ring counter similar to the one implemented in Figure 5.48 can also be devised. The listing in Figure 5.51 shows how.

The microswitch acts to *preset* Q0, but *re*set the three other flip-flops. The three-position slide switch generates the `left` and `right` signals, which are used

Fig. 5.49 *PHDL code for shift register*

```
Module   shreg
Title    '4-bit right-shift register'

Declarations
reset,d_in,clock  pin  14,4,43;
Q3..Q0            pin  16,17,18,19 istype 'reg_d';
Q = [Q3..Q0];

Equations

Q.ar = reset;
Q.clk = clock;

Q3.d = d_in;
Q2.d = Q3;
Q1.d = Q2;
Q0.d = Q1;

end
```

Fig. 5.50 *Simulation of shift-register*

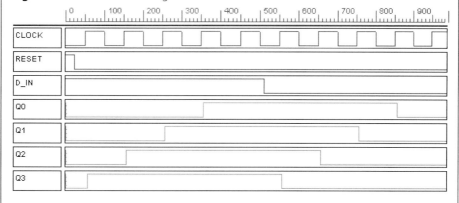

within the equations section to determine the direction of shift. In the case that neither **left** nor **right** is active the final **else** clause ensures that the data is held in position within the shift register.

Enter the code, save, compile, fit and download to the target board. Check that pressing the microswitch sets up the initial 0001 pattern on the LEDs, and that the three-position slide switch then controls the direction of rotation of the ring counter. Edit, save, compile, fit and download a 10-bit version.   ☐

Fig. 5.51 *PHDL code to make a bidirectional ring counter*

```
Module  ring
Title    '4-bit  left-right  ring  counter'

Declarations
load,clock,left,right  pin  14,43,2,1;
Q3..Q0                 pin  16,17,18,19 istype 'reg_d';

Q = [Q3..Q0];

Equations

Q0.ap = load;    "preset Q0 HIGH
Q1.ar = load;    "but all others LOW
Q2.ar = load;
Q3.ar = load;

Q.clk = clock;

when right then
  {                    "shift towards Q0
  Q3.d = Q0;
  Q2.d = Q3;
  Q1.d = Q2;
  Q0.d = Q1;
  }

else when left then
  {                    "shift towards Q3
  Q3.d = Q2;
  Q2.d = Q1;
  Q1.d = Q0;
  Q0.d = Q3;
  }
else Q.d = Q;         "don't shift at all

end
```

Data registers

The last circuit introduced in this chapter is the data register. Registers are humble circuits that just store numbers – the example below will store a 4-bit number. You'll find many registers inside microprocessors; RAM can be thought of as consisting of thousands of data registers, together with decoding and multiplexing circuitry to steer the data to the correct location.

In Figure 5.52 a 4-bit number presented at the D0–D3 inputs will be transferred to the Q0–Q3 outputs on the rising edge of the clock. This number will then simply be stored in the register until the next clock pulse updates the register with any new number presented at the D inputs.

There's a closely related device called a latch. The difference between a latch and a register is explored in the next exercise.

Fig. 5.52 *4-bit data register*

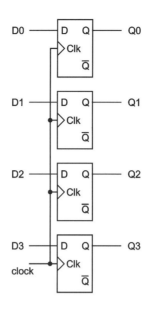

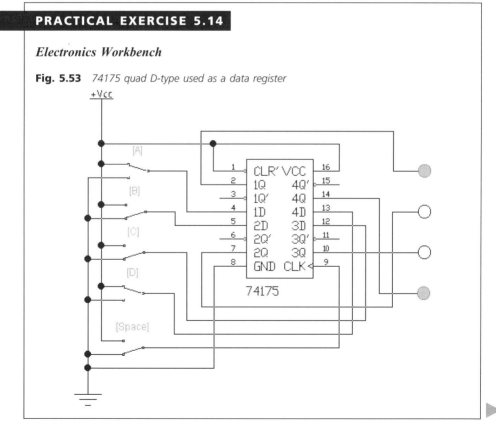

PRACTICAL EXERCISE 5.14

Electronics Workbench

Fig. 5.53 *74175 quad D-type used as a data register*

The file **fig5_53.ewb** uses the 74175 quad D-type to implement a 4-bit data register. Run the simulation, set the input switches A, B, C and D to some arbitrary settings, then hit the space bar to give the CLK signal a LOW-to-HIGH transition. Verify that the data set up on the input is transferred to the output. ☐

Also verify that there's no other way to get the data transferred – there has to be a positive *edge* on the CLK. ☐

Now load the file **fig5_54.ewb** and try the same experiments. You should find that the 7475 is 'transparent' when the CLK is HIGH, with changes to input data immediately appearing at the output. When the CLK is LOW, the last information held is 'latched' and changes at the data input are ignored. ☐

Note: it would be helpful if the industry restricted the use of the term 'latch' to the action of devices like the 7475. However, you will find it used more widely, with some texts referring to an SR latch (= flip-flop), others to edge-triggered latches (= register), and so on.

Fig. 5.54 *4-bit transparent latch*

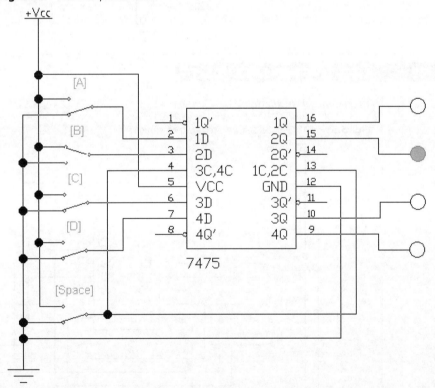

XPLA

The listing in Figure 5.55 is a direct implementation of the circuit of Figure 5.52. Enter the code, compile, fit and download to the target board. Verify that any data

Fig. 5.55 *PHDL code for a 4-bit data register*

```
MODULE   datareg
TITLE    '4-bit data register'

DECLARATIONS
D3..D0  pin  4,6,8,5;
clock   pin  14;
Q3..Q0  pin  16,17,18,19 istype 'reg_d';
D  =  [D3..D0];
Q  =  [Q3..Q0];

EQUATIONS

Q.clk  =  clock;
Q.d  =  D;

END
```

you set on switches SW1, SW2, SW3 and SW4a is transferred to the LED display when you press the microswitch. ☐

Verify that this code generates an edge-triggered system. Hold down the microswitch and check that changes to the input data do *not* appear on the LED display. ☐

The XPLA software doesn't support transparent latches, so if you need one you will have to write some code based on the circuit below – see Figure 5.56.

Fig. 5.56 *One-bit transparent latch*

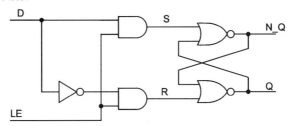

The circuit consists of an SR flip-flop, but the inputs are gated by a couple of AND gates. These gates are 'opened' by the **Latch Enable** signal, LE. Thus, when LE is HIGH, the data from the D input arrives at the S input of the flip-flop, and the complement of D arrives at the R input, forcing the Q output of the flip-flop to take on the logic state of the signal at D. The situation is transparent: wiggling D will wiggle Q.

When LE goes LOW, however, both AND gates give LOW outputs, placing the SR flip-flop into remembering mode – see Figure 5.2 if you've forgotten all about SR flip-flops! The circuit has now latched the data, and changes at D have no effect.

Fig. 5.57 *PHDL code for 4-bit transparent latch*

```
MODULE  transltc
TITLE   '4-bit transparent latch'

DECLARATIONS
D3..D0           pin 4,6,8,5;
clock            pin 14;
Q3..Q0           pin 16,17,18,19;
N_Q3..N_Q0       node;
S3..S0, R3..R0   node;

latch macro  (D,LE,S,R,Q,N_Q)
"see Figure 5.56
  {
  ?S = ?D & ?LE;
  ?R = !?D & ?LE;
  ?N_Q = !(?S # ?Q);
  ?Q = !(?R # ?N_Q);
  };

EQUATIONS

latch(D3,clock,S3,R3,Q3,N_Q3);
latch(D2,clock,S2,R2,Q2,N_Q2);
latch(D1,clock,S1,R1,Q1,N_Q1);
latch(D0,clock,S0,R0,Q0,N_Q0);

END
```

The code in Figure 5.57 makes use of a macro to define a one-bit latch, which is then used four times to create the 4-bit system.

PRACTICAL EXERCISE 5.15

Enter the code. Note that within the macro you have to say !?D rather than ?!D. It took the author an hour or so to discover that! Save, compile, fit, download and check now that if you hold the microswitch down, the latch behaves transparently to changes in the data input. It should, of course, latch that data when the microswitch is released.　　　　　　　　　　　　　　　　　　　　　　　　　　　　　　□

Summary

This chapter has introduced you to the fundamental memory element available to digital logic designers: the flip-flop. You should now be familiar with the functional behaviour of RS, JK, T and D types, and how they are represented within PHDL listings. The chapter has covered some of the new things you can make now that memory is available: counters (both asynchronous (ripple-through) and synchronous types), shift registers and data registers. You should be aware of the possible pitfalls of asynchronous designs.

If you worked through all the practical exercises then you have simulated these circuits using Electronics Workbench, and built and tested them using the CPLD chip and the target hardware.

In the next chapter further methods of designing synchronous circuits will be presented.

Modulo-sixty counter

Introduction

With 60 seconds in a minute, and 60 minutes in an hour, there is a need for a counter that will count in 60s. This is normally made from a decade (BCD) counter and a six's counter. You have seen how various BCD counters can be designed; your task in this assignment is to design, simulate, implement and test a counter that counts 0, 1, 2, 3, 4, 5, 0 . . . then use it, together with a BCD counter to count 0, 1, 2 . . . 58, 59, 0 . . .

Task 1

Using Electronics Workbench or other simulator, design, enter and simulate a 3-bit, ripple-through modulo-6 up counter. Your design should use the same idea as the modulo-10 (BCD) ripple-through up counter of Figure 5.25. Select suitable devices from the Digital ICs library (74 or 4000 series) to implement the circuit, rather than using devices from the Logic Gates or Digital library. Check the relevant details of the chosen devices against information supplied by manufacturers' data sheets.   □

Task 2

Now design a synchronous modulo-6 up counter. Start by sketching the required waveforms, then devise suitable circuitry to drive the JK (T) inputs of each flip-flop, along the lines of the synchronous BCD up counter discussed – see Figure 5.37 *et seq*. Test your design using Electronics Workbench or some other simulator, using Digital ICs (as opposed to devices within the Logic Gates or Digital libraries).   □

Task 3

Implement both your designs in PHDL code, along the lines of Figure 5.26 and 5.39. Simulate the designs to show that they behave as required. Fit, download to the target board, and test each one.   □

Task 4

Combine your synchronous circuit with a synchronous BCD counter to give a modulo-60 up counter. Investigate using the falling edge of Q3 of the BCD counter to act as the clock for the 'BC6' counter. Verify your circuit using Electronics Workbench or other simulator.   □

Task 5

Implement your design on the target board. The display could utilise the bar graph in two sections. For instance, the three left-hand LEDs could indicate the tens and the four right-hand LEDs the units. Alternatively, you could use one of the seven-segment displays to display the tens and the bar graph to indicate the units, incorporating appropriate decoders to display the tens as a figure and the units as a dot or bar graph.

Note: if you use a `truth_table` in your code, place no statements between it and the `END` statement (apart from another `truth_table`). ☐

Task 6

Write a report on this assignment. You should describe what you have done and include printouts of Electronics Workbench schematics for tasks 1, 2 and 4, PHDL listings and simulation results for tasks 3 and 5. For task 5, discuss any alternative designs you have considered. ☐

Coverage

This assignment covers all four of the assessment criteria of Outcome 3 of the Edexcel\BTEC H-level unit Combinational and Sequential Logic and all four of the assessment criteria for Outcome 4.

Grading criteria

Pass

- 'interpret manufacturers' literature to select appropriate sequential logic devices for specific purposes' (complete task 1 satisfactorily)
- 'analyse the operation of sequential logic circuits' (complete task 1 satisfactorily)
- 'use formal techniques to design sequential logic circuits' (complete tasks 1 and 2 satisfactorily)
- 'construct and test sequential logic circuits' (complete task 3 satisfactorily)
- 'design sequential logic circuits to meet a given specification' (complete task 4 satisfactorily)
- 'use computer simulation to verify logic designs' (complete task 1 satisfactorily)
- 'construct and test sequential circuits' (complete task 3 satisfactorily)
- 'use programmable logic devices to minimise component count in systems containing sequential logic circuits' (complete task 3 satisfactorily)

Merit

- 'use a range of methods and techniques to collect, analyse and process information/data' (use XPLA and Electronics Workbench simulators)
- 'apply and analyse detailed knowledge and skills, using relevant theories and techniques' (tasks 1 to 5 – basic implementation – completed satisfactorily)
- 'coherently present and communicate work using technical language accurately' (task 6)

Distinction

- 'check validity when collecting, analysing and processing complex information/data' (give sensible discussion of parameters checked in task 1 – check information against manufacturers' data sheets)

- 'evaluate and synthesise relevant theories and techniques to generate and justify conclusions' (task 5 – alternative implementation – completed satisfactorily)
- 'show an individual approach in presenting and communicating work coherently, using technical language fluently' (task 6)

ASSIGNMENT
Pseudo-random bit sequence generator

Introduction
Digital systems are inherently deterministic, so using a digital system to create something random is difficult. Genuinely random action generally entails an interaction between a digital system and some other unrelated system. This other system might be the electronics associated with the display on a computer system, or the pressing of a button at some unpredictable time by a human user.

In this assignment you will generate a stream of 1s and 0s that, although not genuinely random, at first sight looks pretty random. It is based on a shift register.

Task 1
Find out about PRBS. A good account is given in *The Art of Electronics*. □

The Art of Electronics, Horowitz and Hill, Cambridge University Press, 2nd ed., 0-521-37095-7. The authors cover an amazing amount of electronics in this book. Could do with a 3rd edition, but highly readable, highly recommended for practising engineers.

Task 2
Design a 6-bit, maximal length (63) PRBS generator. Simulate with XPLA. The PHDL symbol for Exclusive-OR is $. Note that if the shift register ever gets into the all-zeros state it won't get out again.

Taking the output of any one flip-flop, count the number of 1s you get in the 63-state sequence.

Count the number of times in the 63-state sequence that you get just a single 1 with a 0 before and after. How many times do you get two 1s in a row? Three? (Carry on . . . !)

Examine any two outputs from the shift register. How often are they different? □

Task 3
Use XPLA to simulate an 8-bit, maximal length (255) PRBS generator. Do the same statistics on it as for task 2. □

Task 4
Use a PRBS to make the ten-bar graph LEDs twinkle randomly (or apparently so). □

Task 5
Devise a circuit to implement the same function as the task 4 design, but using 74 series chips. You do not need to build it: just draw a detailed circuit diagram,

including chip type numbers and pin numbers. A suitable drawing package would be Electronics Workbench, in which case, of course, you could simulate the design as well. ☐

Task 6
Write a report discussing the work done and results obtained.

Coverage
This assignment covers all four of the assessment criteria of Outcome 3 of the Edexcel\BTEC H-level unit Combinational and Sequential Logic and all four of the assessment criteria for Outcome 4.

Grading criteria

Pass

- 'interpret manufacturers' literature to select appropriate sequential logic devices for specific purposes' (complete task 5 satisfactorily)
- 'analyse the operation of sequential logic circuits' (complete task 1 satisfactorily)
- 'use formal techniques to design sequential logic circuits' (complete task 2 satisfactorily)
- 'construct and test sequential logic circuits' (complete task 4 satisfactorily)
- 'design sequential logic circuits to meet a given specification' (complete task 4 satisfactorily)
- 'use computer simulation to verify logic designs' (complete task 2 satisfactorily)
- 'construct and test sequential circuits' (complete task 4 satisfactorily)
- 'use programmable logic devices to minimise component count in systems containing sequential logic circuits' (complete task 4 satisfactorily)

Merit

- 'use a range of methods and techniques to collect, analyse and process information/data' (use XPLA and Electronics Workbench simulators)
- 'apply and analyse detailed knowledge and skills, using relevant theories and techniques' (tasks 1 and 2 – completed satisfactorily)
- 'coherently present and communicate work using technical language accurately' (task 6)

Distinction

- 'check validity when collecting, analysing and processing complex information/data' (give sensible discussion of parameters checked in tasks 2 and 3)
- 'evaluate and synthesise relevant theories and techniques to generate and justify conclusions' (task 4 completed satisfactorily)
- 'show an individual approach in presenting and communicating work coherently, using technical language fluently' (task 6)

5.1 (c): Set active HIGH, Reset LOW to force Q HIGH

5.2 (a): Set and Reset LOW, 'remembering', with Q happening to be LOW

   (b): Set LOW, Reset active HIGH to force Q LOW

   (d): Both Set and Reset HIGH to force Q (and $\overline{Q}$) LOW

5.3 (a): Both Set and Reset LOW to force Q (and $\overline{Q}$) HIGH

   (b): Set active LOW, Reset HIGH to force Q HIGH

5.4 (c): Set HIGH, Reset active LOW to force Q LOW

   (d): Set and Reset HIGH, 'remembering', with Q happening to be LOW

5.5 (a): At 500ns the Set input goes inactive LOW, circuit remains Set

5.6 (d): At 1000ns Reset goes active HIGH, circuit is actively Reset

5.7 (b): At 1500ns the Reset goes inactive LOW, circuit remains Reset

5.8 (c): At 2000ns the Set goes active HIGH, circuit is actively Set

5.9 (a): With Preset and Clear inactive HIGH and no change to the Clock the circuit will remain unchanged

5.10 (c): Preset active LOW will definitely set Q HIGH

5.11 (a): HIGH-to-LOW edge on Clock will have no effect on this positive-edge-triggered flip-flop

5.12 (d): JK both HIGH means circuit will toggle on rising edge of Clock

5.13 (c): HIGH-LOW on J-K means data will be transferred to output at rising edge of Clock: Q will go HIGH

5.14 (b): At P the signals are 0011 on Q3..Q0. This is equivalent to the decimal number 3

5.15 (b): At S you should find all four signals are HIGH, equivalent to decimal 15

5.16 (a): At the next interval after S all the outputs go LOW: 0000.

5.17 (b): Q1 toggles at the rising edge of the clock when (and only when) Q0 is HIGH.

5.18 (d): Q3 only toggles when all the preceding outputs are HIGH

5.19 (a): Q0 is LOW, so none of the higher order flip-flops can toggle

5.20 (c): Q2 only toggles when both the preceding outputs are HIGH

5.21 (a): 0101 – the left-hand 0 has been shifted in from the data input, while the 101 comes from the original data

5.22 (a): 0110 (6) will turn into 0011 (3) – note that shifting right is equivalent (in a binary system) to dividing by 2; shifting left is equivalent to multiplying by 2

ANSWERS TO EXERCISES

Paper exercise 5.1

The 74××74 is a dual D-type flip-flop, with active-LOW preset and clear, and a positive-edge triggered clock, all of which coincides with Figure 5.14.

Paper exercise 5.2

Not available as a device in its own right. Use a JK with J and K inputs tied together.

Practical exercise 5.3

The code of Figure 5.18 can be amended to make the toggle action take place when the microswitch is pressed (rather than when it is released) by changing the clock signal to the toggle flip-flop:

```
toggle.clk = N_Q;
```

Paper exercise 5.3

Figure 5.58 shows the completed waveforms. Figure 5.59 shows the alternative form.

Fig. 5.58 *Completed waveforms for binary counter (see Figure 5.20)*

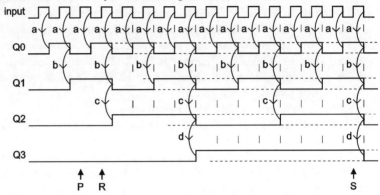

Fig. 5.59 *Waveforms produced when rising edge toggles next flip-flop*

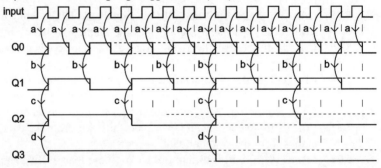

Practical exercise 5.6

To change the code of Figure 5.22 so that a down-counter results, simply remove each ! from the equations. This will ensure that each flip-flop will toggle on the rising edge of its clock, giving down counting, as Figure 5.59 shows.

Practical exercise 5.12

The completed truth table is given in Figure 5.60. The Karnaugh maps for each output are given in Figure 5.61.

Note: the sequence of the variable values along the edges of these Karnaugh maps has been altered for convenience in drawing. This is allowed, as long as the rule 'only change one variable at a time' is obeyed.

Fig. 5.60 *Table showing when flip-flops should toggle to achieve BCD down counting*

count	Q3	Q2	Q1	Q0	Q1	Q2	Q3
		current state				toggle?	
0	0	0	0	0	0	0	1
1	0	0	0	1	0	0	0
2	0	0	1	0	1	0	0
3	0	0	1	1	0	0	0
4	0	1	0	0	1	1	0
5	0	1	0	1	0	0	0
6	0	1	1	0	1	0	0
7	0	1	1	1	0	0	0
8	1	0	0	0	1	1	1
9	1	0	0	1	0	0	0
	1	0	1	0	×	×	×
	1	0	1	1	×	×	×
	1	1	0	0	×	×	×
	1	1	0	1	×	×	×
	1	1	1	0	×	×	×
	1	1	1	1	×	×	×

Fig. 5.61 *Karnaugh maps drawn from information in Figure 5.60*

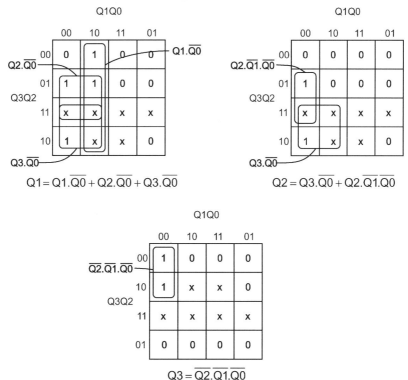

$$Q1 = Q1.\overline{Q0} + Q2.\overline{Q0} + Q3.\overline{Q0}$$

$$Q2 = Q3.\overline{Q0} + Q2.\overline{Q1.Q0}$$

$$Q3 = \overline{Q2.Q1.Q0}$$

6 Finite state machines

Introduction

Chapter 5 introduced the different types of flip-flop, and you saw how they could be used to make circuits from switch de-bouncers to synchronous systems like counters and shift registers. Some of the circuits were presented on a 'Look, if you bung these devices together like this you get a circuit that does that' basis. The synchronous counters were a bit different: first the required behaviour of the outputs was defined by drawing the waveforms, then the problem of working out how to get the individual flip-flops to toggle at the right time was tackled. These circuits were actually *designed*.

The finite state machine is a general-purpose synchronous system that aids the design of a large variety of circuits. In this chapter a general way of designing such systems is presented, and then applied to a few example problems. Like the synchronous BCD down counter design, the method ends up turning a sequential logic problem into a combinational one. Once you've done that, the problem becomes tractable by methods such as Karnaugh maps, Quine–McCluskey minimisation, etc.

Synchronous systems all need clock signals to drive them, so some circuits for generating them are discussed. The chapter concludes by taking a look at the problem of designing circuits where an overall controlling clock is not required – asynchronous designs.

The chapter covers:

- Mealy and Moore finite state machines
- use of D-type, T-type and JK flip-flops to implement state machines
- examples of state machines: counters, detectors, etc.
- Electronics Workbench implementation of state machines
- XPLA implementation of state machines
- state transition diagrams
- PHDL syntax for state machines
- clock generator circuits
- the design of asynchronous sequential circuits
- an extended assignment

Mealy and Moore finite state machines

Fig. 6.1 *General-purpose finite state machine*

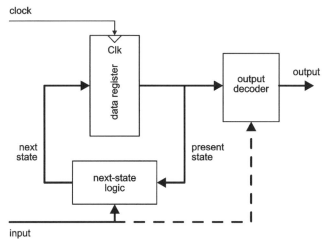

G.H. Mealy and E.F. Moore were pioneers (1955 and 1956) in the design of sequential logic. If you ignore the dotted line, Figure 6.1 illustrates what's known as a 'Moore machine'; a 'Mealy machine' includes it. The heavy lines represent data buses, i.e. collections of individual signals grouped together. At the top of the diagram there's a data register, just like the data register discussed in Chapter 5 – see Figure 5.52. The number of bits in the data register, and the number of bits in the buses leading to and leaving the data register will vary according to the complexity of the system. The number held in the data register represents the 'present state' of the system. When the data register is clocked, the 'next state' is read in. Since the state is held as a number on a finite number of bits in the data register, there can only be a finite number of states that the system can occupy – hence the name 'finite state machine'.

Where does the next state come from? The 'next-state logic' block generates it. This block looks at the present state of the system, and works out what the next state should be, taking into account any possible input signals to the whole system. The behaviour of the whole system is thus governed almost entirely by the way the next-state logic does its job. The thing is, the next-state logic block is *combinational*, so, although it might be tedious work, it's relatively easy to design, using the techniques covered in Chapter 3 – Karnaugh maps, etc.

The output decoder is another combinational logic block. It looks at the current internal state of the system and generates the required outputs. The number of individual signals in the output bus will probably be different from the number of signals making up the present-state, next-state buses. As mentioned above, if the output decoder looks at the input signals as well as the present-state bus then the design is a Mealy type; if it just looks at the current state of the system it's a Moore type. There's no fundamental difference between the two types; it's always possible to convert from one type to the other without having to change the functionality of the system, although sometimes one type is more convenient than the other.

Synchronous binary up counter

As a first example, let's design a 3-bit binary up counter. You already know how to make one using JK or T-type flip-flops – see Figure 5.32 – but now you're going to make one using D-types, and the design methodology of the finite state machine. For this example there are no external inputs to the next-state logic, and the output decoder is not required, so Figure 6.2 results.

Fig. 6.2 *3-bit autonomous finite state machine*

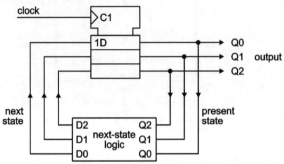

Figure 6.2 is described as 'autonomous' since it is not influenced by any external input signals. To turn this finite state machine into a binary counter the circuitry within the 'next-state logic' block has to be designed, and the first step in this process is to write down its truth table. Note that the Q signals are inputs, while the Ds are outputs. Effectively, three truth tables are needed – one for each output – but they are combined in Figure 6.3 below.

Fig. 6.3 *Truth table (present-state/next-state table) for binary counter FSM*

	present state			next state		
	Q2	Q1	Q0	D2	D1	D0
0	0	0	0	0	0	1
1	0	0	1	0	1	0
2	0	1	0	0	1	1
3	0	1	1	1	0	0
4	1	0	0	1	0	1
5	1	0	1	1	1	0
6	1	1	0	1	1	1
7	1	1	1	0	0	0

How have the entries in this table been derived? Easy! Just look at any given present state, work out what the next state should be (in this case, just count up by one), and write that state down on the right-hand (next state) side of the table. Thus row 0 shows that the next state after 000 is 001. The only (slightly) tricky one is row 7: the next state after 111 is 000.

The next task is to use your circuit minimisation skills to create circuits for each of the three outputs. By just looking at the truth table you can sometimes spot solutions. If you can't see a nice solution, you just work through Karnaugh maps, etc. to arrive at your circuit. Looking at the truth table for D0, it is easy to see that it is simply the complement of Q0, so a single NOT gate will suffice to generate the D0 signal.

You may recognise the 0110 pattern for D1 as exclusive-OR: $D1 = Q1 \oplus Q0$. The 0001 pattern for D2 is AND, while the 1110 pattern is NAND. We need the AND of Q1 and Q0 while Q2 is LOW, but the NAND when it is HIGH. The conditional inverter properties of the exclusive-OR can be utilised here, together with an AND gate. Figure 6.4 shows the complete circuit.

Fig. 6.4 *3-bit binary up counter*

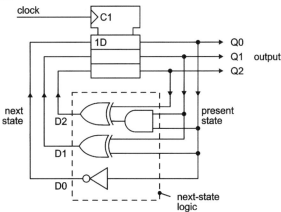

Figure 6.4 may be re-drawn to resemble the circuits of Chapter 5. Figure 6.5 shows the result.

Fig. 6.5 *3-bit binary up counter re-drawn*

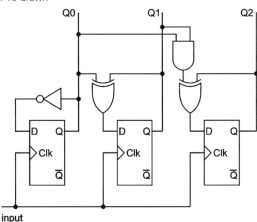

The number of bits in the counter can easily be extended, bearing in mind the work done in Chapter 5. One way to think about the circuit is that the feedback from each flip-flop's output to its own input causes the flip-flop to toggle. The first (Q0) section has a simple inverter, so it toggles at every rising edge of the input clock. The other sections have controlled inverters in the form of the exclusive-OR gates. These feed back inverted forms of their output only when the preceding outputs are all HIGH. Figure 6.6 shows how a 4-bit counter can be implemented using Electronics Workbench.

PRACTICAL EXERCISE 6.1

Electronics Workbench

Fig. 6.6 *4-bit binary up counter*

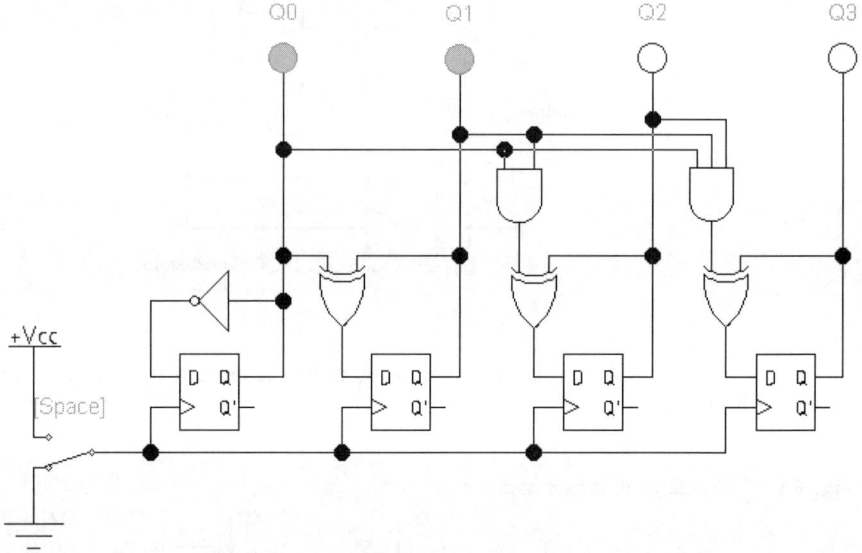

Open Electronics Workbench and run the simulation (file **fig6_6.ewb**). Verify that the circuit counts up in binary. □

XPLA
Enter the code in Figure 6.7 and save. Before you compile, use the **Properties** button to *de*activate D/T register synthesis by un-clicking the box. This prevents the compiler from turning your design from one based on D-type flip-flops into one based on T-types. Hide the **Properties** dialog window, compile, fit and run a timing simulation. (**Simulate Until** 2000ns, 100ns cycle length for the clock.) Verify that you get the correct waveforms. □

Fig. 6.7 *XPLA code based on circuit of Figure 6.6*

```
MODULE  counter
TITLE   '4-bit binary up counter based on Figure 6.6'

DECLARATIONS
clock   pin 43;
Q3..Q0  pin 16,17,18,19 istype 'reg_d';

Q = [Q3..Q0];

EQUATIONS

Q.clk = clock;
Q0.d = !Q0;
Q1.d = Q1 $ Q0;
Q2.d = Q2 $ (Q1 & Q0);
Q3.d = Q3 $ (Q2 & Q1 & Q0);

END
```

Take a look at the **.ph1** (optimised equations) file. You should find something similar to Figure 6.8. ☐

Fig. 6.8 *XPLA optimised equations for binary counter*

```
EQUATIONS

Q0.CLK = clock;                              "--- [PT=1, FI=1, LVL=1] ---
! Q0.D = Q0.Q;                               "--- [PT=1, FI=1, LVL=1] ---
Q1.CLK = clock;                              "--- [PT=1, FI=1, LVL=1] ---
Q1.D = Q0.Q & !Q1.Q
     # !Q0.Q & Q1.Q;                         "--- [PT=2, FI=2, LVL=1] ---
Q2.CLK = clock;                              "--- [PT=1, FI=1, LVL=1] ---
Q2.D = Q0.Q & Q1.Q & !Q2.Q
     # !Q1.Q & Q2.Q
     # !Q0.Q & Q2.Q;                         "--- [PT=3, FI=3, LVL=1] ---
Q3.CLK = clock;                              "--- [PT=1, FI=1, LVL=1] ---
Q3.D = Q0.Q & Q1.Q & Q2.Q & !Q3.Q
     # !Q2.Q & Q3.Q
     # !Q1.Q & Q3.Q
     # !Q0.Q & Q3.Q;                         "--- [PT=4, FI=4, LVL=1] ---

END
```

There are several things to point out. First, notice how the original equation `Q.clk = clock;` has been expanded into four equations, one for each bit of the Q bus. ☐

Also, note how the exclusive-OR equations have been expanded down to the basic Boolean algebra. For instance, $Q1.d = Q1 \oplus Q0$ has become $Q1.d = Q0.\overline{Q1} + \overline{Q0}.Q1$. Use your Boolean algebra skills from Chapter 2 to understand what's happened to the equation for Q3.d. Start by using the definition of exclusive-OR: ☐

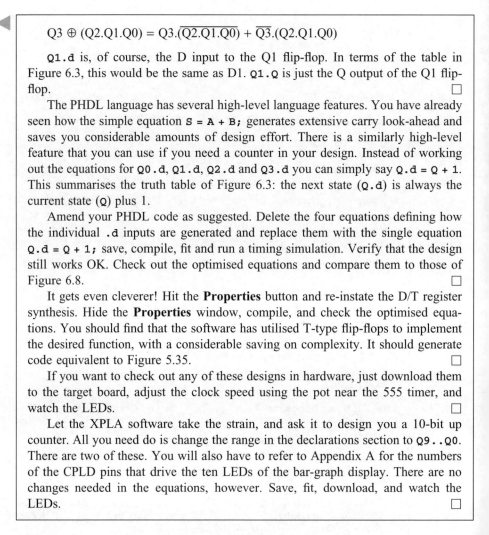

$$Q3 \oplus (Q2.Q1.Q0) = Q3.\overline{(Q2.Q1.Q0)} + \overline{Q3}.(Q2.Q1.Q0)$$

`Q1.d` is, of course, the D input to the Q1 flip-flop. In terms of the table in Figure 6.3, this would be the same as D1. `Q1.Q` is just the Q output of the Q1 flip-flop. □

The PHDL language has several high-level language features. You have already seen how the simple equation `S = A + B;` generates extensive carry look-ahead and saves you considerable amounts of design effort. There is a similarly high-level feature that you can use if you need a counter in your design. Instead of working out the equations for `Q0.d`, `Q1.d`, `Q2.d` and `Q3.d` you can simply say `Q.d = Q + 1`. This summarises the truth table of Figure 6.3: the next state (`Q.d`) is always the current state (`Q`) plus 1.

Amend your PHDL code as suggested. Delete the four equations defining how the individual `.d` inputs are generated and replace them with the single equation `Q.d = Q + 1;` save, compile, fit and run a timing simulation. Verify that the design still works OK. Check out the optimised equations and compare them to those of Figure 6.8. □

It gets even cleverer! Hit the **Properties** button and re-instate the D/T register synthesis. Hide the **Properties** window, compile, and check the optimised equations. You should find that the software has utilised T-type flip-flops to implement the desired function, with a considerable saving on complexity. It should generate code equivalent to Figure 5.35. □

If you want to check out any of these designs in hardware, just download them to the target board, adjust the clock speed using the pot near the 555 timer, and watch the LEDs. □

Let the XPLA software take the strain, and ask it to design you a 10-bit up counter. All you need do is change the range in the declarations section to `Q9..Q0`. There are two of these. You will also have to refer to Appendix A for the numbers of the CPLD pins that drive the ten LEDs of the bar-graph display. There are no changes needed in the equations, however. Save, fit, download, and watch the LEDs. □

Finite state machine for up/down counter

As far as the block diagram is concerned, the only difference between an up counter and an up/down counter is the addition of the up/down control input. In the design below, the counter counts up if the control is HIGH, but down otherwise.

The procedure is the same as before, but this time the truth table for the next-state logic has four inputs: Q2, Q1, Q0 and the up/down control input, dir. The truth table will thus have 16 rows.

As before, the entries in this table are calculated in a straightforward manner. When the direction signal (dir) is LOW the counter is required to count down so the next state is just one less than the present state. Thus, for row 0, the next state is 111 since that is

Fig. 6.9 *3-bit FSM with control input*

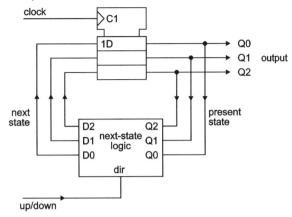

Fig. 6.10 *Truth table (present-state next-state table) for up/down counter*

	dir	present state			next state		
		Q2	Q1	Q0	D2	D1	D0
0	0	0	0	0	1	1	1
1	0	0	0	1	0	0	0
2	0	0	1	0	0	0	1
3	0	0	1	1	0	1	0
4	0	1	0	0	0	1	1
5	0	1	0	1	1	0	0
6	0	1	1	0	1	0	1
7	0	1	1	1	1	1	0
8	1	0	0	0	0	0	1
9	1	0	0	1	0	1	0
10	1	0	1	0	0	1	1
11	1	0	1	1	1	0	0
12	1	1	0	0	1	0	1
13	1	1	0	1	1	1	0
14	1	1	1	0	1	1	1
15	1	1	1	1	0	0	0

one less than 000. When dir is HIGH, on the other hand, the next state is one more than the present state. Row 15 shows 111 rolling over back to 000 as the next state.

Now all you have to do is devise minimised functions for D0, D1 and D2. D0 is again easy: just make it the complement of Q0.

D1 and D2 are less obvious. This time, we will make use of Karnaugh maps to derive solutions.

The chequer-board pattern of bits in Figure 6.11 suggests an exclusive-OR implementation, and in fact there are some slightly neater equations for both the D1 and D2 signals that utilise XOR gates. The Electronics Workbench exercise below uses the equations as derived, however.

Fig. 6.11 $D1 = \overline{dir}.\overline{Q1}.\overline{Q0} + \overline{dir}.Q1.Q0 + dir.Q1.\overline{Q0} + dir.\overline{Q1}.Q0$

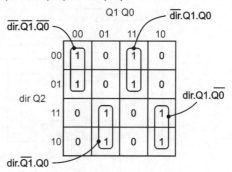

Fig. 6.12 $D2 = \overline{dir}.\overline{Q2}.\overline{Q1}.\overline{Q0} + dir.\overline{Q2}.Q1.Q0 + \overline{dir}.Q2.Q0 + dir.Q2.\overline{Q1} + Q2.Q1.\overline{Q0}$

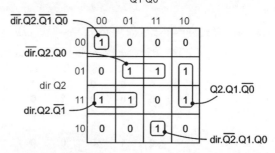

PRACTICAL EXERCISE 6.2

Electronics Workbench

Figure 6.13 shows the 3-bit up/down counter implemented using the equations for D0, D1 and D2 derived above. There is actually a deliberate mistake in the circuit (well, it was originally accidental, but it's a good faultfinding exercise), but run the simulation anyway and record how the circuit behaves both with the dir (keyboard key D) HIGH and with it LOW.   □

Before discussing the error in the circuit, the main points of the implementation are as follows. Since the D-type flip-flops have inverted as well as true outputs, the only extra inverter needed in the system is the one that generates $\overline{dir}$. The AND-OR circuitry in the lower half of the circuit generates the D1 and D2 signals, D1 on the left and D2 on the right. The various AND gates are in the same order (top to bottom) as the product terms in the equations of Figures 6.11 and 6.12.

The error is within the matrix of connections to the AND gates. To find the error you could just check the connections one-by-one against the equations, but it's more interesting to pin it down by a more investigative approach. By studying the way the system *actually* behaves and comparing this with the way it *should* behave, you can work out where the problem lies.

Fig. 6.13 *Electronics Workbench implementation of up/down counter*

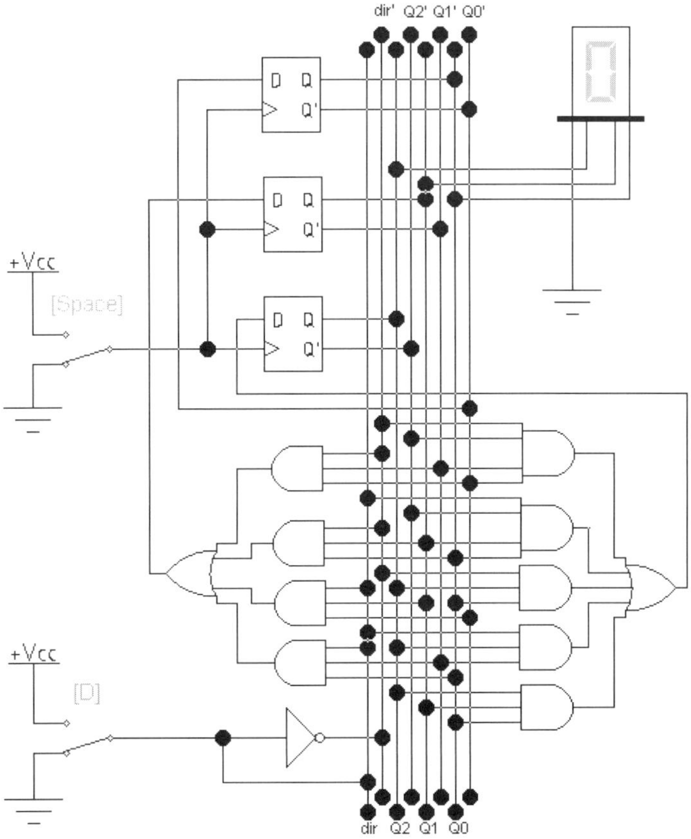

For instance, if it counted 0 ... 1 ... 2 ... 1 ... 2 ... you would identify that bit 1 is at fault since the number 001 (1) is generated instead of 011 (3). And you would know that it goes wrong when the dir/Q2/Q1/Q0 input to the next-state logic is 1010 since the fault occurs when the system is counting up (dir is therefore 1) and the count has reached 2 (010). At this stage D1 should be 1 so that the next count is 3, but D1 must be 0, since the next count is actually 1. Looking at cell 1010 (bottom right) in Figure 6.11 you check that it contains 1, so there's no mistake in the Karnaugh map. You would thus have identified that the problem lies with the AND gate that generates the product term $dir.Q1.\overline{Q0}$ in Figure 6.13 (third one down on left).

Carry out this type of fault identification on the circuit. When you have located the fault, make the correction to the circuit, re-run the simulation and verify that the circuit does indeed count up and down properly. Note that it is easier to move the wires around the AND-gate matrix if you zoom in to 150% or greater. It's also a good idea to turn the simulation OFF while making circuit modifications, to reduce the risk of crashing the software.

XPLA

The design derived from the Karnaugh maps of Figures 6.11 and 6.12 can be entered directly, or you can take advantage of the high-level language features of PHDL to save all the hard work. The two approaches are illustrated below; first the hard way.

Fig. 6.14 *XPLA code based on Figures 6.11 and 6.12*

```
MODULE   counter
TITLE    '3-bit binary up/down counter based on
          Figure 6.11/12'

DECLARATIONS
Clock,dir pin 43,14;
Q2..Q0     pin 16,17,18 istype 'reg_d';

Q = [Q2..Q0];

EQUATIONS

Q.clk = Clock;
Q0.d = !Q0;
Q1.d = !dir & !Q1 & !Q0
     #  !dir & Q1 & Q0
     #  dir & Q1 & !Q0
     #  dir & !Q1 & Q0;
Q2.d = !dir & !Q2 & !Q1 & !Q0
     #  dir & !Q2 & Q1 & Q0
     #  !dir & Q2 & Q0
     #  dir & Q2 & !Q1
     #  Q2 & Q1 & !Q0;

END
```

Enter the code in Figure 6.14, make sure that the D/T register synthesis option of the **Properties** window is *not* checked, compile, fit and download. Verify that the LEDs display 3-bit binary down counting unless you press the microswitch, in which case binary up counting results. ☐

The easy way to get a binary up/down counter is shown in Figure 6.15.

Fig. 6.15 *Use of + and − for up/down counter*

```
MODULE   counter
TITLE    '3-bit binary up/down counter using high-level
          syntax'

DECLARATIONS
Clock,dir pin 43,14;
Q2..Q0     pin 16,17,18 istype 'reg_d';

Q = [Q2..Q0];

EQUATIONS

Q.clk = Clock;
when dir==1 then Q.d = Q + 1;
            else Q.d = Q - 1;

END
```

Enter the code, leave the D/T register synthesis option unchecked, and compile. Check the **.ph1** (optimised equations). You should find that the XPLA software has done the design work for you, and generated the appropriate equations for you. They should be just the same as those in the listing of Figure 6.14. □

As a final variation, open the **Properties** window and check the D/T register synthesis window. As you saw with the up counter exercise, this allows the XPLA software to choose to implement the design using T-type rather than D-type flip-flops if it wishes. Compile the design again and view the new **.ph1** file. You should find a somewhat simpler design, based on T-type devices. Make a note of these equations. □

Finite state machine with T-type flip-flops

As the XPLA software shows, for some systems (such as counters) it's more efficient to use T-type flip-flops to implement the design. The block diagram for such a (3-bit) system is shown in Figure 6.16.

Fig. 6.16 *FSM made with T-type flip-flops*

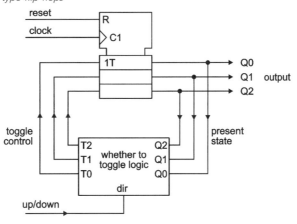

The technique was used in the design of the synchronous BCD down counter in the previous chapter – see Figure 5.41. For every possible state of the system you have to decide what each flip-flop needs to do to get to the next state – whether to toggle or stay put. Figure 6.17 shows the result.

As outlined above, the table is constructed by considering which flip-flops need to toggle to achieve the next state. Thus, the first row of the table shows the system with the present state 000 (0), and counting down (dir = 0). The next required state is thus 111 (7), so all of the flip-flops need to toggle. Similarly, when the count is 4, and the direction is down, all the flip-flops need to toggle to get from 100 (4) to 011 (3). When counting up and you've reached 5, only bits Q1 and Q0 need to toggle to get from 101 (5) to 110 (6).

Fig. 6.17 *Table showing which flip-flops should toggle*

count	dir	present state			toggle?		
		Q2	Q1	Q0	T2	T1	T0
0	0	0	0	0	1	1	1
1	0	0	0	1	0	0	1
2	0	0	1	0	0	1	1
3	0	0	1	1	0	0	1
4	0	1	0	0	1	1	1
5	0	1	0	1	0	0	1
6	0	1	1	0	0	1	1
7	0	1	1	1	0	0	1
0	1	0	0	0	0	0	1
1	1	0	0	1	0	1	1
2	1	0	1	0	0	0	1
3	1	0	1	1	1	1	1
4	1	1	0	0	0	0	1
5	1	1	0	1	0	1	1
6	1	1	1	0	0	0	1
7	1	1	1	1	1	1	1

Note that the table is listed in binary number order, rather than in next-state order, although for the lower half these are the same.

From the truth table you can see that Q0 always needs to toggle, so T0 will be set permanently HIGH: T0 = 1.

Karnaugh maps for T1 and T2 are shown in Figure 6.18.

Fig. 6.18 *Karnaugh maps and Boolean equations for T1 and T2*

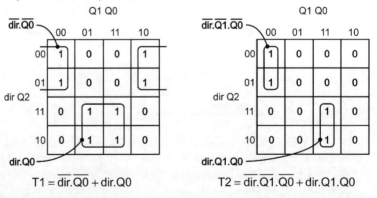

$$T1 = \overline{dir}.\overline{Q0} + dir.Q0$$

$$T2 = \overline{dir}.\overline{Q1}.\overline{Q0} + dir.Q1.Q0$$

PAPER EXERCISE 6.1

Compare these three equations with those created by the XPLA software in the final version of the design in practical exercise 6.2. You should find that they are identical. ☐

Finite state machine with JK flip-flops

As a third and final option, you can use JK flip-flops to implement an FSM. The block diagram is shown below – see Figure 6.19. By way of variation, instead of an up-down control this design incorporates an external input to determine whether the count is in binary or Gray code.

Fig. 6.19 *FSM made with JK flip-flops*

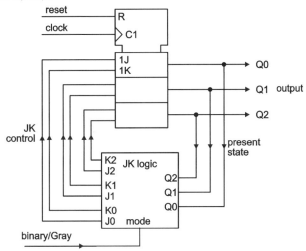

The circuitry within the JK logic block is a bit more difficult to design than either the next-state logic or the whether-to-toggle logic, since the operation of JK flip-flops is more complex than either the D- or T-types. In fact, the way a JK flip-flop behaves needs to be reconsidered in terms of how it is being used here. We need to know what to do to the J and K inputs in order to bring about the required next state at the next clock edge, given knowledge of the current state.

The function of the JK was introduced in Chapter 5 using a table similar to Figure 6.20.

Fig. 6.20 *Function table for JK flip-flop*

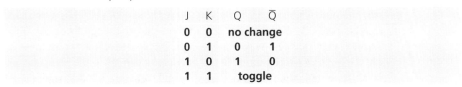

J	K	Q	$\bar{Q}$
0	0	no change	
0	1	0	1
1	0	1	0
1	1	toggle	

The table refers, of course, to the action that will happen at the Q and $\bar{Q}$ outputs at the next edge (falling or rising, depending on the flip-flop details) of the clock input. A more explicit table, and a more useful one for the present discussion, is given in Figure 6.21. For each JK state the two states of the output are listed, before and after the clock edge.

Fig. 6.21 *The eight possible things a JK flip-flop can do*

	J	K	Q	Q̄	Q+	Q̄+
1	0	0	0	1	0	1
2	0	0	1	0	1	0
3	0	1	0	1	0	1
4	0	1	1	0	0	1
5	1	0	0	1	1	0
6	1	0	1	0	1	0
7	1	1	0	1	1	0
8	1	1	1	0	0	1

In Figure 6.21 the state of the outputs before the clock edge are in the Q and Q̄ columns, while the Q+ and Q̄+ columns show the result just after the edge. Rows 1 and 2 show that when J and K are both LOW, the state of the output after the clock edge is the same as it was before. Rows 3 and 4 show that the initial state of the output is irrelevant: the final output is 0, 1 when J, K are 0, 1. Similarly for rows 5 and 6. Rows 7 and 8 illustrate the toggling behaviour.

The table can be recast another way, that is particularly useful when considering the use of JK's in finite state machines – see Figure 6.22.

Fig. 6.22 *How to make a JK do what you want*

	J	K	Q	Q+
a	0	×	0	0
b	×	0	1	1
c	1	×	0	1
d	×	1	1	0

Row a of Figure 6.22 combines rows 1 and 3 of 6.20. If the Q output is currently 0 and you want it to stay that way, make sure the J input is 0, and don't worry about the K.

Similarly, row b combines rows 2 and 6, row c combines 5 and 7 and row d combines 4 and 8. The Q̄ signal is always the complement of Q, of course. To summarise the table: to keep Q LOW make J LOW; to keep Q HIGH make K LOW; to make Q change from 0 to 1 make J HIGH; and to make Q change from 1 to 0 make K HIGH.

Armed with this new way of thinking about JK flip-flops we are now in a position to tackle the binary/Gray counter. The procedure is similar to the one used before: draw up the next-state table then work out what logic level each J and K signal must take at each state of the system. Karnaugh maps can then be used to devise suitable circuitry to drive each J and K input.

The bottom half of the table in Figure 6.23 (where the bin signal is 1) shows binary counting: each 3-bit number in the Q+ columns is just one greater than the number in the Q columns. In the top half each Q+ number is one greater *in Gray code* than the Q number. See Figure 3.16 for Gray code counting.

Fig. 6.23 *Present-state/next-state table for binary/Gray counter*

bin	Q2	Q1	Q0	Q2+	Q1+	Q0+
0	0	0	0	0	0	1
0	0	0	1	0	1	1
0	0	1	0	1	1	0
0	0	1	1	0	1	0
0	1	0	0	0	0	0
0	1	0	1	1	0	0
0	1	1	0	1	1	1
0	1	1	1	1	0	1
1	0	0	0	0	0	1
1	0	0	1	0	1	0
1	0	1	0	0	1	1
1	0	1	1	1	0	0
1	1	0	0	1	0	1
1	1	0	1	1	1	0
1	1	1	0	1	1	1
1	1	1	1	0	0	0

Having established the present-state/next-state requirements, the next step is to work out what each of the J and K signals needs to be for each of the 16 states of the system. Figures 6.24, 6.25 and 6.26 list these levels.

Figures 6.24 to 6.26 have been derived using the table in Figure 6.22. In the first row of Figure 6.26, for instance, the Q0 output is 0 but needs to change to 1 after the next clock edge. According to Figure 6.22 making J0 HIGH (K0 doesn't matter) will ensure this, hence the entries for J0 and K0 in Figure 6.26.

Fig. 6.24 *Logic levels for J2 and K2 to ensure correct behaviour for Q2*

bin	Q2	Q1	Q0	Q2+	J2	K2
0	0	0	0	0	0	×
0	0	0	1	0	0	×
0	0	1	0	1	1	×
0	0	1	1	0	0	×
0	1	0	0	0	×	1
0	1	0	1	1	×	0
0	1	1	0	1	×	0
0	1	1	1	1	×	0
1	0	0	0	0	0	×
1	0	0	1	0	0	×
1	0	1	0	0	0	×
1	0	1	1	1	1	×
1	1	0	0	1	×	0
1	1	0	1	1	×	0
1	1	1	0	1	×	0
1	1	1	1	0	×	1

Fig. 6.25 *Logic levels for J1 and K1 to ensure correct behaviour for Q1*

b/G	Q2	Q1	Q0	Q1+	J1	K1
0	0	0	0	0	0	×
0	0	0	1	1	1	×
0	0	1	0	1	×	0
0	0	1	1	1	×	0
0	1	0	0	0	0	×
0	1	0	1	0	0	×
0	1	1	0	1	×	0
0	1	1	1	0	×	1
1	0	0	0	0	0	×
1	0	0	1	1	1	×
1	0	1	0	1	×	0
1	0	1	1	0	×	1
1	1	0	0	0	0	×
1	1	0	1	1	1	×
1	1	1	0	1	×	0
1	1	1	1	0	×	1

Fig. 6.26 *Logic levels for J0 and K0 to ensure correct behaviour for Q0*

bin	Q2	Q1	Q0	Q0+	J0	K0
0	0	0	0	1	1	×
0	0	0	1	1		
0	0	1	0	0		
0	0	1	1	0		
0	1	0	0	0		
0	1	0	1	0		
0	1	1	0	1	1	×
0	1	1	1	1		
1	0	0	0	1	1	×
1	0	0	1	0		
1	0	1	0	1	1	×
1	0	1	1	0		
1	1	0	0	1	1	×
1	1	0	1	0		
1	1	1	0	1	1	×
1	1	1	1	0		

PAPER EXERCISE 6.2

Complete the remaining entries of Figure 6.26. ☐

Karnaugh maps can now be prepared for each of the three J and three K signals. They are shown in Figures 6.27, 6.28 and 6.29. Figure 6.27 is derived from the table of Figure 6.24, and so on.

Fig. 6.27 *Karnaugh maps and minimised expressions for J2 and K2*

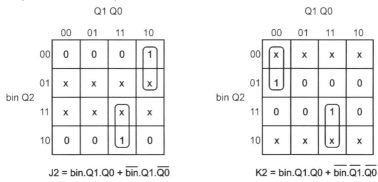

$$J2 = bin.Q1.Q0 + \overline{bin}.Q1.\overline{Q0}$$

$$K2 = \overline{bin}.\overline{Q1}.\overline{Q0} + \overline{bin}.\overline{Q1}.\overline{Q0}$$

Fig. 6.28 *Karnaugh maps and minimised expressions for J1 and K1*

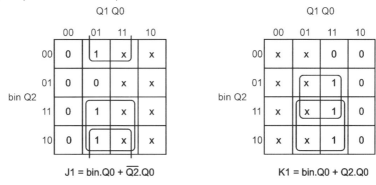

$$J1 = bin.Q0 + \overline{Q2}.Q0$$

$$K1 = bin.Q0 + Q2.Q0$$

Fig. 6.29 *Karnaugh maps and minimised expressions for J0 and K0*

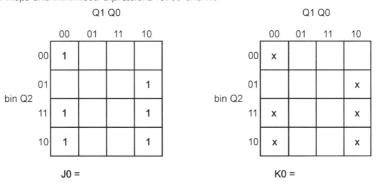

$$J0 =$$

$$K0 =$$

PAPER EXERCISE 6.3

Complete Figure 6.29. Use a product-of-sums type expression. □

We now have minimised Boolean expressions for each of the six outputs from the JK logic block of Figure 6.19, so are in a position to create the circuit.

PRACTICAL EXERCISE 6.3

Electronics Workbench

Figure 6.30 is complete apart from the signals from J0 and K0. Finish off the design, and check that the output counts up in binary when the bin/Gray input signal is HIGH, but in Gray code when it's LOW. Note that the connections are far easier to make if you zoom in to 150% magnification, or more.

Fig. 6.30 *Finite state machine to count in binary or Gray*

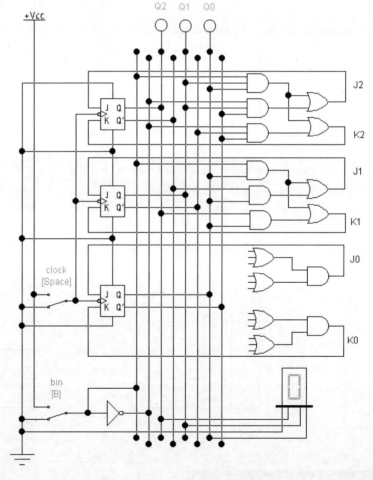

Note that when counting in Gray the seven-segment display should go through the sequence 0, 1, 3, 2, 6, 7, 5, 4, 0 . . . □

XPLA

The XCR5032 chip used on the demonstration target board contains flip-flops that can be configured either as D-types or T-types, but not as JKs. (The exercise in Chapter 5 – Figure 5.12 – effectively built a JK from a D-type. You may care to investigate the **.ph1** code generated from the listing of Figure 5.12 to see how it does it.) There is little point, therefore in trying to implement the design of Figure 6.30 in PHDL. This does not mean that a design with the same overall behaviour cannot be implemented, however. The listing below shows one way of achieving the required result.

Fig. 6.31 *PHDL code for 3-bit binary/Gray code counter*

```
MODULE   counter
TITLE    '3-bit binary/Gray code counter'

DECLARATIONS
Clock,reset,binary pin 43,14,4;
Q2..Q0                 pin 16,17,18 istype 'reg';
Q = [Q2..Q0];

EQUATIONS

Q.clk = Clock;
Q.ar = reset;
when binary==1 then Q.d = Q + 1;
else
   {
   when Q == 0 then Q.d = 1;
   else when Q == 1 then Q.d = 3;
   else when Q == 2 then Q.d = 6;
   else when Q == 3 then Q.d = 2;
   else when Q == 4 then Q.d = 0;
   else when Q == 5 then Q.d = 4;
   else when Q == 6 then Q.d = 7;
   else when Q == 7 then Q.d = 5;
   }

END
```

When the system is required to count up in binary, use is made of the high-level language syntax used before. Thus:

```
when binary==1 then Q.d = Q + 1;
```

This defines the next state (Q.d) as always one more than the current state (Q).

No such neat syntax is available to express the next state when the system is supposed to count in Gray code. The solution here is to list all possible states, from Q == 0 to Q == 7, and just tell the system what the next state (Q.d) is. Note the use of the braces to sort out the structure of the logic.

This solution is OK for a small counter, such as this 3-bit example. It would be a little tedious to type the 65,535 **else** statements for, say, a 16-bit system, however.

State diagrams

For complex systems it is sometimes convenient to illustrate the required behaviour graphically, using what's known as a 'state diagram'. The state diagram for the 3-bit binary/Gray code counter is shown in Figure 6.32.

Fig. 6.32 *Counting in binary (1 arrows) or Gray (0 arrows)*

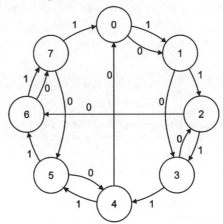

The PHDL language supports syntax for implementing state diagrams. The listing below shows the format, using the binary/Gray counter again as an example.

Fig. 6.33 *Code for binary/Gray code counter, using state diagram syntax*

```
MODULE   counter
TITLE    'Binary/Gray code counter using state_diagram syntax'

DECLARATIONS
Clock,reset,binary  pin 43,14,4;
Q2..Q0              pin 16,17,18 istype 'reg';
Q = [Q2..Q0];

EQUATIONS

Q.clk = Clock;
Q.ar = reset;

state_diagram Q;

state 0: goto 1;
state 1: if binary then 2 else 3;
state 2: if binary then 3 else 6;
state 3: if binary then 4 else 2;
state 4: if binary then 5 else 0;
state 5: if binary then 6 else 4;
state 6: goto 7;
state 7: if binary then 0 else 5;

END
```

In the listing of Figure 6.33 the line `state_diagram Q;` announces the state diagram, and that the 3-bit register Q (consisting of flip-flops Q2..Q0) is to be used to implement the state machine.

The eight `state` lines define the behaviour of the state machine. Note the use of `goto` where the next state is unconditional on any other signals. Note also the use of the `if... then... else` structure where the next state does depend on other signals. (You need to remember to use `if... then... else` to describe the required behaviour of state machines, but `when... then... else` for describing other logic.)

The code of Figure 6.33 produces exactly the same optimised equations as that of Figure 6.31.

State machine with output decoder

None of the state machines discussed so far has required an output decoder: the output of the state register itself has been taken as the output of the entire system. In the next example, however, the states themselves are of no particular interest, but are just a means to an end. The problem solved by this example is how to detect a 1-0-1 sequence in a stream of serial data.

Here's the state diagram – see Figure 6.34.

Fig. 6.34 *State diagram for 1-0-1 sequence detector*

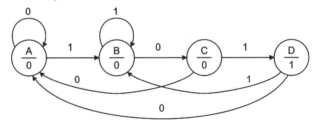

State A is the initial state: nothing has happened so far. The value below the line within each state shows the output of the system – 0 for state A.

The arrows show what happens depending on the input signal. Thus, if the input signal is 0 then the system just stays in state A, but if it's a 1 then we go to state B, since this could be the beginning of a 1-0-1 sequence.

The system still outputs a 0 in state B, of course. If a 0 comes along the system moves to state C since we are two bits through to the sought for sequence. If a 1 arrives while in state B you might think the system should go back to state A but this latest 1 could itself be the start of a 1-0-1 sequence so the correct thing to do is stay in state B.

From state C a 1 signifies that the 1-0-1 sequence has been detected, so the system transitions to state D, and outputs a 1 to signal the fact. A 0 at state C is disaster, so we go right back to state A.

The options from state D are back to A if a 0 arrives, but B if it's a 1.

It can take a great deal of effort to get the state diagram correct for a complex system, but from there on the steps are fairly straightforward. The first is to create a present-state/next-state table. This just lists what the next state is, given the logic level on the input signal, S. See Figure 6.35.

Fig. 6.35 *Present-state/next-state table for 1-0-1 detector*

input (S)	present state	next state
0	A	A
0	B	C
0	C	A
0	D	A
1	A	B
1	B	B
1	C	D
1	D	B

Thus row 1 shows that the system stays in state A if the input signal is 0, while row 5 shows it going from state A to state B if the input is 1.

The next step is to allocate codes to the states. For this example, binary coding will be used: A = 00; B = 01; C = 10 and D = 11. A 2-bit system is sufficient to code this 4-state machine, and the two flip-flops could be D-, T- or JK-types. Using D-types is the most straightforward in terms of design effort, although neater circuits are sometimes possible with the other types. Labelling the MSB flip-flop Q1, with input D1, and the LSB flip-flop Q0, with input D0, gives a new version of the present-state/next-state table. See Figure 6.36.

Fig. 6.36 *Present-state/next-state table encoded in binary*

input S	present state Q1	present state Q0	next state D1	next state D0
0	0	0	0	0
0	0	1	1	0
0	1	0	0	0
0	1	1	0	0
1	0	0	0	1
1	0	1	0	1
1	1	0	1	1
1	1	1	0	1

We can now devise circuitry to generate the D1 and D0 signals. Figure 6.36 shows that D0 can be generated directly from the input signal, S. D1 isn't quite so straightforward but a Karnaugh map may help – see Figure 6.37.

Fig. 6.37 *Karnaugh map for D1*

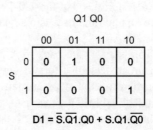

$$D1 = \bar{S}.\bar{Q1}.Q0 + S.Q1.\bar{Q0}$$

It turns out that the Karnaugh map reveals that no minimisation is possible. We now have the information to create a circuit that will obey the state diagram of Figure 6.34. Two D-type flip-flops are needed, and the circuitry to drive the D inputs (the next-state logic) has been derived above. The only additional task is to make an output signal that goes HIGH when machine state D is reached. This is the 'output decoder' of Figure 6.1. In this case a 2-input AND gate will do, since both Q1 and Q0 are HIGH in state D.

PRACTICAL EXERCISE 6.4

Electronics Workbench
Figure 6.38 is an Electronics Workbench implementation of the 1-0-1 detector.

Fig. 6.38   *1-0-1 detector*

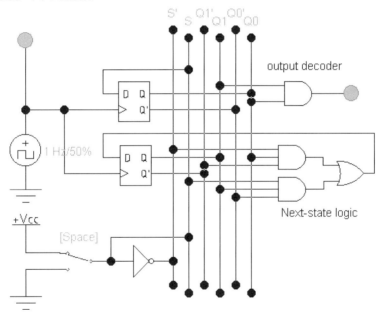

The clock is a 1Hz square wave. To make the output of the circuit go HIGH you need to control the input signal (with the Space bar) so that it's HIGH for one active clock edge, then LOW for an edge, then HIGH again. Slow the clock down if you can't quite see what's happening.   □

XPLA
The state machine syntax of PHDL allows the state machine of Figure 6.34 to be described directly. The XPLA software can then do all the hard work of generating present-state/next-state tables and minimising the equations.
    This is similar to the previous listing (Figure 6.33) except that the states are named A, B, C and D rather than numbered 0, 1, 2 and 3. This has been done simply

Fig. 6.39 *PHDL code to implement 1-0-1 detector*

```
MODULE  detector
TITLE    '1-0-1 detector. See Figure 6.34'

DECLARATIONS
Clock,S,clock_out,output  pin 43,11,16,27;
Q1,Q0                     node istype 'reg';
Q  =  [Q1,Q0];
A  =  [0,0];
B  =  [0,1];
C  =  [1,0];
D  =  [1,1];

EQUATIONS

Q.clk  =  Clock;
clock_out  =  Clock;
output  =  (Q==D);

state_diagram Q;

state A:  if S  then  B  else  A;
state B:  if S  then  B  else  C;
state C:  if S  then  D  else  A;
state D:  if S  then  B  else  A;

END
```

to show the parallel between the PHDL listing and the graphical representation of Figure 6.34. Because of this it has been necessary, within the **DECLARATIONS** section, to define how the various states are to be encoded.

Note the way the **output** signal is generated. Alternative syntax options are: **when Q==D then output = 1;** or simply **output = Q1 & Q0;** Enter the code, save and compile. Take a look at the optimised equations that have been generated – you should find that D1 is generated as per Figure 6.37, that D0 is simply connected to S, and the output is the AND of Q1 and Q0. □

Fit and download the design to the target board. Slow the clock down to about 1Hz and, using the microswitch to control signal S, see if you can get the output LED (the right-hand one) to light up. Note that the microswitch defaults to HIGH, but inputs a LOW when pressed. Challenge your friends to see who can cope reliably with the fastest clock! □

As it stands, the system designed from Figure 6.34 does not allow 'overlapping' patterns. In other words, the output would only go HIGH once if the sequence 1-0-1-0-1 were input. See if you can make a system that *does* allow overlapping. Its output should go HIGH when the last 1 is clocked in as well as the middle 1. You will have to start by re-defining the state diagram: the equivalent of Figure 6.34. Next, draw up the present-state/next-state table (like Figure 6.35), the encoded present/next-state table (like Figure 6.36), devise minimised circuitry and amend the Electronics Workbench file. □

Redesign the XPLA system as well, going straight from the amended state diagram to the PHDL code. □

Flashy turn indicator: a Mealy type finite state machine

The 1-0-1 detector is a Moore type state machine since the output depends purely on the state of the machine. The next FSM example in this chapter is a Mealy type since the output will depend on both the state of the machine and the input signals. The state diagram is shown in Figure 6.40.

Fig. 6.40 *State diagram for flashy turn indicator*

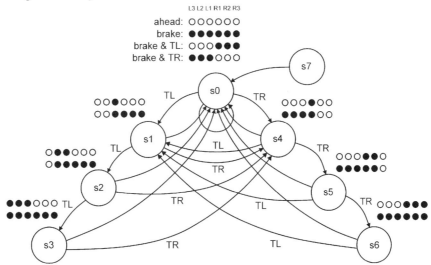

Figure 6.40 illustrates the various states and the required transitions; the blobs show how the six output indicator lamps should behave. The different rows of output blobs show what should happen given different input conditions. The top row of blobs shows what should happen provided the brake pedal is *not* pressed. When turning right, for example, the TR signal will be active so the machine will cycle through states s0, s4, s5, s6, s0 ... and the right-hand set of indicator lamps will progressively light up. When the brake signal *is* active, the other indicators light up as well, as shown in the bottom row of blobs.

State s0 is the straight-ahead state and slightly more complicated; the top row of blobs shows that normally no lights should light up, but they should all do so when the brake pedal is pressed (second row of blobs). The third and fourth rows show what should happen when braking and turning left or right respectively.

The labels on the transition arrows show that the TR signal controls turning right, while TL is for turning left. Transition arrows without labels are the default, i.e. neither turning right nor left.

Seven states are needed for this system, and they will be coded using a 3-bit encoder. The spare eighth state (s7) is not used but has an unconditional transition to s0 just in case the state is entered accidentally. The block diagram for the system is given in Figure 6.41.

Fig. 6.41 *Block diagram for flashy turn indicator*

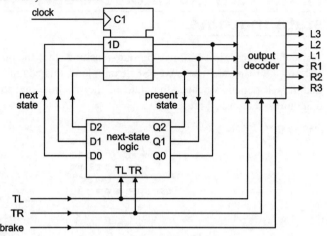

Fig. 6.42 *Encoded next-state table for flashy turn indicator*

	TL	TR	Q2	Q1	Q0	D2	D1	D0
0	0	0	0	0	0	0	0	0
1	0	0	0	0	1	0	0	0
2	0	0	0	1	0	0	0	0
3	0	0	0	1	1	0	0	0
4	0	0	1	0	0	0	0	0
5	0	0	1	0	1	0	0	0
6	0	0	1	1	0	0	0	0
7	0	0	1	1	1	0	0	0
8	0	1	0	0	0	1	0	0
9	0	1	0	0	1	1	0	0
10	0	1	0	1	0	1	0	0
11	0	1	0	1	1	1	0	0
12	0	1	1	0	0	1	0	1
13	0	1	1	0	1	1	1	0
14	0	1	1	1	0	0	0	0
15	0	1	1	1	1	0	0	0
16	1	0	0	0	0	0	0	1
17	1	0	0	0	1	0	1	0
18	1	0	0	1	0	0	1	1
19	1	0	0	1	1	0	0	0
20	1	0	1	0	0	0	0	1
21	1	0	1	0	1	0	0	1
22	1	0	1	1	0	0	0	1
23	1	0	1	1	1	0	0	0
24	1	1	0	0	0	×	×	×
25	1	1	0	0	1	×	×	×
26	1	1	0	1	0	×	×	×
27	1	1	0	1	1	×	×	×
28	1	1	1	0	0	×	×	×
29	1	1	1	0	1	×	×	×
30	1	1	1	1	0	×	×	×
31	1	1	1	1	1	×	×	×

The design of the next-state logic and the design of the output decoder are tackled separately. Taking the next-state logic first, there are five input signals, so the next-state table will have 32 rows. It is shown in Figure 6.42, with the states encoded in binary order (s0 = 000, s1 = 001, etc.). Row 0 shows state s0 staying in s0 when neither TL nor TR is active. The next seven rows show the system returning to state s0 from whatever state it is in when both TL and TR cease to be active.

In row 8 the TR signal is active, so the system moves from s0 to s4. Rows 9, 10 and 11 show the transitions from the turning left states (i.e. s1, s2 and s3) to the first of the turn right states (s4). The remaining rows up to row 23 are interpreted in similar fashion. The last eight rows have 'don't-care × symbols' since we assume that it will not be possible to generate a TR *and* a TL signal at the same time.

Devising minimised expressions for D2, D1 and D0 would be a little tedious to perform manually. A five-variable Karnaugh map (as per Figure 3.20) or the Quine–McCluskey method could be used for each one. A less tedious approach is to use the Electronics Workbench facility to find simplified expressions, as explained in Chapter 3 (practical exercise 3.1). The results are:

$$D2 = TR.\overline{Q2} + TR.\overline{Q1}$$
$$D1 = TR.Q2.\overline{Q1}.Q0 + TL.\overline{Q2}.\overline{Q1}.Q0 + TL.\overline{Q2}.Q1.\overline{Q0}$$
$$D0 = TR.Q2.\overline{Q1}.\overline{Q0} + TL.Q2.\overline{Q1} + TL.\overline{Q0}$$

The design of the next-state logic is thus complete.

The output decoder has six inputs, so requires a 64-row table to be fully defined. Making use of 'don't-care × symbols' on both the input and output sides, it is shown in Figure 6.43.

Figure 6.43 reflects the output requirements (the blobs) as shown on the state diagram of Figure 6.40. Row 0 states that, so long as the brake isn't pressed, none of the output indicators should light up, even if you are turning. Rows 1, 2 and 3 show the

Fig. 6.43 *Output decoder truth table for flashy turn indicator*

	Q2	Q1	Q0	brake	TL	TR	L3	L2	L1	R1	R2	R3
0	0	0	0	0	×	×	0	0	0	0	0	0
1	0	0	0	1	0	0	1	1	1	1	1	1
2	0	0	0	1	0	1	1	1	1	0	0	0
3	0	0	0	1	1	0	0	0	0	1	1	1
4	0	0	0	1	1	1	×	×	×	×	×	×
5	0	0	1	0	×	×	0	0	1	0	0	0
6	0	0	1	1	×	×	0	0	1	1	1	1
7	0	1	0	0	×	×	0	1	1	0	0	0
8	0	1	0	1	×	×	0	1	1	1	1	1
9	0	1	1	0	×	×	1	1	1	0	0	0
10	0	1	1	1	×	×	1	1	1	1	1	1
11	1	0	0	0	×	×	0	0	0	1	0	0
12	1	0	0	1	×	×	1	1	1	1	0	0
13	1	0	1	0	×	×	0	0	0	1	1	0
14	1	0	1	1	×	×	1	1	1	1	1	0
15	1	1	0	0	×	×	0	0	0	1	1	1
16	1	1	0	1	×	×	1	1	1	1	1	1
17	1	1	1	×	×	×	×	×	×	×	×	×

situation if the brake is pressed and the various possible turns (no turn, turn right or turn left) are taking place. Row 4 takes care of state 0, brake pressed, and the impossible turning left and turning right situation.

Rows 5 to 16 enumerate states s1 to s6, and the two possible levels of the brake signal for each case. For these states the logic levels on the TL and TR signals are irrelevant, as far as the output signals are concerned.

The last row deals with state s7, which should never be reached.

Using the truth-table-to-simplified-Boolean-expression facility of Electronics Workbench, the following expressions can be derived for L3 to R3:

$$L3 = \overline{Q1}.\overline{Q0}.brake.\overline{TL} + Q1.Q0 + Q2.brake$$
$$L2 = \overline{Q0}.brake.\overline{TL} + \overline{Q2}.Q1 + Q2.brake$$
$$L1 = \overline{Q2}.Q1 + \overline{Q2}.Q0 + brake.\overline{TL} + Q2.brake$$
$$R1 = Q1.brake + brake.\overline{TR} + Q0.brake + Q2$$
$$R2 = \overline{Q2}.brake.\overline{TR} + Q2.Q0 + Q0.brake + Q2.Q1 + Q1.brake$$
$$R3 = \overline{Q2}.brake.\overline{TR} + \overline{Q2}.Q0.brake + Q2.Q1 + Q1.brake$$

PRACTICAL EXERCISE 6.5

Electronics Workbench

Fig. 6.44 *Flashy turn indicator*

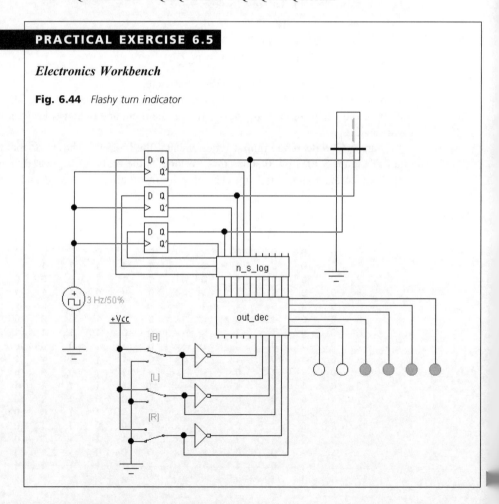

The design is now complete. Figure 6.44 shows an Electronics Workbench implementation. The next-state logic and output decoder circuit blocks were drawn out normally but then captured as sub-circuits, otherwise there would not be sufficient room to draw the complete schematic. Double-clicking on a sub-circuit reveals what's inside. The connections along the top and bottom of each sub-circuit are as follows (left to right): $\overline{Q2}$, Q2, $\overline{Q1}$, Q1, $\overline{Q0}$, Q0, $\overline{brake}$, brake, $\overline{TL}$, TL, $\overline{TR}$ and TR.

The diagram shows the system in state s1 (first of the turn left states) with the brake pedal pressed. Run the simulation (the Electronics Workbench file is **fig6_44.ewb**) and verify that the circuit behaves in accordance with the state diagram, Figure 6.40. □

XPLA

Even using the Electronics Workbench facility for generating Quine–McCluskey simplified Boolean expressions, getting from the state diagram to the circuit diagram for the flashy turn indicator takes a considerable amount of time and effort. Building the circuit in hardware would take a lot of further work. By contrast, the XPLA system allows the design to be entered using state diagram and truth-table syntax, and after that the design process is automatic: just compile, fit (simulate if you want to) and download.

Figure 6.45 shows the PHDL listing for the system.

The state diagram part of the listing deals with the way the system moves from one state to another and is a straightforward description of state transitions part of Figure 6.40. The truth table defines how the outputs depend on the state of the machine, and on the three input signals. It is almost exactly the same as Figure 6.43, except that rows 4 and 17 have been omitted. Note the use of **.x.** for the 'don't care' condition. When the compiler gets to work, the state diagram part of the listing is used to create the next-state logic, while the truth table part creates the output decoder.

The listing is available on the CD (**fig6_45.phd**). Load the file, compile, fit and download to the demonstration target board. You should find that it works as expected, with the microswitch acting as the brake pedal, and the three-position slide switch as the indicator. You can control the speed of the lights by the potentiometer near the 555 timer. □

If you examine the optimised equations you will find that they are similar but not identical to the ones derived from Figures 6.42 and 6.43. The differences arise

Fig. 6.45 *PHDL listing for flashy turn indicator*

```
MODULE  Flashy
TITLE   'Flashy turn indicator'
/* See Figure 6.40                                          */

DECLARATIONS
BRAKE,TL,TR,CLK   pin 14,2,1,43;       "inputs
L3..L1            pin 16,17,18;        "outputs
R1..R3            pin 25,26,27;
```

Fig. 6.45 *(cont'd)*

```
q2..q0              node istype 'reg' ; "internal nodes
state_reg = [q2..q0] ;

EQUATIONS
state_reg.clk = CLK ;

STATE_DIAGRAM  state_reg;
STATE 0:           "straight ahead
  if TL then 1
  else if TR then 4
  else 0;
STATE 1:           "turn left, first state
  if TL then 2
  else if TR then 4
  else 0;
STATE 2:           "turn left, second state
  if TL then 3
  else if TR then 4
  else 0;
STATE 3:           "turn left, third state
  if TR then 4
  else 0;
STATE 4:           "turn right, first state
  if TR then 5
  else if TL then 1
  else 0;
STATE 5:           "turn right, second state
  if TR then 6
  else if TL then 1
  else 0;
STATE 6:           "turn right, third state
  if TL then 1
  else 0;
STATE 7:
  goto 0;          "should never reach state 7

TRUTH_TABLE
  ([state_reg,BRAKE,  TR,   TL] -> [L3, L2, L1, R1, R2, R3])
   [ 0 ,        0 , .x., .x.] -> [ 0,  0,  0,  0,  0,  0];
   [ 0 ,        1 ,   0,   0] -> [ 1,  1,  1,  1,  1,  1];
   [ 0 ,        1 ,   0,   1] -> [ 0,  0,  0,  1,  1,  1];
   [ 0 ,        1 ,   1,   0] -> [ 1,  1,  1,  0,  0,  0];
   [ 1 ,        0 , .x., .x.] -> [ 0,  0,  1,  0,  0,  0];
   [ 1 ,        1 , .x., .x.] -> [ 0,  0,  1,  1,  1,  1];
   [ 2 ,        0 , .x., .x.] -> [ 0,  1,  1,  0,  0,  0];
   [ 2 ,        1 , .x., .x.] -> [ 0,  1,  1,  1,  1,  1];
   [ 3 ,        0 , .x., .x.] -> [ 1,  1,  1,  0,  0,  0];
   [ 3 ,        1 , .x., .x.] -> [ 1,  1,  1,  1,  1,  1];
   [ 4 ,        0 , .x., .x.] -> [ 0,  0,  0,  1,  0,  0];
   [ 4 ,        1 , .x., .x.] -> [ 1,  1,  1,  1,  0,  0];
   [ 5 ,        0 , .x., .x.] -> [ 0,  0,  0,  1,  1,  0];
   [ 5 ,        1 , .x., .x.] -> [ 1,  1,  1,  1,  1,  0];
   [ 6 ,        0 , .x., .x.] -> [ 0,  0,  0,  1,  1,  1];
   [ 6 ,        1 , .x., .x.] -> [ 1,  1,  1,  1,  1,  1];

END
```

because the XPLA system uses a different algorithm from the Quine–McCluskey one to minimise Boolean expressions. The listing shown in Figure 6.46 has the equations entered directly and when compiled, fitted and downloaded gives a system that behaves exactly as before.

Fig. 6.46 *Flashy turn indicator using Quine–McCluskey derived equations*

```
MODULE  Flashy
TITLE   'Flashy turn indicator'
/* From Quine-McCluskey derived equations              */

DECLARATIONS
BRAKE,TL,TR,CLK  pin 14,2,1,43;           "inputs
L3..L1           pin 16,17,18;            "outputs
R1..R3           pin 25,26,27;
Q2..Q0           node istype 'reg' ;      "internal nodes
state_reg = [Q2..Q0];

EQUATIONS
state_reg.clk = CLK ;

"next-state logic
Q2.d = TR & !Q2
     # TR & !Q1;
Q1.d = TR & Q2 & !Q1 & Q0
     # TL & !Q2 & !Q1 & Q0
     #TL & !Q2 & Q1 & !Q0;
Q0.d = TR & Q2 & !Q1 & !Q0
     # TL & Q2 & !Q1
     # TL & !Q0;

"output decoder
L3 = !Q1 & !Q0 & BRAKE & !TL
   # Q1 & Q0
   # Q2 & BRAKE;
L2 = !Q0 & BRAKE & !TL
   # !Q2 & Q1
   # Q2 & BRAKE;
L1 = !Q2 & Q1
   # !Q2 & Q0
   # BRAKE & !TL
   # Q2 & BRAKE;
R1 = Q1 & BRAKE
   # BRAKE & !TR
   # Q0 & BRAKE
   # Q2;
R2 = !Q2 & BRAKE & !TR
   # Q2 & Q0
   # Q0 & BRAKE
   # Q2 & Q1
   # Q1 & BRAKE;
R3 = !Q2 & BRAKE & !TR
   # !Q2 & Q0 & BRAKE
   # Q2 & Q1
   # Q1 & BRAKE;

END
```

Clock generators

The main topic of this chapter is the design of synchronous finite state machines. All such systems need a clock signal to drive the flip-flops that hold the state of the machine, so we now take a look at methods of generating such clock signals.

Relaxation oscillators

Perhaps the simplest way to generate a clock signal is to use a 'relaxation oscillator' configured around an inverter. An Electronics Workbench implementation of such a circuit is shown in Figure 6.47.

Fig. 6.47 *Relaxation oscillator using 74HC Schmitt inverter*

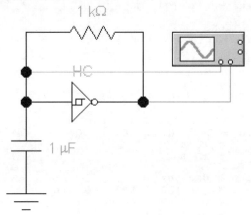

The circuit is built around a single Schmitt-input inverter, and the way it works is quite straightforward. Suppose you've just turned the circuit on and the capacitor is discharged. The input to the inverter is thus LOW. The output will therefore be HIGH, and the capacitor will charge up, with a time constant of CR seconds. (1ms for the component values shown.) This continues until the capacitor voltage reaches the upper threshold of the Schmitt-trigger input (typically about 1.6V for 74HCT). See cursor 1 of Figure 6.48. At this point the input signal is regarded as HIGH so the output goes LOW, and the capacitor starts to discharge. (This is the 'relaxation' bit of the relaxation oscillator.) The discharge continues until the capacitor voltage drops to the lower threshold of the Schmitt-trigger input (typically about 0.9V for 74HCT) – see cursor 2 in Figure 6.48. The input signal to the inverter is now regarded as LOW again, and the cycle repeats.

The frequency of such a clock depends on the capacitor and resistor values, and upon the going-up and going-down threshold voltages of the particular device. You can see from Figure 6.48 that the overall period of the oscillator is about 0.8 time constants, giving a frequency of 1250Hz with the component values shown.

Fig. 6.48 *Electronics Workbench oscilloscope used to monitor waveforms around Schmitt-trigger inverter relaxation oscillator.*

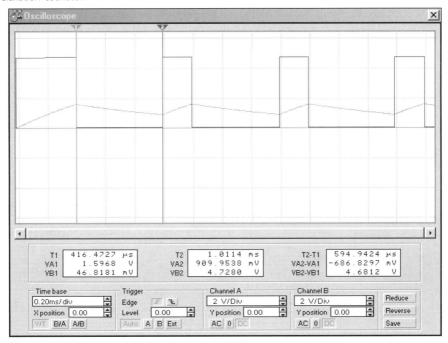

The clock generator circuit used on the demonstration board is another relaxation oscillator, but based on the 555 timer IC. Figure 6.49 gives the circuit diagram.

The operation of this circuit is almost identical to that of the previous circuit, except that the threshold voltage of the 555 timer sets the upper threshold. This is two thirds of the supply voltage, i.e. 3.33V. Similarly, the trigger voltage of the 555 timer sets the

Fig. 6.49 *Relaxation oscillator using 555 timer*

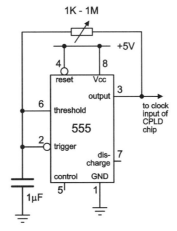

lower threshold, and this is one third of the supply voltage, i.e. 1.67V. Since the capacitor has to charge up and discharge further, the 555 timer version of the relaxation oscillator has a longer period of oscillation than the inverter – about 1.4 time constants as opposed to about 0.8. With the component values shown, when the variable resistor is set to minimum then the period of oscillation is 1.4ms; set to maximum it is 1.4s.

A third type of relaxation oscillator is built around two inverters, but the advantage of this circuit over the single-inverter circuit of Figure 6.47 is that it does not need to have Schmitt-trigger input characteristics. In fact, it is possible to build this circuit using two inverters inside the CPLD chip, and a single external capacitor and resistor. Figure 6.50 shows how.

Fig. 6.50 *Two-inverter relaxation oscillator*

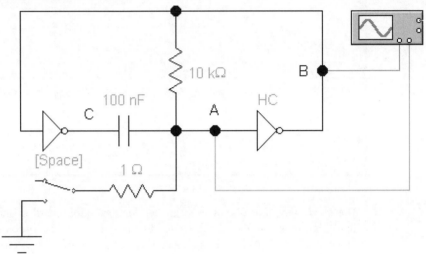

The switch and 1Ω resistor are present simply to persuade the simulator to start the proper action of the circuit. In reality the circuit starts up spontaneously and these components are not required. Similarly, the left and right inverters are shown here as different technologies, but this is also a trick to help get the simulation to come to life.

If you wish to run the simulation, start with the switch closed. You should get an oscilloscope screen-full with trace A at 0V and B at 5V, and the simulation should then pause. Now set the switch open circuit and click the **Resume** button – you should now get an oscilloscope display similar to Figure 6.51.

The curvy trace is signal A and the square wave is B. Signal C is not shown, but is simply the complement of signal B.

The action of the circuit is a bit more difficult to understand than the previous two circuits because the charging and discharging of the capacitor is less easy to visualise. Suppose the capacitor is initially discharged, with points C and A being both at 0V. Signal B will thus sit at 5V. Current will flow down through the 10kΩ resistor, charging up the capacitor, with the voltage at point A rising towards 5V with a $C \times R$ (1ms with the circuit values shown) time constant. This is shown at the left side of the oscilloscope display in Figure 6.51.

Fig. 6.51 *Waveforms at points A and B of Figure 6.50*

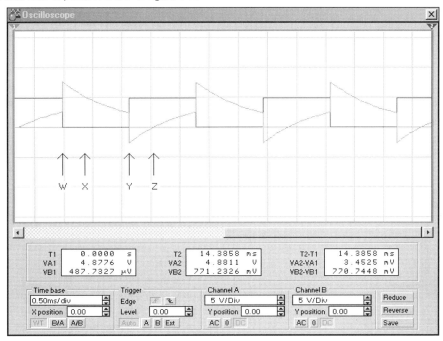

At position W on the figure the voltage at A reaches the threshold level for the logic family used, so node B switches from HIGH to LOW, causing node C to switch from LOW to HIGH. This fast, positive going 5V edge at C is AC-coupled through the capacitor to node A, giving the fast, positive-going 5V edge displayed on A's waveform. A is now more positive than B, so the capacitor first discharges through the 10kΩ resistor until both plates are at 5V (see position X on Figure 6.51) then charges up with A going negative with respect to C.

This situation persists until node A falls to the threshold voltage for the logic family being used, at which point the logic levels all swap. This is position Y on the waveform. B goes from LOW to HIGH, C goes from HIGH to LOW, and this fast-negative-going 5V edge is AC coupled through to A. A is now more negative than B, so first the capacitor discharges until both A and C are at 0V (see point Z on the waveform), and then charges up again with A going positive compared to C. This is where we started the description of the circuit action, and the cycle repeats indefinitely.

Note that the capacitor is charged in both directions, so a non-polarised type should be used. Also, the waveforms are not quite as depicted by Electronics Workbench because of the input protection diodes on the logic. These prevent the signal at node A from going quite so far positive and negative as shown, so the period of oscillation is reduced. With the component values shown, and using the CPLD chip to provide the two inverters, a period of about 1.7ms is obtained, as opposed to the 2.3ms measured on the simulation.

Crystal oscillators

Relaxation oscillators are cheap, reliable and easy to build, but may not have high enough predictability or stability for your application. Oscillators based on small crystals of quartz provide excellent accuracy and stability and are used extensively in applications where precise timekeeping is required.

Quartz crystals oscillate mechanically. Being piezoelectric, they generate oscillating electric charges as they do so. They can be modelled electrically as a series RLC circuit with a further parallel capacitor, giving rise to the possibility of both series resonance and parallel resonance at closely spaced frequencies. In between these two frequencies the behaviour of the circuit changes very rapidly with frequency, leading to circuits possessing very high Q factor and very precise frequency characteristics.

Chips such as microprocessors have internal circuitry designed to work with crystals, so you just decide what frequency you want for your system clock and buy a crystal with that frequency stamped on the case. You put the components together in accordance with the microprocessor data sheet (a couple of low value capacitors are usually the only additional parts needed), turn the circuit on, and everything works.

Designing a crystal oscillator circuit from scratch is a lot trickier, and the best advice is to buy in ready-made crystal oscillator modules. These have the crystal built in, are available (like crystals) in standard frequencies, such as 32.768kHz (divide by 2, 15 times to get exactly 1Hz), 1.000MHz, 3.579545MHz (colour sub-carrier frequency in NTSC TV systems) and so on. Some modules are programmable allowing you to divide down the basic crystal frequency to give a choice of, for instance, 12MHz, 6MHz, 3MHz, 1.5MHz, 750kHz, 375kHz, 187.5kHz, 93.75kHz or 46.875kHz.

Asynchronous state machines

Most of this chapter has been concerned with a formal method for designing state machines that use synchronously clocked flip-flops as the storage element. The flip-flops can be D-type, T-type or JK and the methodology is automated in many development systems such as XPLA. The need for a clock, independent of the other input signals, is a feature of such machines, but it is not always a natural feature of design situations. For example, in an electronic lock, where a user has to press various pushbuttons in a particular sequence, the requirement is simply that the buttons are pressed in the right order, not that the presses are synchronised to a clock. Similarly, coins entering a vending machine will arrive at random intervals, unrelated to any system clock.

The need thus arises for a design method for creating reliable *asynchronous* machines. Generally, asynchronous systems are more difficult to design than synchronous machines since there is a much greater possibility of logic races. (We saw the effect of such races in the asynchronous counters discussed in the previous chapter.) Satisfactory asynchronous systems can be designed, however, using a process similar to that used for synchronous machines: the required behaviour is first represented as a state diagram, then the transitions within the diagram are tabulated. Next the general method of implementing the design is decided (e.g. whether to use flip-flops and, if so, what type), then the combinational logic circuits are designed that drive the flip-flops. Simulation and hardware testing complete the process.

Asynchronous designs fall into two categories: those where the various input signals arise as logic levels, and those where the inputs are non-overlapping pulses. An example of the first is the electronic lock while the vending machine is a pulse-driven system.

Level-driven asynchronous design example

Suppose a (rather simple) electronic lock has two inputs A and B, and the sequence to open the lock is 00,01,11,10 on AB. After entering this sequence the output L should go HIGH to operate the lock mechanism, but any other sequence should result in the warning signal W going permanently HIGH.

State diagram

Fig. 6.52   *State diagram for electronic lock*

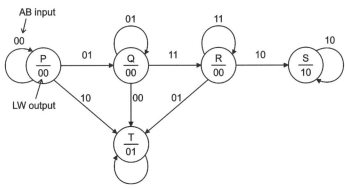

Although the state diagram for this asynchronous machine looks similar to that for a synchronous system, there are some important details that are different. The first is that not all the possible input combinations are indicated. The initial state, state P, has no transition arrow for the case where the input is 11, for instance. The reason for this is that it is assumed that it is not possible for both input bits to change simultaneously from 00 to 11. In the case of this electronic lock, with its separately operated input switches, it would not be possible for them both to be pressed at exactly the same time: one or other would win, even if only by a few nanoseconds. If B is first the system will go to state Q, otherwise to state T. Similarly, state Q has no exit arrow for 10, and R no arrow for 00.

The other difference is that every state has to have a holding 'sling', i.e. a transition arrow leaving and returning to the same state. This is required to give stability to the states. In the case of states P, Q, R and S the input condition attached to the holding sling is the same as the condition that causes the transition to that state; for state T the holding sling is unconditional on the input, i.e. once in state T you can't escape.

Figure 6.52 is incomplete: what happens after reaching state S? For illustrative purposes let's leave it for the time being as 'don't care', but some thought ought to be given for every eventuality in a real design. Possibly 00 would take the system back to the initial state P, while 11 would return it to state R. Another alternative would be an unconditional sling, with an additional reset signal being used to take the system back to state P from any other state.

Initial flow table

The next step in the design process is to turn the state diagram into a flow table. This initially allocates a physical state to each of the conceptual states of the state diagram, and shows how the input signals cause the system to change (flow) from one (physical) state to another. In the flow table shown in Figure 6.53 the conceptual states are labelled P, Q, R, S and T as per the state diagram, while the physical states are listed down the left of the table as F_0 to F_4. In addition some unstable, almost-states are given, labelled q, r, s and t. These are the short-lived states that exist while the system settles down following a change at an input. Short-lived state q leads to stable state Q, and so on. Finally, there are some don't care states, ×, which apply either when we don't care what the system does, or when it's impossible for the system to reach that state.

Fig. 6.53 *Flow table for electronic lock*

		AB input			
		00	01	11	10
physical state	F_0	P	q	×	t
	F_1	t	Q	r	×
	F_2	×	t	R	s
	F_3	×	×	×	S
	F_4	T	T	T	T

From the table you can see that when the system is in physical state F_0 and the input is 00, then the stable conceptual state P is implemented. If the input changes to 01, the system moves horizontally to almost-state q, then vertically to physical state F_1 and conceptual state Q. On the other hand, if the input changes from 00 to 10 then the flow is from P to t, then t to T (F_4). As discussed above, it's assumed that it is not possible for the input to change from 00 to 11, hence the × in the 11 column for physical state F_0.

The system output signals L and W are not shown on the flow table. The state diagram indicates that L should go HIGH when conceptual state S holds, i.e. physical state F_3 persists; similarly, physical state F_4 should cause signal W to go HIGH.

Reduced flow table

It is possible to merge a couple of the rows in Figure 6.53, and hence reduce the flow table to just four physical states. Physical state F_3 can be merged with F_2 since the don't-care ×s can be replaced with the t and R states, and almost-state s can be replaced with stable state S. The reduced flow table is shown in Figure 6.54.

Merging two conceptual states into one physical state means that the output signals cannot now be derived just from the physical state of the system. Signal L is required to

Fig. 6.54 *Reduced flow table for electronic lock*

	AB input			
	00	**01**	**11**	**10**
F_0	**P**	**q**	×	**t**
F_1	**t**	**Q**	**r**	×
F_2	×	**t**	**R**	**S**
F_4	**T**	**T**	**T**	**T**

(physical state on the left)

go HIGH when, and only when, in state S. It will have to be generated by checking that the system is in physical state F_2 *and* the input signal is 10. (The system has changed from being a Moore type of machine to a Mealy type.)

State assignment

The next job is to decide how the four physical states F_0, F_1, F_2 and F_4 will be assigned. A two-bit system will be sufficient to implement the four states. For synchronous systems the decision regarding which two-bit number should represent which state was fairly arbitrary, but for asynchronous systems the designer has to check for logic races.

If we allocate 00 to F_0, 01 to F_1, 10 to F_2 and 11 to F_4 then a race is likely to occur when changing from state r to state R since the system has physically to change from F_1 (01) to state F_2 (10). Both bits have to change, and there is no guarantee they will change simultaneously. There is a great danger of the system falling into the 11 (F_4, T) state and never getting out.

A better allocation is 00, 01, 11 and 10 respectively, for physical states F_0, F_1, F_2 and F_4. The r to R transition now involves just one bit changing so there is no possibility of a race. A new race has been introduced, however, when changing from t to T while the input is 00. This involves F_1 (01) becoming F_4 (10). Matters can be improved by changing the × in this column into a t. This will cater for the 01 – 11 – 10 ($F_1 - F_2 - F_4$) route. The 01 – 00 – 10 ($F_1 - F_0 - F_4$) route is still problematical since the system would fall into stable state P instead of transitioning from t to T. Let's press on with the design, however, despite this race worry, and see what the next stage involves.

Physical next-state tables

First, the reduced flow table (Figure 6.54) is translated into a next-state table, where the states are physically represented by the two-bit variable Q1,Q0 using the implementation $F_0 = P = 00$, $F_1 = Q = 01$, $F_2 = R = S = 11$ and $F_4 = T = 10$. For stable states (shown with upper-case letters in Figure 6.54) the next state is the same is the present one,

Fig. 6.55 *Next-state table for Q1,Q0*

	AB input			
	00	**01**	**11**	**10**
00	**00**	**01**	××	**10**
01	**10**	**01**	**11**	××
11	**10**	**10**	**11**	**11**
10	**10**	**10**	**10**	**10**

(Q1,Q0 on the left)

while for the unstable states (lower-case letters) the next state is the one indicated by the letter. Figure 6.55 shows the result.

The next step is to use Karnaugh maps to minimise the expressions for Q1 and Q0. It is a little easier to do this if the combined table of Figure 6.55 is split into separate maps – see Figures 6.56 and 6.57.

Fig. 6.56 *Karnaugh map for Q1. Q1 = A + Q1 + Q0.$\bar{B}$*

		AB input			
		00	01	11	10
Q1,Q0	00	0	0	×	1
	01	1	0	1	×
	11	1	1	1	1
	10	1	1	1	1

Fig. 6.57 *Karnaugh map for Q0. Q0 = Q0.A + $\overline{Q1}$.B*

		AB input			
		00	01	11	10
Q1,Q0	00	0	1	×	0
	01	0	1	1	×
	11	0	0	1	1
	10	0	0	0	0

Fig. 6.58 *Electronics Workbench implementation of electronic lock*

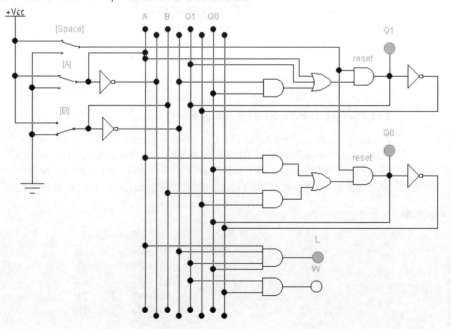

The L and W output signals can also be derived. Remember that L is true only in state S, which is physically implemented in state F_2 while the AB input is 10. F_2 itself is implemented with Q1,Q0 = 11. Thus $L = A.\overline{B}.Q1.Q0$. Similarly, W is true only in state T, which is physically implemented in state F_4 which is in turn implemented with Q1,Q0 = 10. Thus $W = Q1.\overline{Q0}$.

Circuit diagram

We now have all the equations for the variables, so can construct the circuit itself. Figure 6.58 shows an Electronics Workbench representation.

The circuit shown in Figure 6.58 has a reset facility that is provided by the two AND gates marked 'reset' and the Space bar-operated switch. When the switch is in the down position LOWs are forced through the AND gates to reset the system into the 00 (F_1, P) state.

PRACTICAL EXERCISE 6.6

Load the circuit (**fig6_58.ewb**) and run the simulation. Check that the lock will open (indicator L illuminates) after the sequence 00, 01, 11, 10 has been input on the AB switches (press B then A then B again). ☐

Check that any other sequence takes you to the T state (F_4, Q1,Q0 = 11) with indicator W alight. ☐

The worry discussed above when going from state t to state T when the input is 00 should be checked. Verify that the circuit does go to the alarm state, with the W indicator showing, if the sequence 00, 01, 00 is input on AB. This takes the system through states P, q → Q, t → T. ☐

Try re-designing the system to accept the sequence 00, 10, 00, 01. ☐

XPLA version of electronic lock

Fig. 6.59 *PHDL code for electronic lock*

```
MODULE   asynchronous
TITLE    'asynchronous  00,01,11,10  detector'

DECLARATIONS
A,B      pin 4,6;
Q1,Q0    pin 16,17;
L,W      pin 26,27;
reset    pin 11;

EQUATIONS

Q1 = reset & (A # Q1 # !B & Q0);
Q0 = reset & (A & Q0 # B & !Q1);
L = A & !B & Q1 & Q0;
W = Q1 & !Q0;

END
```

Figure 6.59 shows the PHDL version of the circuit shown in Figure 6.58, including the reset facility. The pin numbers are designed for the demonstration board, with the microswitch functioning as the reset, SW1 as input A and SW2 as input B. The two left-hand LEDs of the bar-graph display show the Q1,Q0 status, while the right-most LED shows the alarm signal, W. The 'open-the-lock' signal, L, is displayed on the LED next to W.

Unfortunately, switch bounce on SW1 and SW2 makes it impossible to input the correct sequence, but simulation shows that the system should behave correctly if de-bounced input signals could be generated. Note that the reset signal is active-LOW, so should remain HIGH after a short initial period LOW in the simulation.

If you wish to experiment with the hardware, enter the code, compile, fit and download. Now try setting both input switches HIGH then click the reset switch. When the reset is pressed the system is forced into the 00 state (P). When the reset is released the system follows the horizontal arrow shown in Figure 6.60 below to the unstable 11 state. Note that the ×s of Figure 6.55 have been replaced by 11s since this is how the ×s of Figures 6.56 and 6.57 were interpreted. The flow then follows the vertical arrow to the stable 11 state (R). Operating SW2 now allows the system to move horizontally to enter the other stable 11 state (S), causing the L output (open the lock) to go HIGH. Check that any other sequence of switch operations will lead to the 10 (T) state, with the alarm output (W) going active. □

Fig. 6.60 *Flow for electronic lock when reset is clicked and AB input is 11*

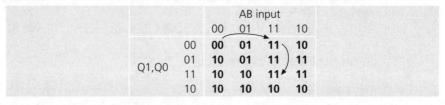

		AB input			
		00	01	11	10
	00	00	01	11	10
	01	10	01	11	11
Q1,Q0	11	10	10	11	11
	10	10	10	10	10

Pulse-driven asynchronous design example

The bouncy nature of the switch operation can be taken into account at the definition stage of the system as the following example illustrates. An electronic lock system should accept at least one pulse from input switch SW1, followed by at least one pulse on SW2, at least one on SW3, at least one on SW2, at least one on SW3, then at least one on SW1. The design assumes that only one switch will go HIGH at a time.

As before, the first step in the design process is to draw up a state transition diagram – see Figure 6.61.

Fig. 6.61 *State diagram for pulse version of electronic lock*

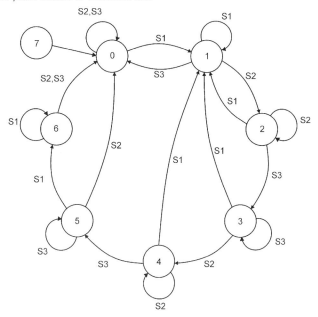

The sequence of actions on S1, S2 and S3 takes the system clockwise around Figure 6.61 from the reset state (state 0) through to the unlock state (state 6). This is a Moore-type machine in that the output signal should go HIGH when (and only when) the system occupies state 6. The system requires seven states, so a three-bit system will be needed to implement it. State 7 is the eighth, unused state.

In this example, each state (apart from 7) has a sling looping back to itself, but, unlike the previous example, the reason for these slings is to cater for the unpredictable switch bounce rather than to give stability to the states. Stability will be provided by the use of flip-flops – this example will need three T-type flip-flops. Each T input will be held permanently HIGH and the design process from here is to devise the three clock signals for the flip-flops. The pulse inputs will be positive going and we want the system to change from one state to another on the falling edge of these pulses, hence negative-edge triggered flip-flops will be needed.

Since flip-flops are to be used, we don't need to worry about the way physical states are assigned to the conceptual states of Figure 6.61, although some care will be needed to ensure that all clock signals arrive at their flip-flops simultaneously. Referring to the three flip-flops as Q2, Q1 and Q0, state 0 can be implemented as 0,0,0, state 1 as 0,0,1, . . . state 7 as 1,1,1.

Figure 6.62 tabulates the state diagram according to this scheme. It is partially completed – fill in the blanks. □

Fig. 6.62 *Present-state/next-state table derived from Figure 6.61*

	present state Q2,Q1,Q0	next state S1 = 1	S2 = 1	S3 = 1
0	000	001	000	000
1	001	001	010	
2	010	001		
3	011	001		
4	100	001		
5	101	110		
6	110	110		
7	111	000		

The next step in the design process is to work out which flip-flops need to toggle for each of the eight possible states and three possible inputs. (Remember that, although there are eight mathematically possible combinations of HIGHs and LOWs on the three input switches, the only three of practical interest are the ones where just one of the switches is HIGH.) For instance, if the present state is 000 and S1 is HIGH then Q0 needs to toggle to get to the next state, while Q1 and Q2 should remain un-clocked. If S2 or S3 is HIGH, none of the flip-flops needs to change. On the other hand, if the present state is 001 and S1 is HIGH nothing needs to change, but if S2 is HIGH flip-flops Q1 and Q0 both need clocking to make them toggle.

The partially completed table of Figure 6.63 has been derived from Figure 6.62 as described above. Using your completed version of Figure 6.62, complete Figure 6.63. □

Fig. 6.63 *Table showing which flip-flops need to toggle*

present state Q2,Q1,Q0	toggle? S1 = 1	S2 = 1	S3 = 1
000	001	000	000
001	000	011	
010	011		
011	010		
100	101		
101	011		
110	000		
111	111		

Fig. 6.64 *PHDL code for pulse-driven lock*

```
MODULE  asynch2
TITLE   'See figure 6.63'

DECLARATIONS
S1,S2, S3               pin 4,6,8;
reset                   pin 14;
z                       pin 16;
a,b,c,d,e,f,g pin 41,37,31,40,34,36,39;
tr                      pin 29;
Q2..Q0                  node;
clock2..clock0          node;
Q = [Q2..Q0];

EQUATIONS
tr = 1;                 "turn on left seven-segment display
Q.t = ^b111;            "Q.t = 1 sets just Q0.t to 1
Q.ar = reset;
Q2.clk = !clock2;       "for negative edge triggering
Q1.clk = !clock1;
Q0.clk = !clock0;
z = Q2 & Q1 & !Q0;      "unlock in state 6

truth_table([Q2,Q1,Q0, S1, S2, S3] -> [clock2, clock1, clock0]);
         [ 0, 0, 0,  1,.x.,.x.] -> [  0,       0,       1    ];
         [ 0, 0, 0,.x.,  1,.x.] -> [  0,       0,       0    ];
         [ 0, 0, 0,.x.,.x.,  1] -> [  0,       0,       0    ];
         [ 0, 0, 1,  1., x.,.x.] -> [  0,       0,       0    ];
         [ 0, 0, 1,.x.,  1,.x.] -> [  0,       1,       1    ];
         [ 0, 0, 1,.x.,.x.,  1] -> [  0,       0,       1    ];
         [ 0, 1, 0,  1,.x.,.x.] -> [  0,       1,       1    ];
         [ 0, 1, 0,.x.,  1,.x.] -> [  0,       0,       0    ];
         [ 0, 1, 0,.x.,.x.,  1] -> [  0,       0,       1    ];
         [ 0, 1, 1,  1,.x.,.x.] -> [  0,       1,       0    ];
         [ 0, 1, 1,.x.,  1,.x.] -> [  1,       1,       1    ];
         [ 0, 1, 1,.x.,.x.,  1] -> [  0,       0,       0    ];
         [ 1, 0, 0,  1,.x.,.x.] -> [  1,       0,       1    ];
         [ 1, 0, 0,.x.,  1,.x.] -> [  0,       0,       0    ];
         [ 1, 0, 0,.x.,.x.,  1] -> [  0,       0,       1    ];
         [ 1, 0, 1,  1,.x.,.x.] -> [  0,       1,       1    ];
         [ 1, 0, 1,.x.,  1,.x.] -> [  1,       0,       1    ];
         [ 1, 0, 1,.x.,.x.,  1] -> [  0,       0,       0    ];
         [ 1, 1, 0,  1,.x.,.x.] -> [  0,       0,       0    ];
         [ 1, 1, 0,.x.,  1,.x.] -> [  1,       1,       0    ];
         [ 1, 1, 0,.x.,.x.,  1] -> [  1,       1,       0    ];
         [ 1, 1, 1,  1,.x.,.x.] -> [  1,       1,       1    ];
         [ 1, 1, 1,.x.,  1,.x.] -> [  1,       1,       1    ];
         [ 1, 1, 1,.x.,.x.,  1] -> [  1,       1,       1    ];

truth_table (Q -> [a,b,c,d,e,f,g]);
         0 -> [1,1,1,1,1,1,0];
         1 -> [0,1,1,0,0,0,0];
         2 -> [1,1,0,1,1,0,1];
         3 -> [1,1,1,1,0,0,1];
         4 -> [0,1,1,0,0,1,1];
         5 -> [1,0,1,1,0,1,1];
         6 -> [1,0,1,1,1,1,1];
         7 -> [1,1,1,0,0,0,0];

END
```

The information contained in Figure 6.63 shows how the three clock signals depend on Q2, Q1, Q0, S1, S2 and S3 – a six-variable combinational logic problem. Circuit minimisation could be carried out by hand using Quine–McCluskey tables or you could use the facilities within Electronics Workbench. Since this problem is aimed at the XPLA system we may as well use the truth table syntax within PHDL. Figure 6.64 shows the listing. Compile, fit and download the design to the target board, then test for correct operation. □

As well as using a truth table to define the way the three clock signals are generated, the listing includes a truth table to display the state of the system on the seven-segment display. Verify that states 0 through 6 are entered as the switches are switched up and back in the correct order (SW1, SW2, SW3, SW2, SW3, SW1). The left-hand LED of the bar graph display should also illuminate when state 6 is reached. □

Try redesigning the system so that state 7 is entered if the incorrect sequence is given at any point. It should not be possible to exit from state 7, except by pressing the reset switch. State 6 should be made similarly inescapable. □

Summary

The finite state machine has been introduced as a method that converts a difficult problem (how to design synchronous sequential systems) into an easy one (how to design combinational logic circuits). Machines based on D-type, T-type and JK flip-flops have been examined and a variety of designs have been completed. Various circuits for generating the clock signal required to drive synchronous sequential systems have been discussed. The more difficult task of designing asynchronous finite state machines that do not have an external clock has also been introduced.

ASSIGNMENT
Start of Frame detector

In a Fast Ethernet data communications system, the **Start of Frame** delimiter is indicated by a 10101011 sequence in the in-coming data stream. This assignment is concerned with the design of a module to detect such a sequence.

Task 1
Sketch the state transition diagram for the system, referring to Figure 6.34 for the type of thing required. The system should respond to non-overlapping sequences only.

Task 2
Design a finite state machine to implement the state transition diagram. Base your design around D-type flip-flops.

Task 3

Simulate your design using Electronics Workbench. Verify that the output goes HIGH when, and only when, the 10101011 sequence is presented to the input.

Task 4

Implement the design in the XPLA system, using the equations derived in task 2. Fit the design to the CPLD chip on the demonstration board, simulate and download the design to verify correct operation.

Task 5

Implement the design in the XPLA system, but using the state diagram syntax. Compare the optimised equations produced by this method with those produced at task 4. Fit, download to the demonstration board and verify correct operation.

Task 6

Write a report on this assignment. Include an introduction summarising the aim of the design and the work done. Include the state transition diagram, the derivation of the minimised Boolean algebra equations of the next-state logic, a print-out of the Electronics Workbench circuit, print-outs of the two PHDL listings, a brief discussion of each task, and a comparative discussion of the different design processes.

Coverage

This assignment covers the last two of the three assessment criteria for Outcome 3 of the Edexcel/BTEC H-level unit Digital and Analogue Devices and Circuits (DADC). It also covers most aspects of Outcomes 3 and 4 of the unit Combinational and Sequential Logic (CASL).

Grading criteria

Pass

- DADC: 'design digital electronic circuits' (complete task 1 and task 2 and/or 5 satisfactorily)
- DADC: 'test digital electronic circuits' (at least one design simulated, downloaded to target hardware and tested, with an account given of results)
- CASL: 'analyse the operation of sequential logic circuits' (task 1 completed satisfactorily)
- CASL: 'use formal design techniques to design sequential logic circuits' (task 2 completed satisfactorily)
- CASL: 'construct and test sequential circuits' (task 4 and/or 5 completed satisfactorily, including account given of results)
- CASL: 'design sequential logic circuits to meet a given specification' (tasks 1 to 3/4 completed satisfactorily)
- CASL: 'use computer simulation to verify logic designs' (tasks 3 and/or 4 completed satisfactorily)

- CASL: 'construct and test sequential logic circuits' (task 4 and/or 5 completed satisfactorily, including account given of results)
- CASL: 'use programmable logic devices to minimise component count in systems containing sequential logic devices' (task 4 and/or 5 completed satisfactorily)

Merit

- 'use a range of methods and techniques to collect, analyse and process information/data' (use XPLA and Electronics Workbench simulators)
- 'apply and analyse detailed knowledge and skills, using relevant theories and techniques' (tasks 1 and 2 completed satisfactorily)
- 'coherently present and communicate work using technical language accurately' (task 6)

Distinction

- 'check validity when collecting, analysing and processing complex information/data' (not necessarily covered in this assignment)
- 'evaluate and synthesise relevant theories and techniques to generate and justify conclusions' (give sensible comparative discussion – tasks 4 and 5)
- 'show an individual approach in presenting and communicating work coherently, using technical language fluently' (task 6)

ANSWERS TO EXERCISES

Paper exercise 6.2

The completed truth table is shown in Figure 6.65.

Fig. 6.65 *Figure 6.26 completed (logic levels for J0 and K0 to ensure correct behaviour for Q0)*

bin	Q2	Q1	Q0	Q0+	J0	K0
0	0	0	0	1	1	×
0	0	0	1	1	×	0
0	0	1	0	0	0	×
0	0	1	1	0	×	1
0	1	0	0	0	0	×
0	1	0	1	0	×	1
0	1	1	0	1	1	×
0	1	1	1	1	×	0
1	0	0	0	1	1	×
1	0	0	1	0	×	1
1	0	1	0	1	1	×
1	0	1	1	0	×	1
1	1	0	0	1	1	×
1	1	0	1	0	×	1
1	1	1	0	1	1	×
1	1	1	1	0	×	1

Paper exercise 6.3
The completed Karnaugh maps are given in Figure 6.66.

Fig. 6.66 *Figure 6.29 completed (Karnaugh maps and minimised expressions for J0 and K0)*

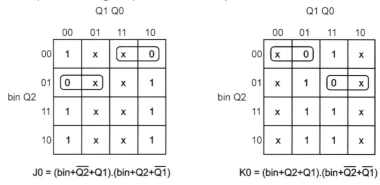

$$J0 = (bin+\overline{Q2}+Q1).(bin+Q2+\overline{Q1})$$

$$K0 = (bin+Q2+Q1).(bin+\overline{Q2}+\overline{Q1})$$

Practical exercise 6.4
Figures 6.67–6.72 include details of the answer.

Fig. 6.67 *State diagram for 'overlapping' 1-0-1 detector*

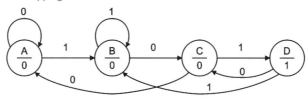

Fig. 6.68 *Present-state/next-state table for overlapping 1-0-1 detector*

input (S)	present state	next state
0	A	A
0	B	C
0	C	A
0	D	C
1	A	B
1	B	B
1	C	D
1	D	B

Fig. 6.69 *Encoded present-state/next-state table for overlapping 1-0-1 detector*

input S	present state Q1	present state Q0	next state D1	next state D0
0	0	0	0	0
0	0	1	1	0
0	1	0	0	0
0	1	1	1	0
1	0	0	0	1
1	0	1	0	1
1	1	0	1	1
1	1	1	0	1

Fig. 6.70 *Karnaugh map for D1 for overlapping 1-0-1 detector*

Q1 Q0

	00	01	11	10
0	0	1	1	0
1	0	0	0	1

S

$$D1 = \bar{S}.Q0 + S.Q1.\overline{Q0}$$

Fig. 6.71 *Electronics Workbench implementation of overlapping 1-0-1 detector*

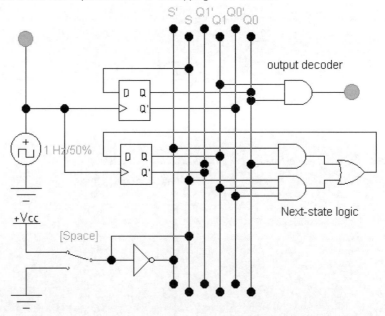

In order to implement the 'overlapping' 1-0-1 detector in PHDL code, just change the code for state D of Figure 6.39:

```
state D: if S then B else C;
```

Fig. 6.72 *As Figure 6.52 but amended to detect 00, 01, 00, 10 sequence*

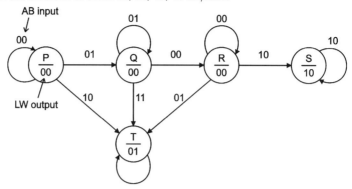

Practical exercise 6.6

Figures 6.73–6.75 show the steps in developing the flow table.

Fig. 6.73 *As Figure 6.53 (flow table) but for new sequence*

		AB input			
		00	01	11	10
physical state	F₀	P	q	×	t
	F₁	r	Q	t	×
	F₂	R	t	×	s
	F₃	×	×	×	S
	F₄	T	T	T	T

Fig. 6.74 *As Figure 6.54 (reduced flow table) but for new sequence*

		AB input			
		00	01	11	10
physical state	F₀	P	q	×	t
	F₁	r	Q	t	×
	F₂	R	t	×	s
	F₄	T	T	T	T

Fig. 6.75 *As Figure 6.55 (next-state table) but for new sequence.*

		AB input			
		00	01	11	10
	00	00	01	10	10
Q1,Q0	01	11	01	10	××
	11	11	10	10	11
	10	10	10	10	10

Note that the same allocation of Q1,Q0 to states has been made as before, namely F_0 (=P) = 00; F_1 (=Q) = 01; F_2 (= R = S) = 11 and F_4 (=T) = 10. A possible race when transforming t into T while the input is 11 has been eliminated by making all the next states 10 in that column.

Figures 6.76 and 6.77 show the Karnaugh maps for Q1 and Q0.

Fig. 6.76 *As Figure 6.56 (Karnaugh map for Q1). Q1 = A + Q1 + Q0.$\bar{B}$ (as before)*

		AB input			
		00	01	11	10
	00	0	0	1	1
	01	1	0	1	×
Q1,Q0	11	1	1	1	1
	10	1	1	1	1

Fig. 6.77 *As Figure 6.57 (Karnaugh map for Q0). Q0 = $\overline{Q1}.\overline{A}.B$ + Q0.$\bar{B}$ for new sequence*

		AB input			
		00	01	11	10
	00	0	1	0	0
	01	1	1	0	×
Q1,Q0	11	1	0	0	1
	10	0	0	0	0

The L and W signals can be derived as before: L = S = A.$\bar{B}$.Q1.Q0 and W = T = Q1.$\overline{Q0}$.

An Electronics Workbench implementation of these equations is shown in Figure 6.78.

Fig. 6.78 *As Figure 6.58 but for new sequence*

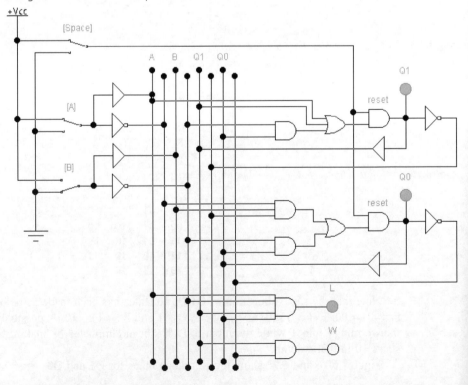

Note the non-inverting buffers introduced into Figure 6.78 as well as the change to the circuitry for Q0. These are required to equalise the delays through the circuit for the A and $\overline{A}$ signals, for B and $\overline{B}$, Q0 and $\overline{Q0}$, Q1 and $\overline{Q1}$. Without these in place the circuit oscillates when changing from 01 back to 00 in the 00, 01, 00, 10 sequence. The fact that the circuit shown in Figure 6.58 appears not to need such buffers is just luck!

Paper exercise 6.4

Figure 6.79 shows the completed truth table.

Fig. 6.79 *Figure 6.62 completed*

	present state	next state		
	Q2,Q1,Q0	S1 = 1	S2 = 1	S3 = 1
0	000	001	000	000
1	001	001	010	000
2	010	001	010	011
3	011	001	100	011
4	100	001	100	101
5	101	110	000	101
6	110	110	000	000
7	111	000	000	000

Practical exercise 6.7

Figures 6.80–6.84 include details of the answer to this exercise.

Fig. 6.80 *Figure 6.63 completed*

present state	toggle?		
Q2,Q1,Q0	S1 = 1	S2 = 1	S3 = 1
000	001	000	000
001	000	011	001
010	011	000	001
011	010	111	000
100	101	000	001
101	011	101	000
110	000	110	110
111	111	111	111

Fig. 6.81 *As Figure 6.61 but for new behaviour*

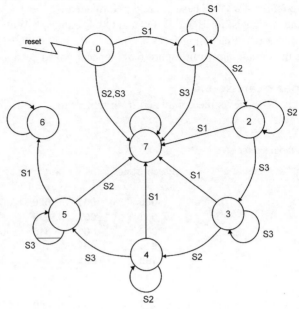

Fig. 6.82 *Present-state/next-state table derived from Figure 6.81*

	present state Q2,Q1,Q0	next state S1 = 1	S2 = 1	S3 = 1
0	000	001	111	111
1	001	001	010	111
2	010	111	010	011
3	011	111	100	011
4	100	111	100	101
5	101	110	111	101
6	110	110	110	110
7	111	111	111	111

Fig. 6.83 *Whether to toggle table, derived from Figure 6.82*

present state Q2,Q1,Q0	toggle? S1 = 1	S2 = 1	S3 = 1
000	001	111	111
001	000	011	110
010	101	000	001
011	100	111	000
100	011	000	001
101	011	010	000
110	000	000	000
111	000	000	000

Fig. 6.84 *Amended truth table for Figure 6.64*

```
truth_table([Q2,Q1,Q0,  S1,  S2,  S3] -> [clock2,  clock1,  clock0]);
            [ 0, 0, 0,   1, .x., .x.] -> [   0,       0,       1    ];
            [ 0, 0, 0, .x.,   1, .x.] -> [   1,       1,       1    ];
            [ 0, 0, 0, .x., .x.,   1] -> [   1,       1,       1    ];
            [ 0, 0, 1,   1.,  x., .x.] -> [   0,       0,       0    ];
            [ 0, 0, 1, .x.,   1, .x.] -> [   0,       1,       1    ];
            [ 0, 0, 1, .x., .x.,   1] -> [   1,       1,       0    ];
            [ 0, 1, 0,   1, .x., .x.] -> [   1,       0,       1    ];
            [ 0, 1, 0, .x.,   1, .x.] -> [   0,       0,       0    ];
            [ 0, 1, 0, .x., .x.,   1] -> [   0,       0,       1    ];
            [ 0, 1, 1,   1, .x., .x.] -> [   1,       0,       0    ];
            [ 0, 1, 1, .x.,   1, .x.] -> [   1,       1,       1    ];
            [ 0, 1, 1, .x., .x.,   1] -> [   0,       0,       0    ];
            [ 1, 0, 0,   1, .x., .x.] -> [   0,       1,       1    ];
            [ 1, 0, 0, .x.,   1, .x.] -> [   0,       0,       0    ];
            [ 1, 0, 0, .x., .x.,   1] -> [   0,       0,       1    ];
            [ 1, 0, 1,   1, .x., .x.] -> [   0,       1,       1    ];
            [ 1, 0, 1, .x.,   1, .x.] -> [   1,       1,       0    ];
            [ 1, 0, 1, .x., .x.,   1] -> [   0,       0,       0    ];
            [ 1, 1, 0,   1, .x., .x.] -> [   0,       0,       0    ];
            [ 1, 1, 0, .x.,   1, .x.] -> [   0,       0,       0    ];
            [ 1, 1, 0, .x., .x.,   1] -> [   0,       0,       0    ];
            [ 1, 1, 1,   1, .x., .x.] -> [   0,       0,       0    ];
            [ 1, 1, 1, .x.,   1, .x.] -> [   0,       0,       0    ];
            [ 1, 1, 1, .x., .x.,   1] -> [   0,       0,       0    ];
```

7 Programmable logic devices

Introduction

If you have followed this book chapter by chapter, you should now be quite good at using the XPLA system to create designs for the 5032 CPLD on the demonstration target board, even though you don't know what's inside the chip. This situation contrasts with microprocessor design – you cannot get very far without a good knowledge of the registers, memory, input/output subsystems, etc. (the 'architecture') of the particular device on which your program will run.

It is a tribute to the designers of the XPLA system software that we have been able to come so far without taking a look at CPLD architecture; their systems have taken care of the details, leaving you to think about what you want the overall behaviour to be. You simply describe that behaviour, using the Philips Hardware Description Language, the compiler turns your description into optimised Boolean algebra equations, the fitter works out how to implement those equations in the hardware inside the chip, and the ISP software sends the final design to the chip itself. Piece of cake!

So long as it works, that is. If it doesn't, you may need to think about the actual hardware inside the chip. This chapter discusses the architecture of the CPLD chip that has been used on the demonstration target board, some of its siblings and some of its friends.

The chapter covers:

- drawing conventions used for PLDs
- PLAs and PALs
- architecture of the 22V10
- architecture of the 5032, and other members of the XPLA family
- architecture of the Altera 7128, and other members of its family
- architecture of the Xilinx 4003E, and other members of its family
- discussion of PLD development systems
- practical exercises on the 22V10 and 5032 chips

Drawing conventions used for PLDs

PLDs have gates with large numbers of inputs; if all these inputs were drawn out separately, the drawings would become unwieldy, so they are condensed into a single line. This is similar to the way a multi-wire bus may be drawn as a single line. Thus,

Fig. 7.1 *Alternative ways to show an AND gate with inputs dir, $\overline{Q1}$ and Q0*

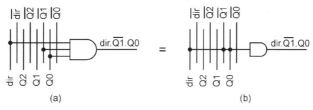

(a)   (b)

instead of drawing an AND gate with three connections as shown in Figure 7.1(a), it is drawn as Figure 7.1(b).

The implication of Figure 7.1(b) is that the AND gate could be connected to *any* of the vertical signal lines. In this example there are eight lines, so the AND gate has eight inputs. Three of them have been programmed so that they are connected as the blobs indicate, while the other five float inactive HIGH.

By way of example of a larger circuit, the combinational logic part of Figure 6.13 is reproduced in Figure 7.2, drawn conventionally. In Figure 7.3 it is drawn using the new method.

Fig. 7.2 *Conventional way of drawing an AND–OR circuit*

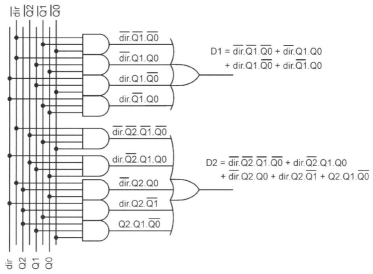

Fig. 7.3 *Same circuit as Figure 7.2, but drawn using PLD conventions*

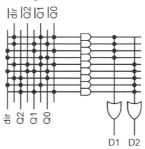

As explained above, each of the nine AND gates has a potential of eight inputs, with the blobs indicating which ones are actually connected. Similarly, each of the two OR gates has a potential of nine inputs; the one that generates signal D1 makes use of four of them, while the other uses five. Recalling the vocabulary of Chapter 2, the AND gates generate 'product terms' while the OR gates 'sum' them together, giving a sum-of-products type circuit.

A circuit such as Figure 7.3, containing both programmable AND gates and programmable ORs, is referred to as a Programmable Logic Array, or PLA. Having the OR gates fully programmable was found to be an under-used facility in most applications, so the PAL (Programmable Array Logic) was devised in which the AND gates were grouped together in fixed numbers. This gives birth to a circuit that is a mixture of Figures 7.2 and 7.3: it would have the programmable AND array of Figure 7.3, but the fixed OR gates of Figure 7.2.

Add some D-type flip-flops (registers) so that you can build a finite state machine and you have a 'registered PAL'. Now make it possible to choose whether or not to use the flip-flops and you get 'Generic Array Logic' or GAL.

The 22V10 GAL

The 22V10 is the most advanced GAL chip available. Its circuit is shown in Figure 7.4.

The details of the ten 'output macro-cells' will be discussed later, but study Figure 7.4 and answer the following questions.

QUESTIONS

7.1 The number of inputs to each of the AND gates shown is ... ?
(a) 8   (b) 20   (c) 44   (d) 64

7.2 The number of inputs to the top OR gate is ... ?
(a) 8   (b) 10   (c) 12   (d) 14

7.3 Given that the circuitry driving output F_4 is similar to that driving F_5, and F_3 is similar to F_7 ... F_0 is similar to F_9, the total number of AND gates is ... ?
(a) 60   (b) 80   (c) 100   (d) 120

7.4 The true and complement versions of input I_5 connect to vertical signals numbered ... ?
(a) 18 & 19   (b) 20 & 21   (c) 22 & 23   (d) 24 & 25

7.5 The true and complement versions of the feedback from output F_4 connect to vertical signals numbered ... ?
(a) 18 & 19   (b) 20 & 21   (c) 22 & 23   (d) 24 & 25

7.6 The total number of inputs and outputs is ... ?
(a) 10   (b) 12   (c) 22   (d) 44

Fig. 7.4 *Architecture of the 22V10*

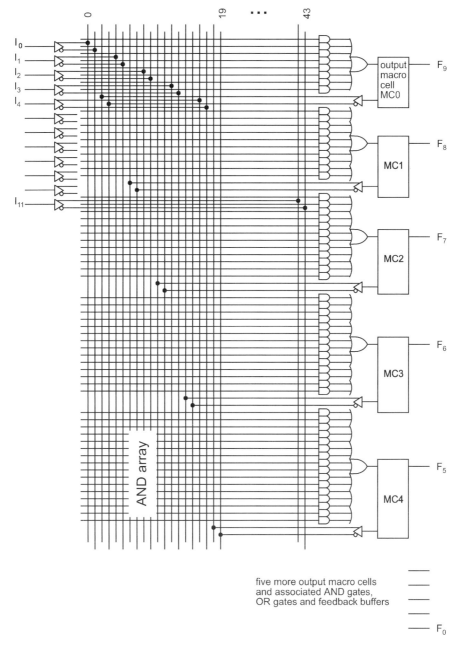

22V10 output macro-cells

Each macro-cell shown in Figure 7.4 contains a D-type flip-flop together with further circuitry that gives considerable versatility to the device. (The 'V' in 22V10 stands for 'versatile'.) Figure 7.5 shows the details.

Fig. 7.5 *22V10 output macro-cell*

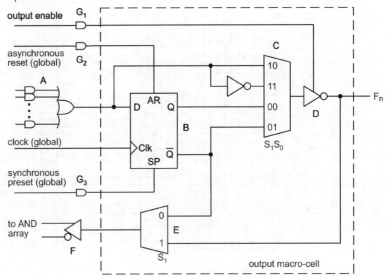

The AND-OR circuit labelled A is just one of the 10 AND-OR circuits shown on the overall diagram, Figure 7.4. Similarly, the true/complement buffer, F, is one of those shown on Figure 7.4.

The macro-cell itself contains the D-type flip-flop, B. The clock signal for this (and all the other flip-flops on the chip) has to come from the I_0 input pin, which means that if you are using the flip-flops in a 22V10 chip, input I_0 cannot be used separately as a combinational input. The reset and preset inputs of the flip-flop can be left disconnected, if you don't wish to use them. If you do want to use them then you can drive them from the programmable array with a single product term, but, like the clock signal, all the flip-flops are driven by the same (global) reset and preset signals, so they will all be set or reset together. Note the *asynchronous* reset signal (i.e. the reset takes place immediately the reset signal is asserted), but the *synchronous* preset (i.e. the flip-flop is set at the next clock edge after the preset signal goes HIGH.)

If you don't wish to use a flip-flop then you can bypass it. Multiplexer C chooses whether the signal to the output pin comes straight from the OR gate, or via the flip-flop. This multiplexer is set up by program bits S_1 and S_0 when the design is downloaded to the chip. As well as allowing you to choose whether you wish your signal output to be registered or combinational, the multiplexer lets you decide whether the signal is inverted on its way to the output.

Tri-state buffer D determines whether the signal actually reaches the output pin, F_n. The output enable signal for this buffer comes, via AND gate G_1, from the programmable array, so you can control the output buffer by a single product term Boolean expression. Provided bit S_1 is set (i.e. the output is a combinational type rather than registered) and the output buffer is disabled, the associated pin can be used as an input port. The signal is routed via programmable multiplexer E into the AND array. When the output is registered (S_1 is 0) the signal from the flip-flop is fed back into the array.

The effect of the status bits is summarised in the table, Figure 7.6.

Fig. 7.6 *Effect of status bits on 22V10 output macro-cell*

S_1	S_0	macro-cell behaviour
0	0	Registered output, inverting, feedback from flip-flop
0	1	Registered output, non-inverting, feedback from flip-flop
1	0	Combinational output, inverting, pin can be input, output or bi-directional
1	1	Combinational output, non-inverting, pin can be input, output or bi-directional

Implications of the architecture

Having studied the physical structure of the 22V10 the limitations of the chip can now be better understood. There is the obvious limit implied by the size of the device – you are not going to be able to build a 16-bit counter in a device with just 10 flip-flops, for instance. The global nature of the clock means that you have to use designs where all the flip-flops are clocked simultaneously, but this is generally a good design aim in any case. Similarly, the global reset and preset signals lead to similar observations. The synchronous nature of the preset as opposed to the asynchronous nature of the reset should be remembered; in some situations the synchronous signal will avoid logic races like those encountered in Chapter 5.

The way the AND gates are grouped means that Boolean expressions with more than 16 product terms have to be generated by using the feedback feature. The penalties are the loss of a macro-cell and increased propagation delay.

PRACTICAL EXERCISE 7.1

You can use the XPLA development system to create designs for the 22V10. Although hardware to test the designs is not provided with this book, you can use the software to investigate the chip. The first exercise takes a very simple design and

Fig. 7.7 *PHDL code to check JEDEC file*

```
MODULE  simple
TITLE    'Simple circuits to check JEDEC file'

DECLARATIONS
I0, I1, I2        pin 2, 3, 4;
F9, F8, F7, F6 pin 27, 26, 25, 24;
F0                pin 17 istype 'reg';

EQUATIONS

F9 = I0;
F8 = I1;
F7 = I2;
F6 = I0 & I1 & I2;
F0.clk = I0;
F0.d = I1;
F0.sp = I2;

END
```

examines the nature of the resulting JEDEC file, while the second looks at chip limitations.

The pin numbers used in the listing assume that the target is a 22V10 in a 28-pin PLCC package; the input and output variables are named as per Figure 7.4. Enter the listing, save, set the **DEVICE** to **xcr22V10-7pc28c** and compile, then fit. ☐

In order to understand the JEDEC file it needs to be compared with Figure 7.4, so you may find it convenient to print out the **.jed** file for this design.

The first of the equations in Figure 7.7 connects **F9** (macro-cell 0) to input **I0**. This connection is shown in the JEDEC file on line L000088. Take a look at this line; you should find a 0 followed by 43 1s. You can think of the 0 as a connection blob at the top left of the AND array of Figure 7.4, while all the other 1s are connections to the array that have been blown up.

The very first line (L000000) of the JEDEC file shows the connection to the AR (asynchronous reset) AND gate for the flip-flops. This is not used in this particular listing, so all 44 of these connections remain intact (i.e. 0).

Line L000044 shows the connections to the OE (output enable) AND gate for macro-cell 0. The tri-state buffer for this macro-cell needs to be permanently enabled, so all 44 connections to the AND gate have been blown away, the gate input floats HIGH and the buffer is enabled as required. The same remarks apply to all the other macro-cells used in this design, namely cells 1, 2, 3 and 9 – see lines L000440, L000924, L001496 and L005368.

The other seven lines for macro-cell 0 are not used, so all the connections from L000132 to L000439 remain intact, and the AND gate outputs are all LOW. These AND gates are the other seven shown connected to the top OR gate of Figure 7.4.

Line L000484 shows input **I1** connected to output **F8** (macro-cell 1); line L000968 shows input **I2** connected to output **F7** (macro-cell 2). Line L001540 shows how the AND function is implemented – connection 0s are shown connecting inputs **I0**, **I1** and **I2** to the top AND gate for output **F6** (macro-cell 4).

The flip-flop part of the design utilises macro-cell 9. You can see the connection from input **I1** to the D input of the flip-flop on line L005412. The synchronous preset connection to **I2** is made on line L005764, and the status bits for the flip-flop are on line L005826. S_0 is given first, so the 10 status does tie up with the information given in the second row of Figure 7.6. All the other macro-cells are set up as 11: combinational output, non-inverting.

If you really enjoy pouring over a load of 1s and 0s, you can have endless fun by amending the listing of Figure 7.7 in some small way; save, re-compile, re-fit and take a look at the **.jed** file to see if you can see what's happened. ☐

The next listing shows the code for a 10-bit up/down counter. This will obviously require 10 flip-flops, so will be near the limit of what a 22V10 can accommodate.

Enter the code, save, make sure the **DEVICE** setting is still **xcr22V10-7pc28c** and compile. The software may take a little while to complete the process, but be patient! If you take a look at the **.ph1** (optimised equations) file you will see how hard the compiler had to work.

Fig. 7.8 *PHDL code for 10-bit up/down counter*

```
MODULE   updnbin
TITLE    '10-bit binary up/down counter'

DECLARATIONS
dir      pin;      "count up when dir is HIGH
reset    pin;
clock    pin;
Q9..Q0 pin istype 'reg_d';

Q = [Q9..Q0];

EQUATIONS

Q.ar = reset;
Q.clk = clock;
when (dir == 1)  then Q.d = Q.q + 1;
                 else Q.d = Q.q - 1;

END
```

Now fit the design. Despite the work done by the compiler, you will find that it is not possible to fit the design to the hardware available. The internal node generated by the compiler uses one of the macro-cells, leaving the chip one short for the flip-flops. The compiler had to generate an internal node because it would otherwise need a 20 term sum-of-products equation and the widest available is 16.

A bigger chip is needed: enter the XPLA family.

The XPLA family

The 22V10 is classified as a 'Simple Programmable Logic Device' (SPLD). The step from 10 macro-cells to 32 macro-cells takes us into the realm of 'Complex Programmable Logic Devices' (CPLDs) and the XPLA 5032 chip.

The architecture of this chip is indicated in Figure 7.9.

The 5032 chip is split into two 'Logic Blocks', each of which contains 16 macro-cells. Figure 7.9 shows one of the logic blocks, together with the 'Zero-power Interconnect Array' (ZIA) that connects the two logic blocks together. Within the logic block you can see two programmable arrays; the PAL array is the one driving the AND gates, just like the AND array of the 22V10, while the other array is referred to as the PLA array, and this drives additional OR gates as shown.

If you refer back to the discussion of the 22V10 architecture (Figure 7.4 and Q3) you will recall that the chip contains 120 AND gates, grouped in two lots of 8, two lots of 10, two of 12, two of 14 and two of 16. Study Figure 7.9 then answer the following questions to see how the 5032 compares to the 22V10.

Fig. 7.9 *Architecture of the 5032*

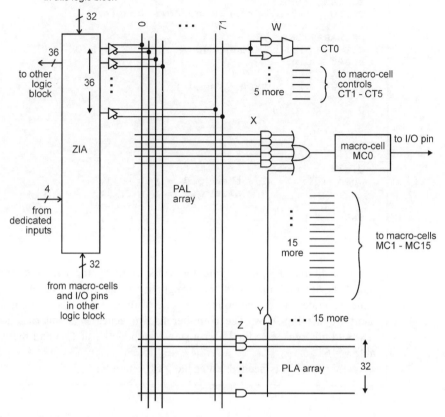

7.12 The total number of Z-type AND gates in one logic block is ...?
   (a) 5   (b) 32   (c) 80   (d) 112

7.13 The total number of control term signals to a macro-cell is ...?
   (a) 1   (b) 5   (c) 6   (d) 12

7.14 Each control term signal to the macro-cells can be ...?
   (a) an AND term composed from up to 36 signals
   (b) an OR term composed from up to 36 signals
   (c) either (a) or (b)
   (d) both (a) and (b)

7.15 The total number inputs and outputs to the 5032 chip is ...?
   (a) 4   (b) 16   (c) 32   (d) 36

XPLA macro-cell

The circuit of the macro-cell itself is shown in Figure 7.10 (This shows the version of the macro-cell on the 5032 device, with enhanced clocking; there is an earlier version with slightly less clock facilities. The type number indicates which version: a 'c' after the number (e.g. **xcr5032c-pc44c**) indicates the enhanced clocking version.)

Most of the circuitry is straightforward. Programmable multiplexer A allows the input signal to the macro-cell to be used in true or complement form, while B allows the output to be combinatorial or registered.

Tri-state buffer C allows the macro-cell to be isolated from its associated pin. If the $\overline{GTS}$ (Global Tri-State) signal is active (LOW) then all the D multiplexers in all the macro-cells force the outputs of the whole chip to be isolated. If you don't need this facility the $\overline{GTS}$ pin should be held inactive HIGH, in which case multiplexer E still allows considerable flexibility in controlling the macro-cell's output.

Fig. 7.10 *XPLA macro-cell (5032, enhanced)*

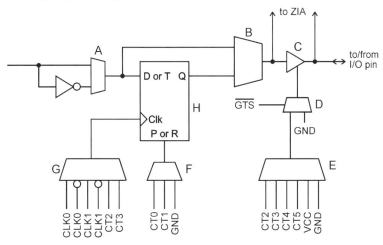

Multiplexer F allows the choice of two signals to preset or reset the macro-cell's flip-flop, or to disable these facilities by connecting them to GND (i.e. logic LOW). Note that you can choose to use either the preset or reset but not both. Also, you can choose whether the preset (or reset) is synchronous or asynchronous. You do this by using appropriate 'dot' extensions in the PHDL code. Thus .SR implies synchronous reset; .AR gives an asynchronous reset to the flip-flop.

Multiplexer G gives you a choice of four clock signals for each flip-flop, and a choice of polarity for signals CLK0 and CLK1. CLK0 comes directly from the dedicated CLK0 input pin on the chip; although it is normally used as a dedicated clock signal, it is possible to use this as a combinatorial input as well. CLK1 can come directly from its input pin, or it can be generated internally, as a Boolean expression. The other two clock options (CT2 and CT3) have to be generated by W-type circuits, i.e. as a Boolean AND or OR expression.

Finally, the flip-flop itself, H, can be set up as a D-type or a T-type, as exercises earlier in the book have shown.

Implications of the architecture

What insights have we gained from examining the architecture of the 5032? As with the 22V10, the basic knowledge about the number of macro-cells gives an indication of the overall size of design that can be implemented in the chip. If 32 macro-cells are not enough, there are versions of the chip with 64, or 128 macro-cells. Other points generally come to light when trying to implement some particular design. The next exercise shows the sort of thing that can happen.

PRACTICAL EXERCISE 7.2

This exercise explores the same 10-bit up/down counter as in Figure 7.8. The listing in Figure 7.11 is the same, but pin numbers have been added to suit the demonstration target board.

Enter the code and save. Use the **Properties** button of the **Project Panel** to set the compiler/fitter properties as follows:

- Max P-term per equation: 37 (Note that the minimum is five, maximum is 37; knowing about the architecture of the 5032 you should appreciate where these limits come from.)
- Optimising effort: Fast
- Activate D/T register synthesis: *un*-tick
- Auto Node Collapse Mode: tick
- Pin preassignment: Keep
- Pin assignment source: **.phd**
- Reserve ISP pins: tick

Now **Hide** the **Properties** box and hit the **Compile** button. The design should compile within a second or so. □

Fig. 7.11 *Up-down counter for demonstration board*

```
MODULE  updnbin
TITLE   '10-bit binary up/down counter'

DECLARATIONS
dir     pin 4;                "count up when dir (SW1) is HIGH
reset   pin 14;               "micro-switch
clock   pin 43;               "555 timer
Q9..Q0  pin 16,  17,  18,  19,  20,  21,  24,  25,  26,  27 istype
                 'reg_d';  "bar-graph;  LSB  on  right
Q = [Q9..Q0];

EQUATIONS

Q.ar = reset;
Q.clk = clock;
when (dir == 1) then Q.d = Q.q + 1;
                else Q.d = Q.q - 1;

END
```

Now take a look at the **.ph1** (optimised equations) file. Near the top of this listing (just after the **TITLE** line) is a summary of the equations that have been generated. You should find that they range in size from Q0 with just one product term (pt) to Q9, which needs 20. In terms of AND gates, equations with more than five product terms will need to use the Z gates of Figure 7.9. (These are referred to as the PLA product terms, as opposed to the PAL product terms – the X gates.) The third line of the **.ph1** file actually tells you about this usage. For this design, with the compiler properties set as above, 10 macro-cells, 64 PLA (Z) AND gates and 45 PAL (X) AND gates will be needed. No buried nodes will be required, so only one 'level' will be used. This looks hopeful: in the whole chip there are 32 macro-cells, 64 PLA gates and 160 PAL gates, so the design should fit.

Now hit the **Fit** button. Problem! Although the entire chip has 64 PLA gates, each logic block has just 32. Because of the way the pins are allocated, outputs Q9 down to Q4 are implemented in a logic block A, and these functions need 60 of the 64 PLA gates mentioned above. Logic block A has just 32 PLA gates, hence the error message when you try to fit this design.

One way around this would be to distribute the Q outputs between the two logic blocks (by re-allocating pin numbers) so that the PLA terms are distributed evenly. This would mean that the order of the bits within the bar graph display would be rather haphazard, however.

Another way to solve the problem is to force the compiler to use fewer product terms. It will have to create a buried node to do so, but there are plenty of macro-cells on the chip, so, although it will increase the propagation delay, at least the design should fit. Open the **Properties** window again and set the **Max P-term** per equation to 12. Hide the **Properties** window and re-compile (it will take a bit longer this time) and have another look at the **.ph1** file. You should find that the compiler has devised a way to keep the number of PLA terms down to just 31, while introducing just one buried node. Hit the **Fit** button and verify that the design gets through the fitting process OK. □

A better solution to the design is to use T-type flip-flops rather than forcing the compiler to use D-types. Open the **Properties** window and tick the **Activate D/T register** synthesis option. Hide the window and re-compile. (Although you have specified `istype 'reg_d'` in the source code, the compiler now ignores this.) If you take a look at the new **.ph1** file, line three should inform you that this is much more efficient in terms of resources used. No PLA terms are used at all, only 19 PAL terms, 1 level, and 10 macro-cells. □

Fit this version of your design and download it to the demonstration board. □

Switch SW1 (the one at the left-hand side of the board) controls the direction of the count, the microswitch resets the count to all zeros, and the pot next to the 555 timer controls the count speed. Adjust the speed to a suitable value, and verify that the counter behaves as expected. □

If you look carefully, you may find that the counter does *not* behave correctly. Set the clock to minimum speed (i.e. fully anti-clockwise), switch SW1 to the down position, and press (and release) the reset microswitch. At the next count you should get all 1s, but you may not find this to be the case. It is not clear just what is the cause of this error. A timing simulation reveals no problem. Disconnecting the LED loads from the chip output (by switching switch 4d down) does not improve matters. Increasing the value of the de-coupling capacitor underneath the CPLD chip seems to make things worse. Hanging an oscilloscope probe, or a finger, on the clock signal from the 555 timer to the CPLD chip sometimes improves matters, so it would appear to be something to do with the nature of the clock signal. Inverting the clock signal (by using the equation `Q.clk = !clock;`) does appear to get rid of the problem, but that solution was found more or less by trial and error, rather than by understanding the problem; it is not guaranteed to work in all situations. Another solution is to add a buffer between the clock input pin and the `.clk` connection on the flip-flops thus:

```
clock_buf node istype 'keep';   "add this line to
                                "the declarations
                                "section

clock_buf = clock;              "drive the clock
                                "buffer from the
                                "clock

Q.clk = clock_buf;              "and drive the flip-
                                "flops from the
                                "buffer
```

The problems encountered above of trying to fit this design into the 5032 chip were a little bit contrived, i.e. forcing the compiler to use D-type flip-flops when knowing that T-types are much more efficient for binary counters. They serve, however, to show how knowledge of the internal architecture of the chip is sometimes useful. The problem of getting the hardware to work reliably was more realistic, and shows how what should have been a five-minute job can sometimes take five hours, five days or longer. At least having the ISP facilities means that new designs can be tested very quickly.

The Altera 7128

Much of this book has been written with the XPLA development software and associated 'Coolrunner' CPLD chips in mind, but it is only one of a number of similar systems. This chapter continues by taking a look at a couple of alternative devices, the first of which is the Altera EPM7128S, a 128-macro-cell member of the MAX 7000 family. It has a similar architecture to the Xilinx 5032 CPLD. In both devices the macro-cells are divided into groups of 16. Altera refer to such a group as a Logic Array Block. The 8 LABs of the EPM7128S are interconnected by a Programmable Interconnect Array (PIA).

The EPM7128S comes in a range of packages, ranging from the 84-pin PLCC (Plastic Leaded Chip Carrier, like the 44-pin version on the demonstration board) to the 160-pin PQFP (Plastic Quad Flat Pack, surface-mount) package. How do you get access to the 128 macro-cells with only an 84-pin package? The answer is you don't. In fact, only half the 16 macro-cells in each of the 8 LABs have pins, giving 64 I/O pins on the chip. Even with the 160-pin package only 96 of the macro-cells are accessible. The reason is that you are very unlikely to need access to all the macro-cells since it is almost inevitable that some will be used for internal ('buried') nodes.

Figure 7.12 illustrates the PIA and architecture for one Logic Array Block.

This is a little more complex than the Coolrunner chip, but there are some general points that can be made. The five AND gates marked X perform a similar function to the X gates of the Coolrunner architecture. They have access to 36 signals from the PIA (in true and complement form) together with 16 signals generated by 'shareable expanders' from the local Logic Array Block. A maximum of five 52-signal product terms can thus be summed by the OR gate Y, passed through the switch arrangement and through the exclusive-OR to the data input of the associated macro-cell. The Product-term select matrix can also route the product terms to the preset, clock and clear inputs of the macro-cell.

If more than five product terms are needed, a certain amount of borrowing and lending of AND gates can be arranged between macro-cell driver blocks. using the 'shareable expanders'. These provide a similar function to the additional PLA (Z type) AND gates of the Coolrunner architecture. One AND gate is sacrificed if the shareable expander is used. In addition, all five AND gates can be donated to an adjacent macro-cell driver via the parallel expander chain. In Figure 7.12 these gates can be donated to the macro-cell driver lower down the diagram by means of the switch arrangement shown in the macro-cell driver. The Altera development system software sorts out the

Fig. 7.12 *Altera MAX 7128S PIA and Logic Array Block Architecture*

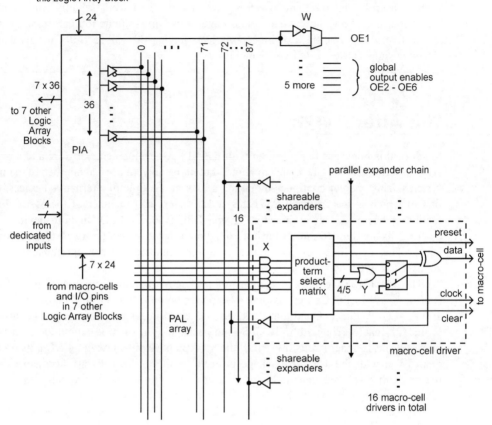

from 16 macro-cells
and 8 I/O pins in
this Logic Array Block

best arrangements. As with the Coolrunner system, small increases in timing delays are incurred when these facilities are used. The circuit marked W generates six output enable signals in true or complement form that feed into all the macro-cells on the chip.

The details of the macro-cell itself are shown in Figure 7.13.

Programmable multiplexer A allows fast input signals to be connected directly into a macro-cell flip-flop.

Multiplexer B allows the generation of combinatorial outputs, bypassing the flip-flop altogether.

Tri-state buffer, C, allows the macro-cell to be isolated from its I/O pin, allowing the macro-cell to be used as a buried node, or simply to tri-state the output. The designer can set up two further characteristics for the output buffer, C: there is a facility to set the slew rate of the output signal, and the output can be set as an open-drain type.

Multiplexer D selects the signal that controls C's output enable input. These OE signals come from the W circuitry shown in Figure 7.12.

Multiplexer E selects between the global clear signal and one generated by the macro-cell driver.

Fig. 7.13 *Altera MAX7000S macro-cell*

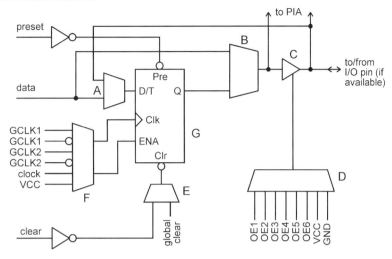

Multiplexer F allows the designer to clock the macro-cell flip-flop from the true or complement of one of the two global clock signals, or from the locally generated one. It also selects a clock enable signal, if required.

Finally, the flip-flop itself (G) can be set up to behave as either D- or T-type.

Altera development software

The 7128 chip described above is a member of the MAX 7000E family. (MAX stands for Multiple Array matriX, referring to the multiple logic array blocks interconnected by the programmable interconnect array.) The largest member of the 7000E family has 512 macro-cells, with the chip containing over 10,000 gates. Other Altera CPLD families are the FLEX 10K with up to 250,000 gates and the APEX 20K with up to 1,000,000 gates. FLEX stands for Flexible Logic Element matriX, referring to the way logic is implemented in small chunks of memory (look-up tables) rather than AND-OR arrays. (APEX is a mnemonic for Advanced Programmable Logic Matrix.)

These chips can implement very complex designs – complete systems on a chip – and designing these systems calls for very advanced development software. Altera provide the MAX+PLUS and QUARTUS software to help designers handle such complexity. Designs can be shared among engineers, and can be entered using the AHDL language (Altera Hardware Description Language – similar to PHDL), VHDL (the V is for Very high-speed integrated circuit; VHDL is a manufacturer-independent, industry-standard HDL), Verilog (another manufacturer-independent, industry-standard HDL) or by graphical means. Compilers can be set up to optimise speed on certain signal paths, or for optimum use of chip resources, or to maintain pin usage, and so on.

There is a growing use of pre-designed subsystems ('cores') that a designer can incorporate to save on the development time. It is also important to be able to integrate the development system software for the Altera chips into the EDA (Engineering Design Automation) software that may be used for an overall engineering project.

The Xilinx XC4003E

The 5032 XPLA chip and software development system was described earlier in this book as a Xilinx product, but it was actually designed by Philips and bought up by Xilinx in 1999. One of its distinguishing features is the very low power that the chip itself consumes – hence the name 'Coolrunner'. As far as this book is concerned, it provides a very convenient entry point into the world of PLDs. There is no charge for the development system software, which is, nevertheless, quite powerful, the learning curve is fairly gentle, and there are few problems installing the software on a PC.

Prior to acquiring the XPLA system, Xilinx provided a family of CPLD chips but their main PLD products are described as Field Programmable Gate Arrays. 'Field programmable' means, of course, that the device can be programmed while in the field, i.e. away from the manufacturer's premises. In fact, it has to be programmed each time it is powered up; unlike the CPLD chips, its internal logic configuration is volatile. This is no great problem. A small non-volatile memory chip can be used to store the configuration data, which is automatically downloaded to the FPGA chip on power-up.

By way of example, the FPGA device covered in this chapter is the XC4003E. This has two different kinds of macro-cells: the ones that communicate to the outside world are known as Input/Output Blocks (IOBs) and there are 80 of these. The internal ones are called Configurable Logic Blocks (CLBs) and there is a 10×10 matrix (i.e. 100) of these. Everything is connected up by a hierarchical, programmable wiring system.

Each IOB has two flip-flops – one for inputs (A) and one for outputs (B) – which gives the designer the option of registering the signal to/from the I/O pad. The input flip-flop can be set up either as an edge-triggered device, or as a 'transparent' (level-driven) latch. There is an optional delayed route (C) for the input signal, so that it won't arrive before the clock in cases where the clock signal is derived from an input pad.

There is a control on the slew rate of the output, there are optional pull-up or pull-down resistors on the I/O pin, and there's tri-state functionality on the output. Most signals can be inverted.

Figure 7.14 illustrates the structure of an IOB.

The structure of a CLB is shown in Figure 7.15. You can see that it has two flip-flops, together with three 'function generators', F, G and H. The F and G function generators are each implemented as a 16×1 high speed RAM, allowing any 4-input truth table (i.e. any 4-input logic function) to be implemented as a look-up table. In terms of Boolean expressions, one of these function generators can implement *any* Boolean expression containing four input variables. Expressions containing up to nine variables can be implemented by using both the F and G function generators, the programmable multiplexer shown at the top left of the diagram, and function generator H. There is a small penalty to pay, however, in additional propagation delay.

The numerous programmable multiplexers within the CLB allow an enormous amount of flexibility in the way each one is configured.

As well as the 80 IOBs and the 100 CLBs, the XC4003E chip architecture includes tri-state buffers for driving 'longline' connections between the CLBs, dedicated logic for generating carry (and borrow) signals between adjacent CLBs, a global set/reset, and an on-chip oscillator. There are also 'wide decoders' on each side of the chip. These are

Fig. 7.14 *XC4000E IOB*

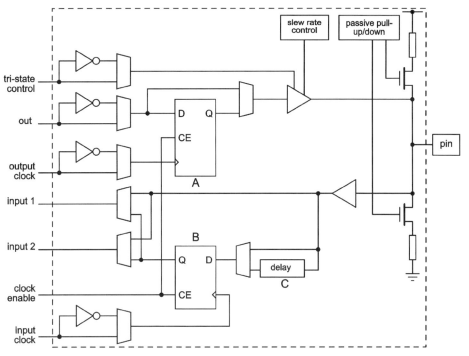

Fig. 7.15 *XC4000E CLB*

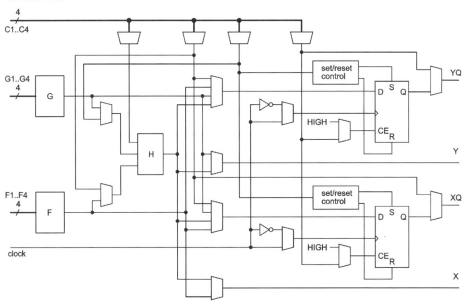

programmable AND gates that will recognise (decode) a pattern of 1s and 0s on the signals on their side of the chip – useful when used for address decoding in microprocessor systems, and faster than the CLB function generators when there are more than nine signals to decode.

The overall architecture allows different parts of each macro-cell to be used independently. The flip-flops to be used independently of the rest of CLB and unused function generators can be used to implement on-chip fast RAM.

Obtaining a detailed appreciation of the architecture, and knowing how to apply that knowledge takes a considerable amount of effort. Most designs, however, can be entered, compiled and fitted with the designer relying on the development software ('Foundation') to make efficient use of the resources available in the chip. As discussed with the Altera development system, this allows extremely complex designs to be handled by teams of engineers. The use of 'core' circuits consisting of complex building blocks that users can customise to their own requirements, but which are optimised to fit the FPGA circuitry, becomes more and more prevalent as time-to-market has to be minimised. Many of these are available from Xilinx, but increasingly third-party designs are available, at a cost, from 'Alliance' partners. Interfacing to general-purpose EDA software is also possible, so that not only the functionality of the design within the FPGA chip, but also of the chip within the entire system can be simulated. Integration of design entry, simulation, PCB manufacture, production and documentation are then also feasible.

Summary

The architecture of the 22V10 SPLD and the 5032 CPLD chips has been examined in detail, and some of the implications of the architecture have been investigated in terms of implementing designs.

The architecture of the Altera 7128 CPLD and the Xilinx 4003E FPGA has also been discussed. When creating complex designs for these and larger (million-gate) chips the necessity for very powerful development system software, and the option to buy in ready-compiled sub-systems (cores), has been emphasised.

ANSWERS TO QUESTIONS

7.1   (c)
7.2   (a)
7.3   (d)
7.4   (b)
7.5   (c)
7.6   (c)
7.7   (d)
7.8   (a): There are 36 independent signals, but each is available in true and complement form, hence the different answers for 7.7 and 7.8.
7.9   (a)

7.10 **(d)**: Five from the X gates and another 32 from the Zs.

7.11 **(c)**: 16 lots of five.

7.12 **(b)**

7.13 **(c)**: There are also two clock signals and the $\overline{\text{GTS}}$.

7.14 **(c)**: The multiplexer allows you to choose either the AND gate or the OR. If you need a more complex expression the software will allow it, but at the expense of a macro-cell, and additional delay.

7.15 **(d)**: 32 macro-cells with associated I/O pins, plus four dedicated inputs.

Appendix A:
Circuit diagram

Fig. A.1 *Circuit diagram for 5032 demonstration board*

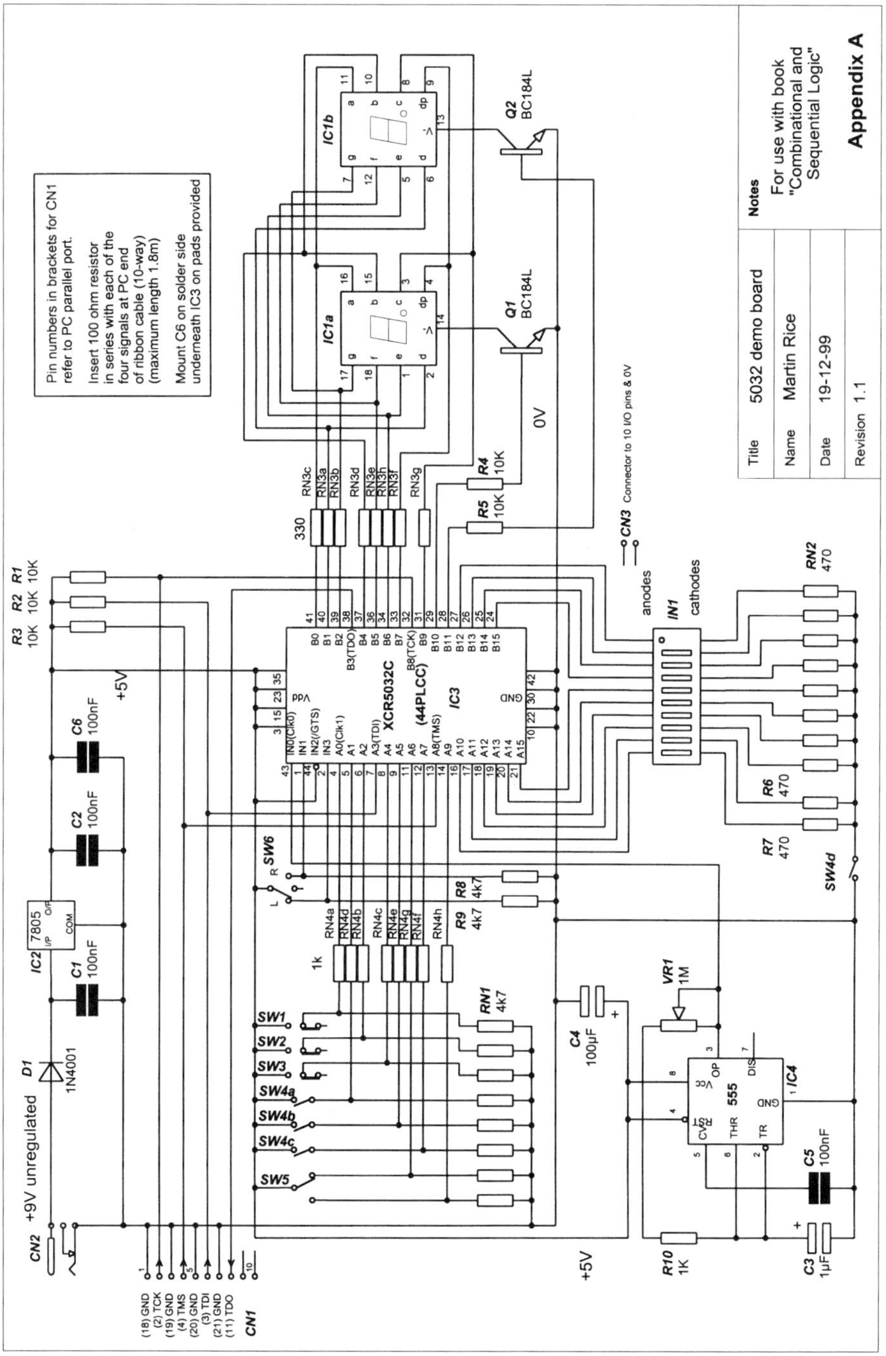

Appendix B: Hardware construction, testing and ordering

You have three options as far as acquiring a target board is concerned. You will need a target board in order to carry out the practical work required by Edexcel. Your options are:

- build from scratch
- buy a PCB, then build
- buy the target board and download cable built and tested.

To make your own PCB photocopy the artwork printed in Figure B.1. The text is shown mirror image in the figure, but make sure that when you view the finished PCB from the track side, the text reads normally. The layout measures 100mm × 80mm, i.e. half a standard Eurocard 100mm × 160mm single-sided board.

The artwork is also provided in PCBWizard format on the CD. You will need that software in order to print it.

Fig. B.1 *Artwork for 5032 demonstration board PCB*

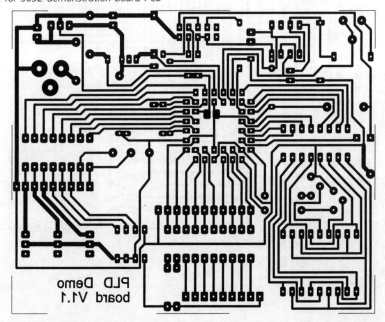

Fig. B.2 *Component layout diagram for 5032 demonstration board*

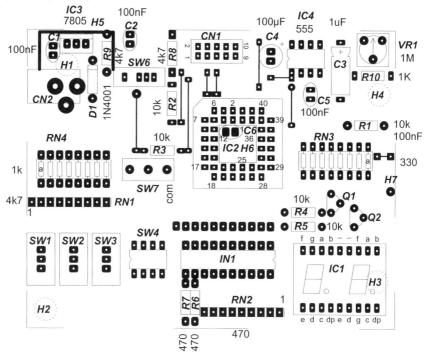

When laser printing or photocopying the use of special PCB artwork film is recommended, such as that provided by Rapid Electronics (order code 34-0774). All holes should be drilled 0.8mm except for the regulator (IC3), diode (D1), terminal pin (H7) and power socket (CN2). The regulator, diode and terminal pin require 1mm holes, while the three pins of the power socket need 3mm (unless you can drill slots).

The component layout is shown in Figure B.2, and the component list is given in Figure B.3. The only items not listed are some rubber stick-on feet that you may care to use to keep the board off the work surface, and a nut and bolt to secure the heat-sink to the regulator IC.

Note that the 44-pin PLCC chip holder (H6) has to be orientated correctly, the bargraph display (IN1) has a slight chamfer to indicate pin 1, the SIL resistor packs have a blob to indicate pin 1, and the DIL resistor packs can be fitted either way round. The common pin of SW7 (the micro-switch) is at the hinge end of the activating lever. There are nine links required, and the terminal pin (H7) is useful for connecting the earth clip of a scope-probe, etc.

An unregulated or regulated power supply of 7.5–9V at 300mA is required with a centre-positive, 2.5mm plug. Rapid Electronics part 85-1680 (£6.20 + VAT) or Argos 982-5712 (£4.50 including VAT) should be suitable.

To test the finished board, connect to a power supply and check that you get +5V at the output of the regulator. A convenient test point is the link just below the three-way slide switch, SW6. Next, connect to the parallel port of your PC and run the PC-ISP

Fig. B.3 *Bill of materials (July 2000 prices, excluding VAT)*

name	supplier	stock code	unit cost	quantity	total (£)
1µF Axial Electrolytic Capacitor	Rapid Electronics	11-0105	0.09	1	0.09
100µF Radial Electrolytic Capacitor	Rapid Electronics	11-0250	0.05	1	0.05
100nF Capacitor	Rapid Electronics	08-0275	0.06	4	0.24
10K Resistor (pack of 100)	Rapid Electronics	62-0394	0.60	0.05	0.03
10-Segment Red Bar Graph Display	Rapid Electronics	55-0190	1.10	1	1.10
1K Resistor (pack of 100)	Rapid Electronics	62-0370	0.60	0.01	0.01
1k 8-resistor DIL pack	Rapid Electronics	63-0645	0.28	1	0.28
1M Potentiometer – finger adjustable	Rapid Electronics	68-0710	0.78	1	0.78
1N4001 Rectifier Diode	Rapid Electronics	1N4001	0.04	1	0.04
32 pin SIL	Rapid Electronics	22-0460	0.55	1	0.55
330 8-resistor DIL pack	Rapid Electronics	63-0635	0.28	1	0.28
470 8-resistor SIL pack	Rapid Electronics	63-0205	0.11	1	0.11
470 Resistor (pack of 100)	Rapid Electronics	62-0362	0.60	0.02	0.01
4k7 8-resistor SIL pack	Rapid Electronics	63-0225	0.11	1	0.11
4k7 Resistor (pack of 100)	Rapid Electronics	62-0386	0.60	0.02	0.01
555 timer	Rapid Electronics	NE555	0.22	1	0.22
7805 Regulator	Rapid Electronics	7805-STM	0.35	1	0.35
2-digit 7-segment display	Rapid Electronics	57-0135	0.80	1	0.80
BC184L Transistor	Rapid Electronics	BC184L	0.07	2	0.14
Micro-miniature slide switch	Farnell	733-659	0.60	1	0.60
Micro-switch	Rapid Electronics	78-0735	0.38	1	0.38
Miniature Slide Switch	Rapid Electronics	76-0200	0.55	3	1.65
PCB DC Power socket 2.5mm	Rapid Electronics	20-0975	0.11	1	0.11
10-way IDC boxed header	Rapid Electronics	19-0500	0.19	1	0.19
5032 CPLD	Insight-Memec	xcr5032c-10pc44c	2.75	1	2.75
SPST Slide Switch DIL 4	Rapid Electronics	80-0100	0.45	1	0.45
100 × 160 PCB (use half)	Rapid Electronics	34-0205	1.75	0.5	0.88
Heatsink	Rapid Electronics	36-0115	0.19	1	0.19
Terminal pin (pack of 100)	Rapid Electronics	34-0610	0.48	0.01	0.01
10-way IDC cable socket	Rapid Electronics	19-0300	0.21	1	0.21
25-way D-connector plug	Rapid Electronics	15-0110	0.26	1	0.26
25-way D-connector cover	Rapid Electronics	15-0310	0.48	1	0.48
10-way IDC cable (use 6ft)	Rapid Electronics	01-0167	5.55	0.06	0.33
100 min resistor (pack of 100)	Rapid Electronics	64-0044	0.70	0.04	0.03
				Total	**13.72**

software. Details for constructing the cable are given in Appendix A, but refer to Figure B.2 for pin-numbering for the 10-way IDC connector. If you get the message **Checking ISP download cable/Board connection...** followed by **ISP HyperCable/ Board found!** and **There is 1 JTAG device in the system** then the cable and connections to the programming pins of the chip are sound. If you don't get these reassuring messages, use a 'scope to check for signals on the four connections. These can conveniently be monitored on the two long link wires just to the left of the CPLD chip, on the link wire between the IDC connector and the 100µF capacitor, C4, and on the short link near the terminal pin.

The rest of the board can be tested using the `cnt60.jed` file provided on the CD. First, copy this file to a writable disk, then use the PC-ISP software to send this file to the target board. Appendix C gives details about installing and running the PC-ISP software. When the file has been successfully processed and sent to the board you should find that the bar graph display steadily lights up from the left. All the slide switches need to be in the up position for this to happen. Check that adjusting the pot near the 555 timer chip controls the speed with which this happens. Keep the rightmost switch on the DIL slide switch in the up position, but check that the six other switches control individual elements of the bar graph. The three-position slide switch near the top of the board controls which one of the two seven-segment displays is activated. The display should count up from 0 to 5, then reset. When pressed, the micro-switch should reset the display to 0.

Refer to Appendix C for information about installing and running the XPLA and PC-ISP software.

Appendix C: Software installation

XPLA software

This is used for design entry and simulation, is installed from the CD by running the **setup.exe** program found within the XPLA folder of the CD. The process is very straightforward, using the install wizard. The default options are OK, but you can change directories, etc., if you wish. You need 32MB of RAM to run the software.

PC-ISP software

This is used for converting the output of the XPLA software into a binary file, and downloading this file to the CPLD chip. It is installed from the CD by running the **setup.exe** program found within the ISP folder of the CD. The process is again straightforward. One warning, however: do not install in a directory whose path includes a name that includes a space (like **Program Files**). The names of your working files and folders should also have no spaces. (If you don't do this you will get a message when you try to download saying **No output bin/isp files generated!** and **Operation Aborted!**)

The PC-ISP software communicates with your target board via a 10-way ribbon cable and the PC parallel port, and normally it can ascertain the address of the port automatically. If you are having trouble communicating with the target board it may be worth specifying the port address (if you know it) or just trying different options. This is done with the **Port Setup...** menu, then clicking the **Check cable/check connection** button.

Refer to Chapter 1 (see Figure 1.32) for detailed instructions for sending a design to the target board.

To send the cnt60.jed file to it:

- Double-click on the **Device Name** cell on row 1 of the **Device** tab of the **Configure JTAG chain devices** window. Select **XCRx032_CA** from the list that pops up.
- Now double-click in the **Design filename** on row 1. Browse to the (writable) location where you have copied the cnt60.jed file from the CD, and open the file.
- Double-click the **Operation** cell, and select **Prog_&_Verify**.
- Press the **Execute** button. Some messages reporting progress should appear in the Message window (cable and device checking, checksum calculation, erase, program and verify each side, end operation).

Note that after this process you should find two files have been created in addition to the original `cnt60.jed` file: `cnt60.bin` and `scan___.jcd`. In order to write these two files to disk you must have write access to the disk while using PC-ISP.

If you have a printer connected to your printer port you may consider adding another parallel port to your PC to save swapping cables over (this is not expensive: about £10). Use the original parallel port for the printer, and the new one for the ISP system. You will have to set up the address of the new parallel port when you fit it. The address of the original port is probably **378(hex)** so make the new one **278(hex)**.

Appendix D:
XPLA schematic editor

As well as entering designs using PHDL code, the XPLA development system allows designs to be entered as a circuit diagram – a schematic. This is sometimes a convenient way to think about a design, although you lose the high-level constructs of the PHDL language. Unfortunately, you cannot mix schematic and HDL descriptions in a design. This appendix introduces you to the use of the schematic editor.

The very first PHDL design discussed in Chapter 1 consisted of a three-input AND gate – see Figure 1.27. To enter the same circuit as a schematic rather than as PHDL code run the XPLA software and load the **basic_gates** project (or create a new project with that name). Remove any existing PHDL source file (**Source/Remove from Project**) and create a new source file (**Source/New File...**). Click on **Schematic** in the **Type** field of the **Create New File** dialog box, choose a name for the file (**and_cct**, for example) then hit the **New** button. The schematic editor should run, providing you with a new blank sheet on which to draw your AND-gate circuit.

Actually, the sheet is not entirely blank: a border is provided, and a title block in the bottom right-hand corner. The title block and its contents form a symbol and you will learn how to edit this symbol later. For now, just use the **Zoom** facilities to fit the whole drawing onto the screen. There are several ways to achieve this: you can press **CTRL-F**; you can use the **View\Full Fit** menu item, or you can click on the magnifying-glass-in-a-box icon near the top of the window. In any case, the cursor changes to a Z shape, and a message in the information bar at the bottom of the window tells you what to do next. When you have the full drawing in view, drag the Z cursor around the title block so that when you release the mouse button it is enlarged enough to read the text within the symbol. You should find today's date, the name of the file, and a few other items.

Check out the **Zoom In** (magnifying glass with + sign) and **Zoom Out** (magnifying glass with − sign) facilities.

Note that a right-click on the mouse disables the zoom commands.

The circuit consists of a three-input AND gate, three buffers, and some input and output connectors. The AND gate is a further example of a symbol, and is added to the drawing using the **Add/Symbol...** menu (or pressing the F2 key). Symbols are kept in libraries, so you first have to choose the correct library from the two that are on offer in the **Symbol Libraries** dialog box. The MISC library contains nothing but the **Title** symbol, while the **Coolpld.lib** library contains several hundred symbols, ranging from a 16-bit accumulator to an 8-input exclusive-OR gate. Select the **Coolpld.lib** library, then scroll down to find the three-input AND gate – **AND3**. Click on it to highlight it, then move the mouse cursor over the drawing area – you should find that a 3-input AND-gate symbol hangs on the mouse. Click in a central part of the drawing area to deposit it, then go back to the **Symbol Library** to find the buffer – **BUF**. Place three of these in the drawing area. Right-click to lose the **BUF** symbol that still hangs on the mouse, then close the **Symbol Library** dialog box.

See Figure D.1 for an example of the completed diagram.

If you accidentally place a symbol you can delete it by means of the **Edit/Delete** menu (or by pressing F5). Follow the instructions in the information bar. An item can be moved using the **Edit/Move** command (or the F7 key) or it can be dragged using the **Edit/Drag** command (or the F8 key). The difference between moving and dragging is this: dragging retains connectivity, while moving disconnects the moved item from any wires attached to it. You haven't added any wires as yet, but remember this distinction for later!

Having placed the AND gate and the three buffers, the next thing to do is add some wires. (After adding the wires you will add net names to the wires and after adding the net names you will add I/O markers to the net names.)

Use the **Add/Wire** menu command (or F3 key) to add wires as shown in Figure D.1. Click on a component node (little red square) then click again where you want the wire to go, including corners. Right-click to quit a wire. Draw the three wires to the three inputs of the AND gate, then the four output wires, then the three joining up the buffer inputs. Note that you can start and finish wires wherever you want; little red squares indicate incomplete nets (wires). At this stage you should have three such red squares at the three inputs, and four at the outputs. There should also be three little blue squares at the three T-junctions.

Remember you can use the draw wire (F3), delete (F5), move (F7) and drag (F8) facilities to edit wires if you need to tidy them up. It's worth dragging or moving some of the components, then editing them back into place, then tidy up the wiring to practise these functions.

The seven nets now need labelling. Use the **Add/Net Name** (F4) facility to do so. After pressing the F4 key the process is:

- type the net name – watch the information bar
- press the **Enter** key – the net name should appear on the mouse cursor
- click on the little red square at the end of the net you wish to name – the net name should attach itself to the net

When you have entered and attached all seven net names, the I/O markers can be added. Click the **Add/I/O Marker** menu item (or press Alt + M), choose I/O type then click on the net name, just at the end of the wire. You have three input markers and four output markers to add. After doing so, your circuit schematic should look similar to Figure D.1.

The design is now complete, so save it, then compile as for a PHDL file. You will need to use the **Pin Editor** to specify chip connections; remember to set the **Properties/ Fitter Options/Pin** assignment source to **.paf** so that the **Pin Editor** settings are enforced at the fitter stage. Before the **Pin Editor** can be used a fit run has to be made, so the process is fit, pin-edit, then re-fit. As for the PHDL version of this circuit, suitable

Fig. D.1 *Schematic version of Figure 1.27*

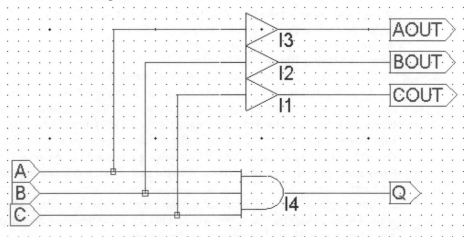

pin numbers are 4, 6 and 8 for the three inputs, and 16, 17, 18 and 27 for the four outputs. The design can now be downloaded to the target board ready for testing.

As mentioned above, in order to edit the entries in the title block of the drawing, the title block symbol needs editing. This is achieved using the **Symbol Editor**. Click on the **Edit/Symbol** menu item, then (as instructed in the information bar) pick the title bar symbol to edit (by clicking on it). The **Symbol Editor** should run, and you should now be able to delete any unwanted text, add new text, etc. as required. Note that text size may be altered (before you type the text itself) using the **Options/Graphic Options...** menu. Further variables (like the **[FileName]**) can be found in the **Edit/Attribute / Attribute Window** menu. When you are happy with your title block, save it and close the **Symbol Editor**. You should find that the title block in your drawing has been updated to your design.

That completes this introduction to the schematic editor. There is a considerable amount more to learn about it, such as the way a complex diagram can be built up as a hierarchy of individual drawings, and how the hierarchy navigator allows you to trace a signal through. The **Help** system provides some clues, but you may have to find out some details by trial and error.

As well as schematic and PHDL entry, the XPLA system allows designs to be described using the Verilog hardware description language. Verilog versions of some of the designs in this book are available at the website for this book.

Although VHDL also appears to be a fourth alternative entry method, the XPLA system (XPLA Professional Version 3.31) does not support it.

Appendix E: Use of the Xilinx Webpack CPLD development system

Installation

The CD contains three files in the **Webpack** folder. Each one is an executable file and the installation process is to run each file, starting with **webpack_hdl_abel.exe**, then **webpack_xpla_fitter.exe**. The third file (**webpack_xpla_programmer.exe**) gives an upgrade (version 4.10 as opposed to version 4.05) of the **XPLA PC-ISP Programmer** software. The files can be run from the CD: locate them using **Windows Explorer** then double-click them. The installation process for each piece of software is straightforward; you will need to reboot the computer once all required items have been installed. The author has tested the software using the default folder names only, but other locations should work, provided you stick to folder names and paths *without* any spaces.

You can check what has been installed using **Start \ Programs \ Xilinx CPLD WebPACK \ About WebPACK**. An HTML viewer should run and tell you about the programs that you have installed. A few others will be listed as not having been installed. These are not necessary for the purposes of the book since they are concerned with the other CPLD families that Xilinx make, and with facilities for VHDL- and Verilog-based projects. If you do wish to obtain them they are available free of charge from the Xilinx website.

Project Navigator

This software enables projects to be created and provides facilities for HDL and schematic design files to be entered and for designs to be compiled and checked for operation. The **Project Navigator** is also used to launch the fitter and download software. This set of operations is similar to the functions provided by the **XPLA Professional** and **PC-ISP** software as described in Chapter 1. The rest of this appendix takes you through the process: from design entry using the ABEL language through to downloading to the chip. As discussed in the preface, PHDL is very closely based on ABEL, so there will be little new to learn as far as the syntax of the language is concerned.

Run **Project Navigator**. If you have accepted the default conditions during installation you should be able to do so by clicking **Start \ Programs \ Xilinx CPLD WebPACK \ Webpack Project Navigator**. □

Click **File \ New Project...** to open the **New Project** dialog box. This dialog box allows you to give the project a name, choose a location for the project, choose the target device, and choose the design entry method (synthesis tool). It automatically creates a new folder in which to keep the new project, giving the folder the same name as you choose for the project. For the purposes of this appendix the **c:\xplawork** folder was chosen as the location, and the project was named **appendix_e**. This software automatically created a folder called **c:\xplawork\appendix_e** and the project file **appendix_e.npl** within it. Choose a similar project name and location, then set the **Device family** to **Xilinx XPLA 5V CPLDs**, the **Device** to **XCR5032C PC44C**, and the **Synthesis tool** to **ABEL XST**. These last three properties may be set by clicking in the value field for each property, then selecting from the drop-down menu. Note that the speed grade is not selectable at this point, and defaults to the fastest (**6ns**). Click **OK** to finalize your choices. □

Next click the **Project \ New Source...** menu item then select **ABEL-HDL Module** as the new source object type. Choose a name for the source file (for example **gates** – make sure it has eight characters or less), leave the location at default (this should be the folder just created in the **New Project** dialog box), and check that the **Add to Project** box is ticked. Click the **Next >** button to progress. □

The **Define ABEL-HDL Source** dialog box appears; this allows you to enter the names of input and output ports. These names will be allocated to pins in the ABEL code that is created. Enter the three names A, B and C separated by commas (A,B,C) in the first **Pin Name** field; enter comma-separated names A_OUT, B_OUT and C_OUT (A_OUT,B_OUT,C_OUT) in the next **Pin Name** field below; and finally Q in the field below that. Click the **Next >** button. □

Check the information in the **New Source Information** box, click the **Finish** button, and wait a second or so while the software carries out its various tasks. You should now have a **Project Navigator** window similar to Figure E.1. □

As you can see from Figure E.1, the **Project Navigator** has created an ABEL file with the **MODULE** name, **PIN** declarations, and **EQUATIONS** and **END** statements already entered. To complete the file simply type the following:

```
A_OUT = A;
B_OUT = B;
C_OUT = C;
Q=A & B & C;
```

between the **EQUATIONS** and **END** statements. Pin numbers for the ports also need to be entered. Insert the following information into the pin lines:

```
A,B,C pin 4,6,8;
A_OUT,B_OUT,C_OUT pin 16,17,18;
Q pin 27;
```

Your ABEL file should now look very similar to the PHDL file of Figure 1.30. Indeed, the PHDL code of Figure 1.30 could be used almost exactly. The keywords (**MODULE**, **PIN**, etc.) should be displayed in blue. □

Having completed the design entry, the source code now needs to be compiled. Do this by double-clicking the **Compile Design** option in the **Processes for Current Source** window of **Project Navigator**. (If you don't have this option showing check that the **.abl** source file in the **Sources in Project** window is highlighted.) After a few seconds

Fig. E.1 *Project Navigator ready to accept ABEL code*

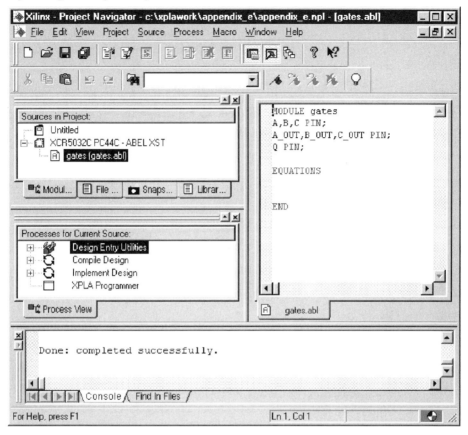

of activity, and a few messages appearing in the console window, compilation should be complete. If there are errors in your source code, a big red cross will appear next to the **Compile Design** option, and you will need to correct these and re-compile before further progress can be made. The console window will give details of the errors. Warnings give rise to a yellow exclamation mark. These should be checked, but will not prevent further processing. □

Having compiled the design successfully it can now be implemented (fitted) so double-click the **Implement Design** option in the **Processes** window. If all goes well, nice big green ticks should appear against both the **Compile Design** and **Implement Design** processes. □

Finally, the XPLA programmer can be invoked, again by double-clicking the option in the **Processes** window. The familiar **PC-ISP** software should run, and the next few steps are similar to those described in Chapter 1. First, select the device; choose **XCR5032C** in the **Device Name** field. Next select **Prog & Verify** for the **Operation**. Now select your JEDEC file for the **Design** filename. Finally, click the **Execute** button. Wait for the download to take place, and check out that your CPLD has turned itself into an AND gate. □

Test vectors

One feature of the XPLA software that the software does not offer is the graphical simulator. (One *is* available from Xilinx, but requires familiarity with the VHDL or Verilog language to use, so is not discussed further in this book.)

Instead of the waveform method of setting inputs and viewing outputs, functional checking of the operation of designs is achieved by the use of 'test vectors'. This involves adding a section of code to the design that lists what the output should do, given certain inputs. For the three-input AND gate example the test vectors can exercise the whole set of possible inputs. The syntax for the test vector definitions is similar to that for entering a truth table. Thus:

```
test_vectors([A,B,C] -> Q);
             [0,0,0] -> 0;
             [0,0,1] -> 0;
             [0,1,0] -> 0;
             [0,1,1] -> 0;
             [1,0,0] -> 0;
             [1,0,1] -> 0;
             [1,1,0] -> 0;
             [1,1,1] -> 1;
```

Enter these lines after the last of the equations (and before the END statement) in your source code file, save and re-compile.   ☐

If you examine the **Sources in Project** window you should now find two sources listed: something like **gates (gates.abl)** and **gates-vectors** – click on the latter. You should find that the **Processes for Current Source** window changes to reflect the processes appropriate to a test vector source. **Compile Test Vectors** (which may already have a green tick) and **Simulate Equations** should be listed. Double-clicking the **Simulate Equations** option should initiate a simulation, during which the functional behaviour of the design is checked for each test vector. You should get a green tick after a few seconds activity.   ☐

If you want to see what happens if a design does not match up to its test vectors, try changing one of the test vector lines, then double-click the **Simulate Equations** option. You should find that the test vectors are re-compiled, and a warning given. Details of where the design fails to meet its test are recorded in a separate text file (for instance **gates.sm1**) which you can view using **File \ Open...** in **Project Navigator**.   ☐

While on the subject of the different information contained in different files, use **Windows Explorer** to view the entire contents of the folder created for this project. You should find that some 60 files have been generated, together with two folders containing a further 21. Some of these are the same as those generated by the XPLA software. For instance, the **.ph1** file shows the optimised equations while the **.tim** file shows timing information. The **.edn** file is an **EDIF** file (Electronic Design Interchange Format) which is a text file describing the design at gate level, while the **.vhf** file is a VHDL version of your design.   ☐

Differences between ABEL and PHDL source code

As you have seen in the example given above, ABEL and PHDL are very similar. However, in order to test designs, the `test_vectors` section needs to be added; note also that the module name *must* be the same as the filename. In addition, the file name has to be DOS-compatible, that is 8 characters or less with no spaces. The file extension must be **.abl** (not **.phd**).

All the PHDL examples in Chapters 1, 2 and 3 convert to the ISE-ABEL system with just these amendments. All of the examples in Chapter 4 also convert, but for the high-level implementation of the adder (see Figure 4.33). The XPLA-PHDL code is shown in Figure E.2 and the equivalent ABEL code is given in Figure E.3.

Fig. E.2 *PHDL code for 4-bit adder, using + syntax*

```
MODULE   adder
TITLE    '4-bit  adder:  high-level  implementation'

DECLARATIONS
A3..A0,  B3..B0  pin;
S4..S0           pin;
A  =  [A3..A0];
B  =  [B3..B0];
S  =  [S4..S0];

EQUATIONS

S  =  A  +  B;

END
```

Fig. E.3 *ABEL code for 4-bit adder, using + syntax*

```
MODULE   adder
TITLE    '4-bit  adder:  high-level  implementation'

DECLARATIONS
A3..A0,  B3..B0  pin;
S4..S0           pin;
A  =  [A3..A0];
B  =  [B3..B0];
S  =  [S4..S0];

EQUATIONS

S  =  [.x.,A]  +  [.x.,B];

test_vectors([A,B]->S);
             [1,2]->3;
             [15,1]->16;

END
```

Note that writing simply `S = A + B` in the ABEL language causes a compiler error since S is specified as a 5-bit quantity while A and B are 4-bit. To get over this, the equation pads out the two 4-bit variables with `.x.` (a 'don't care' bit). Note also that only two of the possible 256 sums have been supplied as test vectors. In reality you should check a few more!

Chapter 5 started to investigate basic sequential systems. All the PHDL source code in Chapter 5 will translate directly into ABEL, but designing test vectors now has to take into account the sequence of events, rather than just testing inputs and outputs. The NOR-gate version of the RS flip-flop, shown in Figure E.4, illustrates the point.

Fig. E.4 *Test vectors for RS flip-flop*

```
Module   NOR_RS
Title    'RS flip-flop made from NOR gates'

Declarations
set,reset  pin 4,8;
Q,N_Q      pin 16,27;

Equations

Q  = !(reset # N_Q);
N_Q = !(set # Q);

test_vectors([set,reset]->[Q,N_Q]);
            [1,0]->[1,0];      "set
            [0,0]->[1,0];      "no change
            [0,1]->[0,1];      "reset
            [0,0]->[0,1];      "no change
            [1,1]->[0,0];      "set AND reset simultaneously
            [0,0]->[.x.,.x.];  "illegal change at input

End
```

The equations simulator happily agrees with the first five vectors, but gets into a tizzy over the last. The test vector output is 'don't care', but the simulator cannot make up its mind as to how the system will behave following the 1,1 to 0,0 transition at its input. If you think back to the discussion over this flip-flop, then you won't be altogether surprised that the simulator fails to converge.

Fig. E.5 *Code and test vectors for JK flip-flop*

```
Module   jkff
TITLE    'jk flip-flop'
  "positive edge triggered, active-HIGH preset

DECLARATIONS
Clock,J,K,Pre  pin 43,4,8,14;
Q              pin 16 istype 'reg_jk';
N_Q            pin 27;
Clock_out      pin 20;

EQUATIONS

Q.clk = Clock;
Q.j  = J;
Q.k  = K;
Q.ap = Pre;
N_Q  = !Q;
Clock_out = Clock;
```

```
test_vectors([J,K,Clock]->[Q,N_Q]);
                [1,0,.c.]->[1,0];        "set
                [0,0,.c.]->[1,0];        "no change
                [0,1,.c.]->[0,1];        "reset
                [0,0,.c.]->[0,1];        "no change
                [1,1,.c.]->[1,0];        "toggle
                [0,0,.c.]->[1,0];        "no change
                [1,1,.c.]->[0,1];        "toggle
                [0,0,.c.]->[0,1];        "no change

End
```

Figure E.5 shows the use of the .c. syntax for a clock signal. Note that the action of the asynchronous preset has not been checked using these test vectors.

Figure E.6 shows the ABEL version of the ripple-through up counter – compare with Figure 5.22. Again, the ABEL and PHDL versions are identical, except for the addition of the test vectors to the ABEL code.

Fig. E.6   *ABEL code for ripple-through up counter*

```
Module  rtbuk
Title   '4-bit ripple-through binary up counter'

Declarations
reset,clock  pin 14,43;
Q3..Q0       pin 20,21,24,25 istype 'reg_t';

Q = [Q3..Q0];

equations

!Q0.clk = clock;
!Q1.clk = Q0;
!Q2.clk = Q1;
!Q3.clk = Q2;

Q.ar = reset;
Q.t = ^b1111;  "this sets all four t inputs to 1

test_vectors([reset,clock]->[Q]);
                [1,.x.]->[0];        "reset
                [0,.c.]->[1];        "counting up
                [0,.c.]->[2];
                [0,.c.]->[3];
                [0,.c.]->[4];
                [0,.c.]->[5];
                [0,.c.]->[6];
                [0,.c.]->[7];
                [0,.c.]->[8];
                [0,.c.]->[9];
                [0,.c.]->[10];
                [0,.c.]->[11];
                [0,.c.]->[12];
                [0,.c.]->[13];
                [0,.c.]->[14];
                [0,.c.]->[15];
                [0,.c.]->[0];

End
```

According to a Xilinx application note (XAPP312), the line `Q.t = ^b1111;` should be replaced with `Q.t = [1,1,1,1];` when converting from PHDL to ABEL. However, either syntax works in this particular situation for either language.

The simulation results are interesting to view, clearly showing the ripple-through effect. Part of the **.sml** file is shown in Figure E.7.

Fig. E.7 *Simulation results for ripple-through counter*

```
Simulate iSE 3.01  Date:  Fri  Oct  06  22:38:02  2000
Fuse file:  'rtbuk.bll'  Vector file:  'rtbuk.tmv'  Part:  'PLA'
4-bit ripple-through binary up counter


           r  c
           e  l
           s  o
           e  c    Q Q Q Q
           t  k    3 2 1 0

   V0001   1  X    L L L L
   V0002   0  C    L L L L
           0  C    L L L L
           0  C    L L L L
           0  C    L L L H
           0  C    L L L H
   V0003   0  C    L L L H
           0  C    L L L H
           0  C    L L L H
           0  C    L L L L
           0  C    L L L L
           0  C    L L H L
           0  C    L L H L
      .
      .
      .
   V0016   0  C    H H H L
           0  C    H H H L
           0  C    H H H L
           0  C    H H H H
           0  C    H H H H
   V0017   0  C    H H H H
           0  C    H H H H
           0  C    H H H H
           0  C    H H H L
           0  C    H H H L
           0  C    H H L L
           0  C    H H L L
           0  C    H L L L
           0  C    H L L L
           0  C    L L L L

17 out of 17 vectors passed.
```

Note how vector V0017 shows first the LSB toggling from H to L, which in turns causes bit 1 to toggle from H to L which causes bit 2 to toggle (H to L) which causes bit 3 to toggle (H to L). The final result (LLLL) agrees with the test vector. Compare this with the simulation results for the synchronous system (see Figure E.8).

Fig. E.8 *Simulation results for synchronous binary counter*

```
Simulate iSE 3.01  Date: Fri Oct 06 22:56:40 2000
Fuse file: 'sybuk.bll'  Vector file: 'sybuk.tmv'  Part: 'PLA'
4-bit synchronous binary up counter

          r  c
          e  l
          s  o
          e  c    Q Q Q Q
          t  k    3 2 1 0

V0001  1  X    L L L L
V0002  0  C    L L L L
       0  C    L L L H
       0  C    L L L H
V0003  0  C    L L L H
       0  C    L L H L
       0  C    L L H L
  .
  .
  .
V0016  0  C    H H H L
       0  C    H H H H
       0  C    H H H H
V0017  0  C    H H H H
       0  C    L L L L
       0  C    L L L L

17 out of 17 vectors passed.
```

The ABEL simulation for the ripple-through BCD counter (see Figure 5.26) indicates that the design will not actually work: the reset from 1001 back to 0000 causes trouble. Although the design does actually work, in practice it is not a good one, as the main text emphasises. All the synchronous designs do simulate correctly.

Fig. E.9 *Possible test vectors for a shift register*

```
test_vectors([reset,clock,d_in]->[Q]);
            [1,.x.,.x.]->[0];       "reset
            [0,.c.,1]->[^b1000];   "shift in a 1
            [0,.c.,0]->[^b0100];   "now keep shifting to right
            [0,.c.,0]->[^b0010];
            [0,.c.,0]->[^b0001];
            [0,.c.,0]->[^b0000];
```

Figure E.9 shows some possible test vectors for a shift register (see Figure 5.49), while Figure E.10 shows some for the left-right barrel shift register (see Figure 5.51).

```
test_vectors([load,clock,left,right]->[Q]);
             [1,.x.,.x.,.x.]->[^b0001];   "preset a 1 in LSB
             [0,.c.,1,0]->[^b0010];       "shift left
             [0,.c.,1,0]->[^b0100];
             [0,.c.,1,0]->[^b1000];
             [0,.c.,1,0]->[^b0001];
             [0,.c.,0,1]->[^b1000];       "shift right
             [0,.c.,0,1]->[^b0100];
             [0,.c.,0,0]->[^b0100];       "no shift
             [0,.c.,0,1]->[^b0010];
             [0,.c.,0,1]->[^b0001];
             [0,.c.,0,1]->[^b1000];
```

The PHDL version of a data-register (Figure 5.55) converts to the ABEL system with no modification except the addition of test vectors. The final PHDL example of Chapter 5 (Figure 5.57) converts with the minor addition of two additional declarations: D = [D3..D0]; and Q = [Q3..Q0]. This allows the test vectors shown in Figure E.11 to be used to test the operation of the design – a 4-bit transparent latch.

Fig. E.11 *Example test vectors for transparent latch*

```
test_vectors([D,clock]->[Q]);
             [^b0101,1]->[^b0101];   "open latch
             [^b1010,1]->[^b1010];   "toggle the inputs
             [.x.,0]->[^b1010];      "close latch
```

Both versions of the 3-bit up-down counter discussed in Chapter 6 work as expected when transferred to the ABEL system (see Figures 6.14 and 6.15). An example set of test vectors suitable for both versions is shown in Figure E.12.

Fig. E.12 *Example test vectors for up-down counter*

```
test_vectors([dir,Clock]->[Q]);
             [1,.c.]->[1];   "assume O/P is reset to 0 before
                             "starting
             [1,.c.]->[2];   "count up...
             [1,.c.]->[3];
             [1,.c.]->[4];
             [1,.c.]->[5];
             [1,.c.]->[6];
             [1,.c.]->[7];
             [1,.c.]->[0];   "roll over
             [0,.c.]->[7];   "count down...
             [0,.c.]->[6];
             [0,.c.]->[5];
             [0,.c.]->[4];
             [0,.c.]->[3];
             [0,.c.]->[2];
             [0,.c.]->[1];
             [0,.c.]->[0];
             [0,.c.]->[7];
```

The binary/Gray counter (Figure 6.30) requires something like Figure E.13 to test its operation. This set of test vectors will also check out the state-diagram version of the design (see Figure 6.32).

Fig. E.13 *Test vectors for 3-bit binary/Gray counter*

```
test_vectors([binary,Clock]->[Q]);
                [1,.c.]->[1];   "assume O/P is reset to 0 before
                                "starting
                [1,.c.]->[2];   "count up in binary
                [1,.c.]->[3];
                [1,.c.]->[4];
                [1,.c.]->[5];
                [1,.c.]->[6];
                [1,.c.]->[7];
                [1,.c.]->[0];   "roll over
                [0,.c.]->[1];   "now count in Gray code
                [0,.c.]->[3];
                [0,.c.]->[2];
                [0,.c.]->[6];
                [0,.c.]->[7];
                [0,.c.]->[5];
                [0,.c.]->[4];
                [0,.c.]->[0];
```

The state machine for detecting a 1-0-1 sequence (see Figure 6.38) compiles satisfactorily (although the variable `output` is coloured pink as if it's a keyword). A possible set of test vectors is given in Figure E.14.

Fig. E.14 *Test vectors for 1-0-1 sequence detector*

```
test_vectors([S,Clock]->[output]);
                [1,.c.]->[0];
                [0,.c.]->[0];
                [1,.c.]->[1];   "found a 1-0-1 sequence
                [0,.c.]->[0];
                [1,.c.]->[0];   "this isn't one
                [1,.c.]->[0];
                [0,.c.]->[0];
                [1,.c.]->[1];   "here's another
```

Figure 6.45 of Chapter 6 is the 'flashy turn indicator'. Some minor changes are needed to the PHDL code. The `/* comment */` syntax is not recognised in ABEL, so the double-quote sign must be used instead. The other complaint is just a warning that the outputs have not been declared as combinatorial. Adding `istype 'com'` to the relevant pin declarations will rectify this. Test vectors are needed to check the operation of the design, and Figure E.15 lists a possible set.

```
test_vectors([BRAKE,TL,TR,CLK]->[L3,L2,L1,R1,R2,R3]);
            [0,1,0,.c.]->[0,0,1,0,0,0];   "turn left, 1st state
            [0,1,0,.c.]->[0,1,1,0,0,0];   "turn left, 2nd state
            [0,1,0,.c.]->[1,1,1,0,0,0];   "turn left, 3rd state
            [0,1,0,.c.]->[0,0,0,0,0,0];   "turn left, 0th state
            [0,1,0,.c.]->[0,0,1,0,0,0];   "turn left, 1st state
            [1,1,0,.c.]->[0,1,1,1,1,1];   "brake + turn left,
                                           2nd state
            [0,1,0,.c.]->[1,1,1,0,0,0];   "turn left, 3rd state
            [0,0,1,.c.]->[0,0,0,1,0,0];   "turn right, 1st state
            [0,0,1,.c.]->[0,0,0,1,1,0];   "turn right, 2nd state
            [0,0,1,.c.]->[0,0,0,1,1,1];   "turn right, 3rd state
            [1,0,1,.c.]->[1,1,1,0,0,0];   "brake + turn right,
                                           0th state
            [0,0,0,.c.]->[0,0,0,0,0,0];   "straight ahead
            [1,0,0,.c.]->[1,1,1,1,1,1];   "straight ahead + brake
            [0,0,0,.c.]->[0,0,0,0,0,0];   "straight ahead
```

The final two designs in Chapter 6 are asynchronous machines. Figure 6.58 is the PHDL code to implement the state diagram of Figure 6.51. This machine requires the data 00,01,11,10 to be entered on inputs A and B respectively to make signal L (un-Lock) go high while any other sequence sets signal W (Warning) permanently HIGH. An active-LOW reset signal is included in the design.

The PHDL code needs no change to convert into ABEL. A set of test vectors that will give a partial check on the operation is given in Figure E.16.

Fig. E.16 *Test vectors for electronic lock*

```
test_vectors([A,B,reset]->[L,W]);
            [.x.,.x.,0]->[0,0];   "reset
            [0,0,1]->[0,0];       "enter 00
            [0,1,1]->[0,0];       "then 01
            [1,1,1]->[0,0];       "then 11
            [1,0,1]->[1,0];       "then 10 to unlock
            [.x.,.x.,0]->[0,0];   "reset
            [0,0,1]->[0,0];       "enter 00
            [1,0,1]->[0,1];       "enter 10 (incorrect)
            [.x.,.x.,1]->[0,1];   "get stuck with warning on
```

Figure 6.63 copes with input signals that are 'bouncy', i.e. signals which oscillate an indeterminate number of times. To get to the treasure you have to make input signal S1 go up and down at least once, then signal S2, then S3, then S2 again, then S3 again, and finally S1. The state transition diagram Figure 6.60 illustrates this required sequence; it also shows what happens if other sequences are followed.

The ABEL system issues a few warnings about type declarations, which can be fixed by adding appropriate `istype` qualifiers to the `PIN` statements. (The design still works even if you don't.) Figure E.17 shows a set of tests that will perform a partial check on the design.

Fig. E.17 *Test vectors to check out pulse-driven lock*

```
test_vectors([S1,S2,S3,reset]->[z]);
            [.x.,.x.,.x.,1]->[0];    "reset
            [1,0,0,0]->[0];          "now make S1 toggle
            [0,0,0,0]->[0];          "a few times
            [1,0,0,0]->[0];
            [0,0,0,0]->[0];
            [0,1,0,0]->[0];          "now S2
            [0,0,0,0]->[0];
            [0,1,0,0]->[0];
            [0,0,0,0]->[0];
            [0,0,1,0]->[0];          "now S3
            [0,0,0,0]->[0];
            [0,1,0,0]->[0];          "now S2 again
            [0,0,0,0]->[0];
            [0,0,1,0]->[0];          "now S3 again
            [0,0,0,0]->[0];
            [1,0,0,0]->[0];          "now S1 again
            [0,0,0,0]->[1];          "to release the gold
```

In Chapter 7 the architectures of the 22V10, the Xilinx 5032, the Altera 7128 and the Xilinx 4003E were discussed. It was discovered that a 10-bit up/down counter would not fit into a 22V10 device since the chip is too small, with only 10 macro-cells. Surprisingly, the ABEL system succeeds where the XPLA-PHDL system failed. The best the XPLA system could do when generating optimised equations for the system was to produce an equation with 20 product terms in it, to drive the D input of the MSB flip-flop. The ABEL system manages to do the same job with a 12-product-term equation. This means that the internal node is no longer required, and the design can be fitted successfully. The ABEL system also takes noticeably less time to produce its design than the XPLA.

Summary

This appendix has covered installation of the **Webpack** software packages needed to enter designs using ABEL, perform functional testing on the designs by means of test vectors, fit designs into the Coolrunner family of CPLDs, and download designs to hardware. It has also given an introduction to the use of the software.

The PHDL designs in the main part of the book have been tested on the **Webpack** system, and found to need very few, if any, amendments in order to import them.

While the **Webpack** system is more versatile than the XPLA system, covering a wider range of chips and languages, it does not offer graphical simulation facilities (or a graphical pin editor). These facilities and more are available, however, to users who are familiar with the VHDL and Verilog design languages.

Index

IMPORTANT: READ CAREFULLY

WARNING: BY OPENING THE PACKAGE YOU AGREE TO BE BOUND BY THE TERMS OF THE LICENCE AGREEMENT BELOW.

This is a legally binding agreement between You (the user or purchaser) and Pearson Education Limited. By retaining this licence, any software media or accompanying written materials or carrying out any of the permitted activities You agree to be bound by the terms of the licence agreement below.

If You do not agree to these terms then promptly return the entire publication (this licence and all software, written materials, packaging and any other components received with it) with Your sales receipt to Your supplier for a full refund.

SINGLE USER LICENCE AGREEMENT

❏ YOU ARE PERMITTED TO:

- Use (load into temporary memory or permanent storage) a single copy of the software on only one computer at a time. If this computer is linked to a network then the software may only be installed in a manner such that it is not accessible to other machines on the network.

- Make one copy of the software solely for backup purposes or copy it to a single hard disk, provided you keep the original solely for back up purposes.

- Transfer the software from one computer to another provided that you only use it on one computer at a time.

❏ YOU MAY NOT:

- Rent or lease the software or any part of the publication.

- Copy any part of the documentation, except where specifically indicated otherwise.

- Make copies of the software, other than for backup purposes.

- Reverse engineer, decompile or disassemble the software.

- Use the software on more than one computer at a time.

- Install the software on any networked computer in a way that could allow access to it from more than one machine on the network.

- Use the software in any way not specified above without the prior written consent of Pearson Education Limited.

ONE COPY ONLY

This licence is for a single user copy of the software
PEARSON EDUCATION LIMITED RESERVES THE RIGHT TO TERMINATE THIS LICENCE BY WRITTEN NOTICE AND TO TAKE ACTION TO RECOVER ANY DAMAGES SUFFERED BY PEARSON EDUCATION LIMITED IF YOU BREACH ANY PROVISION OF THIS AGREEMENT.

Pearson Education Limited owns the software You only own the disk on which the software is supplied.

LIMITED WARRANTY

Pearson Education Limited warrants that the diskette or CD rom on which the software is supplied are free from defects in materials and workmanship under normal use for ninety (90) days from the date You receive them. This warranty is limited to You and is not transferable. Pearson Education Limited does not warrant that the functions of the software meet Your requirements or that the media is compatible with any computer system on which it is used or that the operation of the software will be unlimited or error free.

You assume responsibility for selecting the software to achieve Your intended results and for the installation of, the use of and the results obtained from the software. The entire liability of Pearson Education Limited and its suppliers and your only remedy shall be replacement of the components that do not meet this warranty free of charge.

This limited warranty is void if any damage has resulted from accident, abuse, misapplication, service or modification by someone other than Pearson Education Limited. In no event shall Pearson Education Limited or its suppliers be liable for any damages whatsoever arising out of installation of the software, even if advised of the possibility of such damages. Pearson Education Limited will not be liable for any loss or damage of any nature suffered by any party as a result of reliance upon or reproduction of or any errors in the content of the publication.

Pearson Education Limited does not limit its liability for death or personal injury caused by its negligence.

This licence agreement shall be governed by and interpreted and construed in accordance with English law.